2010 ADA Standards for Accessible Design

D1261867

Department of Justice
September 15, 2010

BNi. Building News

EDITOR-IN-CHIEF
William D. Mahoney, P.E.

TECHNICAL SERVICES
Ana Varela
Katherine Ritch

COVER DESIGN
Robert O. Wright

ANAHEIM
1612 S. Clementine St.
Anaheim, CA 92802

VISTA
990 Park Center Drive, Suite E
Vista, CA 92081

1-800-873-6397

ISBN 978-155701-756-7

Table of Contents

Title II

Title III

2004 ADAAG

Introduction and Editor's Note

The Department of Justice published revised regulations for Titles II and III of the Americans with Disabilities Act of 1990 "ADA" in the *Federal Register* on September 15, 2010. These regulations adopted revised, enforceable accessibility standards called the 2010 ADA Standards for Accessible Design "2010 Standards" or "Standards". The 2010 Standards set minimum requirements – both scoping and technical – for newly designed and constructed or renovated state and local government facilities, public accommodations, and commercial facilities to be readily accessible to and usable by individuals with disabilities.

Adoption of the 2010 Standards also establishes a revised reference point for Title II entities that choose to make structural changes to existing facilities to meet their program accessibility requirements; and it establishes a similar reference for Title III entities undertaking readily achievable barrier removal.

The Department is providing this document with the official 2010 Standards in one publication. The document includes:

- The 2010 Standards for state and local governments, which consist of the Title II regulations at 28 CFR 35.151 and the 2004 ADAAG at 36 CFR part 1191, appendices B and D;
- The 2010 Standards for public accommodations and commercial facilities, which consist of the Title III regulations at 28 CFR part 36, subpart D, and the 2004 ADAAG at 36 CFR part 1191, appendices B and D.

The 2010 ADA Standards for Accessible Design (2010 Standards) govern the construction and alteration of places of public use, commercial buildings, and state and local government facilities. The Department of Justice (DOJ) maintains ADA standards that apply to all ADA facilities except transportation facilities, which are governed by the Department of Transportation.

The 2010 Standards are comprised of three parts. Title II (28 CFR 35.151), Title III (28 CFR 36 subpart D) and the 2004 ADAAG. The Department of Justice published revised guidelines for Titles II and III of the Americans with Disabilities Act of 1990. The 2004 ADAAG, a publication of the United State Access Board, is included within the 2010 Standards in its entirety. These three documents come together to make the 2010 Standards which apply to all construction projects or alterations where the start date is on or after March 15, 2012.

In the places were Title II and Title III differ from the 2004 ADAAG, Title II and III prevail. The regulations in Titles II and III include additional design requirements that supplement the standards set forth in the 2004 ADAAG. The Department of Justice's Title II addresses state and local government facilities whereas Title III covers places of public use and commercial facilities.

The Department included guidance in its revised ADA regulations published on September 15, 2010. This version of the 2010 Standards has been supplemented with the Guidance on 2010 Standards for Accessible Design. This publication has been complied in an effort to create a side-by-side look at the 2010 Standards with the explanatory information of the requirements found in the guidance. Information from the Guidance has been denoted in a shaded box after each applicable section. This guidance provides detailed information about the Department's adoption of the 2010 Standards including changes to the Standards, the reasoning behind those changes, and responses to public comments received on these topics. The document, Guidance on the 2010 ADA Standards for Accessible Design, can be downloaded from www.ADA.gov.

All Guidance will appear throughout the manual in shaded boxes such as this before or after the code that they pertain to.

Eric Mahoney AIA, LEED AP

For More Information

For information about the ADA, including the revised 2010 ADA regulations, please visit the Department's website www.ADA.gov; or, for answers to specific questions, call the toll-free ADA Information Line at 800-514-0301 (Voice) or 800-514-0383 (TTY).

Title II
2010 Standards for State and Local Government Facilities

State and local government facilities must follow the requirements of the 2010 Standards, including both the Title II regulations at 28 CFR 35.151; and the 2004 ADAAG at 36 CFR part 1191, appendices B and D.

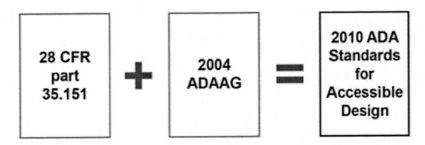

In the few places where requirements between the two differ, the requirements of 28 CFR 35.151 prevail.

Compliance Date for Title II

If the start date for construction is on or after March 15, 2012, all newly constructed or altered State and local government facilities must comply with the 2010 Standards. Before that date, the 1991 Standards (without the elevator exemption), the UFAS, or the 2010 Standards may be used for such projects when the start of construction commences on or after September 15, 2010.

CONTENTS

28 CFR 35.151 New Construction and Alterations
(a) Design and construction (includes the exception for structural impracticability)
(b) Alterations (includes alterations in historic properties, path of travel, and primary function)
(c) Accessibility standards and compliance date
(d) Scope of coverage
(e) Social service center establishments
(f) Housing at a place of education
(g) Assembly areas
(h) Medical care facilities
(i) Curb ramps
(j) Facilities with residential dwelling units for sale to individual owners
(k) Detention and correctional facilities

§ 35.151 New construction and alterations

Guidance on the Revisions to 28 CFR 35.151

Section 35.151(a), which provided that those facilities that are constructed or altered by, on behalf of, or for the use of a public entity shall be designed, constructed, or altered to be readily accessible to and usable by individuals with disabilities, is unchanged in the final rule, but has been redesignated as Sec. 35.151(a)(1). The Department has added a new section, designated as Sec. 35.151(a)(2), to provide that full compliance with the requirements of this section is not required where an entity can demonstrate that it is structurally impracticable to meet the requirements. Full compliance will be considered structurally impracticable only in those rare circumstances when the unique characteristics of terrain prevent the incorporation of accessibility features. This exception was contained in the title III regulation and in the 1991 Standards (applicable to both public accommodations and facilities used by public entities), so it has applied to any covered facility that was constructed under the 1991 Standards since the effective date of the ADA. The Department added it to the text of Sec. 35.151 to maintain consistency between the design requirements that apply under title II and those that apply under title III. The Department received no significant comments about this section.

- **(a) Design and construction.**
  - (1) Each facility or part of a facility constructed by, on behalf of, or for the use of a public entity shall be designed and constructed in such manner that the facility or part of the facility is readily accessible to and usable by individuals with disabilities, if the construction was commenced after January 26, 1992.
  - **(2) Exception for structural impracticability**
    - (i) Full compliance with the requirements of this section is not required where a public entity can demonstrate that it is structurally impracticable to meet the requirements. Full compliance will be considered structurally impracticable only in those rare circumstances when the unique characteristics of terrain prevent the incorporation of accessibility features.
    - (ii) If full compliance with this section would be structurally impracticable, compliance with this section is required to the extent that it is not structurally impracticable. In that case, any portion of the facility that can be made accessible shall be made accessible to the extent that it is not structurally impracticable.
    - (iii) If providing accessibility in conformance with this section to individuals with certain disabilities (e.g., those who use wheelchairs) would be structurally impracticable, accessibility shall nonetheless be ensured to persons with other types of disabilities, (e.g., those who use crutches or who have sight, hearing, or mental impairments) in accordance with this section.
- **(b) Alterations**

Guidance

The 1991 title II regulation does not contain any specific regulatory language comparable to the 1991 title III regulation relating to alterations and path of travel for covered entities, although the 1991 Standards describe standards for path of travel during alterations to a primary function. See 28 CFR part 36, app A., section 4.1.6(a) (2009).

The path of travel requirements contained in the title III regulation are based on section 303(a)(2) of the ADA, 42 U.S.C. 12183(a)(2), which provides that when an entity undertakes an alteration to a place of public accommodation or commercial facility that affects or could affect the usability of or access to an area that contains a primary function, the entity shall ensure that, to the maximum extent feasible, the path of travel to the altered area--and the restrooms, telephones, and drinking fountains serving it--is readily accessible to and usable by individuals with disabilities, including individuals who use wheelchairs.

The NPRM proposed amending Sec. 35.151 to add both the path of travel requirements and the exemption relating to barrier removal (as modified to apply to the program accessibility standard in title II) that are contained in the title III regulation to the title II regulation. Proposed Sec. 35.151(b)(4) contained the requirements for path of travel. Proposed Sec. 35.151(b)(2) stated that the path of travel requirements of Sec. 35.151(b)(4) shall not apply to measures taken solely to comply with program accessibility requirements.

Where the specific requirements for path of travel apply under title III, they are limited to the extent that the cost and scope of alterations to the path of travel are disproportionate to the cost of the overall alteration, as determined under criteria established by the Attorney General.

The Access Board included the path of travel requirement for alterations to facilities covered by the standards (other than those subject to the residential facilities standards) in section 202.4 of 2004 ADAAG. Section 35.151(b)(4)(iii) of the final rule establishes the criteria for determining when the cost of alterations to the path of travel is "disproportionate" to the cost of the overall alteration.

The NPRM also provided that areas such as supply storage rooms, employee lounges and locker rooms, janitorial closets, entrances, and corridors are not areas containing a primary function. Nor are restroom areas considered to contain a primary function unless the provision of restrooms is a primary purpose of the facility, such as at a highway rest stop. In that situation, a restroom would be considered to be an "area containing a primary function" of the facility.

The Department is not changing the requirements for program accessibility. As provided in Sec. 35.151(b)(2) of the regulation, the path of travel requirements of Sec. 35.151(b)(4) only apply to alterations undertaken solely for purposes other than to meet the program accessibility requirements. The exemption for the specific path of travel requirement was included in the regulation to ensure that the specific requirements and disproportionality exceptions for path of travel are not applied when areas are being altered to meet the title II program accessibility requirements in Sec. 35.150. In contrast, when areas are being altered to meet program accessibility requirements, they must comply with all of the applicable requirements referenced in section 202 of the 2010 Standards. A covered title II entity must provide accessibility to meet the requirements of Sec. 35.150 unless doing so is an undue financial and administrative burden in accordance with Sec. 35.150(a)(3). A covered title II entity may not use the disproportionality exception contained in the path of travel provisions as a defense to providing an accessible route as part of its obligation to provide program accessibility. The undue financial and administrative burden standard does not contain any bright line financial tests.

The Department's proposed Sec. 35.151(b)(4) adopted the language now contained in Sec. 36.403 of the title III regulation, including the disproportionality limitation (i.e., alterations made to provide an accessible path of travel to the altered area would be deemed disproportionate to the overall alteration when the cost exceeds 20 percent of the cost of the alteration to the primary function area). Proposed Sec. 35.151(b)(2) provided that the path of travel requirements do not apply to alterations undertaken solely to comply with program accessibility requirements.

The Department received a substantial number of comments objecting to the Department's adoption of the exemption for the path of travel requirements when alterations are undertaken solely to meet program accessibility requirements. These commenters argued that the Department had no statutory basis for providing this exemption nor does it serve any purpose. In addition, these commenters argued that the path of travel exemption has the effect of placing new limitations on the obligations to provide program access. A number of commenters argued that doing away with the path of travel requirement would render meaningless the concept of program access. They argued that just as the requirement to provide an accessible path of travel to an altered area (regardless of the reason for the alteration), including making the restrooms, telephones, and drinking fountains that serve the altered area accessible, is a necessary requirement in other alterations, it is equally necessary for alterations made to provide program access. Several commenters expressed concern that a readily accessible path of travel be available to ensure that persons with disabilities can get to the physical location in which programs are held. Otherwise, they will not be able to access the public entity's service, program, or activity. Such access is a cornerstone of the protections provided by the ADA. Another commenter argued that it would be a waste of money to create an accessible facility without having a way to get to the primary area. This commenter also stated that the International Building Code (IBC) requires the path of travel to a primary function area, up to 20 percent of the cost of the project. Another commenter opposed the exemption, stating that the trigger of an alteration is frequently the only time that a facility must update its facilities to comply with evolving accessibility standards.

In the Department's view, the commenters objecting to the path of travel exemption contained in Sec. 35.151(b)(2) did not understand the intention behind the exemption. The exemption was not intended to eliminate any existing requirements related to accessibility for alterations undertaken in order to meet program access obligations under Sec. 35.149 and Sec. 35.150. Rather, it was intended to ensure that covered entities did not apply the path of travel requirements in lieu of the overarching requirements in this Subpart that apply when making a facility accessible in order to comply with program accessibility. The exemption was also intended to make it clear that the disproportionality test contained in the path of travel standards is not applicable in determining whether providing program access results in an undue financial and administration burden within the meaning of Sec. 35.150(a)(3). The exemption was also provided to maintain consistency with the title III path of travel exemption for barrier removal, see Sec. 36.304(d), in keeping with the Department's regulatory authority under title II of the ADA. See 42 U.S.C. 12134(b); see also H. R Rep. No. 101B485, pt. 2, at 84 (1990) ("The committee intends, however, that the forms of discrimination prohibited by section 202 be identical to those set out in the applicable provisions of titles I and III of this legislation.").

For title II entities, the path of travel requirements are of significance in those cases where an alteration is being made solely for reasons other than program accessibility. For example, a public entity might have six courtrooms in two existing buildings and might determine that only three of those courtrooms and the public use and common use areas serving those courtrooms in one building are needed to be made accessible in order to satisfy its program access obligations. When the public entity makes those courtrooms and the public use and common use areas serving them accessible in order to meet its program access obligations, it will have to comply with the 2010 Standards unless the public entity can demonstrate that full compliance would result in undue financial and administrative burdens as described in Sec. 35.150(a)(3). If such action would result in an undue financial or administrative burden, the public entity would nevertheless be required to take some other action that would not result in such an alteration or such burdens but would ensure that the benefits and services provided by the public entity are readily accessible to persons with disabilities. When the public entity is making modifications to meet its program access obligation, it may not rely on the path of travel exception under Sec. 35.151(b)(4), which limits the requirement to those alterations where the cost and scope of the alterations are not disproportionate to the cost and scope of the overall alterations. If the public entity later decides to alter courtrooms in the other building, for purposes of updating the facility (and, as previously stated, has met its program access obligations) then in that case, the public entity would have to comply with the path of travel requirements in the 2010 Standards subject to the disproportionality exception set forth in Sec. 35.151(b)(4).

The Department has slightly revised proposed Sec. 35.151(b)(2) to make it clearer that the path of travel requirements only apply when alterations are undertaken solely for purposes other than program accessibility.

- (1) Each facility or part of a facility altered by, on behalf of, or for the use of a public entity in a manner that affects or could affect the usability of the facility or part of the facility shall, to the maximum extent feasible, be altered in such manner that the altered portion of the facility is readily accessible to and usable by individuals with disabilities, if the alteration was commenced after January 26, 1992.
- (2) The path of travel requirements of § 35.151(b)(4) shall apply only to alterations undertaken solely for purposes other than to meet the program accessibility requirements of § 35.150.
- (3)
  - (i) Alterations to historic properties shall comply, to the maximum extent feasible, with the provisions applicable to historic properties in the design standards specified in § 35.151(c).
  - (ii) If it is not feasible to provide physical access to an historic property in a manner that will not threaten or destroy the historic significance of the building or facility, alternative methods of access shall be provided pursuant to the requirements of § 35.150.

> **Guidance**
>
> § 35.151(b)(3) Alterations to historic facilities
>
> The final rule renumbers the requirements for alterations to historic facilities enumerated in current Sec. 35.151(d)(1) and (2) as Sec. 35.151(b)(3)(i) and (ii). Currently, the regulation provides that alterations to historic facilities shall comply to the maximum extent feasible with section 4.1.7 of UFAS or section 4.1.7 of the 1991 Standards. See 28 CFR 35.151(d)(1). Section 35.151(b)(3)(i) of the final rule eliminates the option of using UFAS for alterations that commence on or after March 15, 2012. The substantive requirement in current Sec. 35.151(d)(2)--that alternative methods of access shall be provided pursuant to the requirements of Sec. 35.150 if it is not feasible to provide physical access to an historic property in a manner that will not threaten or destroy the historic significance of the building or facility--is contained in Sec. 35.151(b)(3)(ii).

- **(4) Path of travel.** An alteration that affects or could affect the usability of or access to an area of a facility that contains a primary function shall be made so as to ensure that, to the maximum extent feasible, the path of travel to the altered area and the restrooms, telephones, and drinking fountains serving the altered area are readily accessible to and usable by individuals with disabilities, including individuals who use wheelchairs, unless the cost and scope of such alterations is disproportionate to the cost of the overall alteration.
  - **(i) Primary function.** A "primary function" is a major activity for which the facility is intended. Areas that contain a primary function include, but are not limited to, the dining area of a cafeteria, the meeting rooms in a conference center, as well as offices and other work areas in which the activities of the public entity using the facility are carried out.
    - (A) Mechanical rooms, boiler rooms, supply storage rooms, employee lounges or locker rooms, janitorial closets, entrances, and corridors are not areas containing a primary function. Restrooms are not areas containing a primary function unless the provision of restrooms is a primary purpose of the area, e.g., in highway rest stops.
    - (B) For the purposes of this section, alterations to windows, hardware, controls, electrical outlets, and signage shall not be deemed to be alterations that affect the usability of or access to an area containing a primary function.
  - **(ii)** A "path of travel" includes a continuous, unobstructed way of pedestrian passage by means of which the altered area may be approached, entered, and exited, and which connects the altered area with an exterior approach (including sidewalks, streets, and parking areas), an entrance to the facility, and other parts of the facility.
    - (A) An accessible path of travel may consist of walks and sidewalks, curb ramps and other interior or exterior pedestrian ramps; clear floor paths through lobbies, corridors, rooms, and other improved areas; parking access aisles; elevators and lifts; or a combination of these elements.
    - (B) For the purposes of this section, the term "path of travel" also includes the restrooms, telephones, and drinking fountains serving the altered area.
    - (C) **Safe harbor.** If a public entity has constructed or altered required elements of a path of travel in accordance with the specifications in either the 1991 Standards or the Uniform Federal Accessibility Standards before March 15, 2012, the public entity is not required to retrofit such elements to reflect incremental changes in the 2010 Standards solely because of an alteration to a primary function area served by that path of travel.

Guidance

§ 35.151(b)(4)(ii)(C) Path of travel--safe harbor

In Sec. 35.151(b)(4)(ii)(C) of the NPRM, the Department included a provision that stated that public entities that have brought required elements of path of travel into compliance with the 1991 Standards are not required to retrofit those elements in order to reflect incremental changes in the 2010 Standards solely because of an alteration to a primary function area that is served by that path of travel. In these circumstances, the public entity is entitled to a safe harbor and is only required to modify elements to comply with the 2010 Standards if the public entity is planning an alteration to the element.

A substantial number of commenters objected to the Department's imposition of a safe harbor for alterations to facilities of public entities that comply with the 1991 Standards. These commenters argued that if a public entity is already in the process of altering its facility, there should be a legal requirement that individuals with disabilities be entitled to increased accessibility by using the 2010 Standards for path of travel work. They also stated that they did not believe there was a statutory basis for "grandfathering" facilities that comply with the 1991 Standards.

The ADA is silent on the issue of "grandfathering" or establishing a safe harbor for measuring compliance in situations where the covered entity is not undertaking a planned alteration to specific building elements. The ADA delegates to the Attorney General the responsibility for issuing regulations that define the parameters of covered entities' obligations when the statute does not directly address an issue. This regulation implements that delegation of authority.

One commenter proposed that a previous record of barrier removal be one of the factors in determining, prospectively, what renders a facility, when viewed in its entirety, usable and accessible to persons with disabilities. Another commenter asked the Department to clarify, at a minimum, that to the extent compliance with the 1991 Standards does not provide program access, particularly with regard to areas not specifically addressed in the 1991 Standards, the safe harbor will not operate to relieve an entity of its obligations to provide program access.

One commenter supported the proposal to add a safe harbor for path of travel.

The final rule retains the safe harbor for required elements of a path of travel to altered primary function areas for public entities that have already complied with the 1991 Standards with respect to those required elements. The Department believes that this safe harbor strikes an appropriate balance between ensuring that individuals with disabilities are provided access to buildings and facilities and potential financial burdens on existing public entities that are undertaking alterations subject to the 2010 Standards. This safe harbor is not a blanket exemption for facilities. If a public entity undertakes an alteration to a primary function area, only the required elements of a path of travel to that area that already comply with the 1991 Standards are subject to the safe harbor. If a public entity undertakes an alteration to a primary function area and the required elements of a path of travel to the altered area do not comply with the 1991 Standards, then the public entity must bring those elements into compliance with the 2010 Standards.

- **(iii) Disproportionality**
    - (A) Alterations made to provide an accessible path of travel to the altered area will be deemed disproportionate to the overall alteration when the cost exceeds 20 % of the cost of the alteration to the primary function area.
    - (B) Costs that may be counted as expenditures required to provide an accessible path of travel may include:
        - (1) Costs associated with providing an accessible entrance and an accessible route to the altered area, for example, the cost of widening doorways or installing ramps;
        - (2) Costs associated with making restrooms accessible, such as installing grab bars, enlarging toilet stalls, insulating pipes, or installing accessible faucet controls;

- (3) Costs associated with providing accessible telephones, such as relocating the telephone to an accessible height, installing amplification devices, or installing a text telephone (TTY); and
- (4) Costs associated with relocating an inaccessible drinking fountain.

- **(iv) Duty to provide accessible features in the event of disproportionality.**
  - (A) When the cost of alterations necessary to make the path of travel to the altered area fully accessible is disproportionate to the cost of the overall alteration, the path of travel shall be made accessible to the extent that it can be made accessible without incurring disproportionate costs.
  - (B) In choosing which accessible elements to provide, priority should be given to those elements that will provide the greatest access, in the following order—
    - (1) An accessible entrance;
    - (2) An accessible route to the altered area;
    - (3) At least one accessible restroom for each sex or a single unisex restroom;
    - (4) Accessible telephones;
    - (5) Accessible drinking fountains; and
    - (6) When possible, additional accessible elements such as parking, storage, and alarms.

- **(v) Series of smaller alterations**
  - (A) The obligation to provide an accessible path of travel may not be evaded by performing a series of small alterations to the area served by a single path of travel if those alterations could have been performed as a single undertaking.
  - (B)
    - (1) If an area containing a primary function has been altered without providing an accessible path of travel to that area, and subsequent alterations of that area, or a different area on the same path of travel, are undertaken within three years of the original alteration, the total cost of alterations to the primary function areas on that path of travel during the preceding three-year period shall be considered in determining whether the cost of making that path of travel accessible is disproportionate.
    - (2) Only alterations undertaken on or after March 15, 2011, shall be considered in determining if the cost of providing an accessible path of travel is disproportionate to the overall cost of the alterations.

- **(c) Accessibility standards and compliance date.**
  - (1) If physical construction or alterations commence after July 26, 1992, but prior to the September 15, 2010, then new construction and alterations subject to this section must comply with either the UFAS or the 1991 Standards except that the elevator exemption contained at section 4.1.3(5) and section 4.1.6(1)(k) of the 1991 Standards shall not apply. Departures from particular requirements of either standard by the use of other methods shall be permitted when it is clearly evident that equivalent access to the facility or part of the facility is thereby provided.
  - (2) If physical construction or alterations commence on or after September 15, 2010, and before March 15, 2012, then new construction and alterations subject to this section may comply with one of the following: the 2010 Standards, UFAS, or the 1991 Standards except that the elevator exemption contained at section 4.1.3(5) and section 4.1.6(1)(k) of the 1991 Standards shall not apply. Departures from particular requirements of either standard by the use of other methods shall be permitted when it is clearly evident that equivalent access to the facility or part of the facility is thereby provided.
  - (3) If physical construction or alterations commence on or after March 15, 2012, then new construction and alterations subject to this section shall comply with the 2010 Standards.
  - (4) For the purposes of this section, ceremonial groundbreaking or razing of structures prior to site preparation do not commence physical construction or alterations.
  - (5) Noncomplying new construction and alterations.

- **(i)** Newly constructed or altered facilities or elements covered by §§ 35.151(a) or (b) that were constructed or altered before March 15, 2012, and that do not comply with the 1991 Standards or with UFAS shall before March 15, 2012, be made accessible in accordance with either the 1991 Standards, UFAS, or the 2010 Standards.
- **(ii)** Newly constructed or altered facilities or elements covered by §§ 35.151(a) or (b) that are constructed or altered on or after March 15, 2012, and that do not comply with the 1991 Standards or with UFAS shall, on or after March 15, 2012, be made accessible in accordance with the 2010 Standards.

Guidance

§ 35.151(c) Accessibility standards for new construction and alterations

Section 35.151(c) of the NPRM proposed to adopt ADA Chapter 1, ADA Chapter 2, and Chapters 3 through 10 of the Americans with Disabilities Act and Architectural Barriers Act Guidelines (2004 ADAAG) into the ADA Standards for Accessible Design (2010 Standards). As the Department has noted, the development of these standards represents the culmination of a lengthy effort by the Access Board to update its guidelines, to make the Federal guidelines consistent to the extent permitted by law, and to harmonize the Federal requirements with the private sector model codes that form the basis of many State and local building code requirements. The full text of the 2010 Standards is available for public review on the ADA Home Page (http://www.ada.gov) and on the Access Board's Web site (http://www.access-board.gov/gs.htm) (last visited June 24, 2010). The Access Board site also includes an extensive discussion of the development of the 2004 ADA/ABA Guidelines, and a detailed comparison of the 1991 Standards, the 2004 ADA/ABA Guidelines, and the 2003 International Building Code.

Section 204 of the ADA, 42 U.S.C. 12134, directs the Attorney General to issue regulations to implement title II that are consistent with the minimum guidelines published by the Access Board. The Attorney General (or his designee) is a statutory member of the Access Board (see 29 U.S.C. 792(a)(1)(B(vii)) and was involved in the development of the 2004 ADAAG. Nevertheless, during the process of drafting the NPRM, the Department reviewed the 2004 ADAAG to determine if additional regulatory provisions were necessary. As a result of this review, the Department decided to propose new sections, which were contained in Sec. 35.151(e)-(h) of the NPRM, to clarify how the Department will apply the proposed standards to social service center establishments, housing at places of education, assembly areas, and medical care facilities. Each of these provisions is discussed below.

Congress anticipated that there would be a need for close coordination of the ADA building requirements with State and local building code requirements. Therefore, the ADA authorized the Attorney General to establish an ADA code certification process under title III of the ADA. That process is addressed in 28 CFR part 36, subpart F. Revisions to that process are addressed in the regulation amending the title III regulation published elsewhere in the Federal Register today. In addition, the Department operates an extensive technical assistance program. The Department anticipates that once this rule is final, revised technical assistance material will be issued to provide guidance about its implementation.

Section 35.151(c) of the 1991 title II regulation establishes two standards for accessible new construction and alteration. Under paragraph (c), design, construction, or alteration of facilities in conformance with UFAS or with the 1991 Standards (which, at the time of the publication of the rule were also referred to as the Americans with Disabilities Act Accessibility Guidelines for Buildings and Facilities (1991 ADAAG)) is deemed to comply with the requirements of this section with respect to those facilities (except that if the 1991 Standards are chosen, the elevator exemption does not apply). The 1991 Standards were based on the 1991 ADAAG, which was initially developed by the Access Board as guidelines for the accessibility of buildings and facilities that are subject to title III. The Department adopted the 1991 ADAAG as the standards for places of public accommodation and commercial facilities under title III of the ADA and it was published as Appendix A to the Department's regulation implementing title III, 56 FR 35592 (July 26, 1991) as amended, 58 FR 17522 (April 5, 1993), and as further amended, 59 FR 2675 (Jan. 18, 1994), codified at 28 CFR part 36 (2009).

Section 35.151(c) of the final rule adopts the 2010 Standards and establishes the compliance date and triggering events for the application of those standards to both new construction and alterations. Appendix B of the final title III rule (Analysis and Commentary on the 2010 ADA Standards for Accessible Design) (which will be published today elsewhere in this volume and codified as Appendix B to 28 CFR part 36) provides a description of the major changes in the 2010 Standards (as compared to the 1991 ADAAG) and a discussion of the public comments that the Department received on specific sections of the 2004 ADAAG. A number of commenters asked the Department to revise certain provisions in the 2004 ADAAG in a manner that would reduce either the required scoping or specific technical accessibility requirements. As previously stated, although the ADA requires the enforceable standards issued by the Department under title II and title III to be consistent with the minimum guidelines published by the Access Board, it is the sole responsibility of the Attorney General to promulgate standards and to interpret and enforce those standards. The guidelines adopted by the Access Board are "minimum guidelines." 42 U.S.C. 12186(c).

Compliance date. When the ADA was enacted, the effective dates for various provisions were delayed in order to provide time for covered entities to become familiar with their new obligations. Titles II and III of the ADA generally became effective on January 26, 1992, six months after the regulations were published. See 42 U.S.C. 12131 note; 42 U.S.C. 12181 note. New construction under title II and alterations under either title II or title III had to comply with the design standards on that date. See 42 U.S.C. 12183(a)(1). For new construction under title III, the requirements applied to facilities designed and constructed for first occupancy after January 26, 1993--18 months after the 1991 Standards were published by the Department. In the NPRM, the Department proposed to amend Sec. 35.151(c)(1) by revising the current language to limit the application of the 1991 standards to facilities on which construction commences within six months of the final rule adopting revised standards. The NPRM also proposed adding paragraph (c)(2) to Sec. 35.151, which states that facilities on which construction commences on or after the date six months following the effective date of the final rule shall comply with the proposed standards adopted by that rule.

As a result, under the NPRM, for the first six months after the effective date, public entities would have the option to use either UFAS or the 1991 Standards and be in compliance with title II. Six months after the effective date of the rule, the new standards would take effect. At that time, construction in accordance with UFAS would no longer satisfy ADA requirements. The Department stated that in order to avoid placing the burden of complying with both standards on public entities, the Department would coordinate a government-wide effort to revise Federal agencies' section 504 regulations to adopt the 2004 ADAAG as the standard for new construction and alterations.

The purpose of the proposed six-month delay in requiring compliance with the 2010 Standards was to allow covered entities a reasonable grace period to transition between the existing and the proposed standards. For that reason, if a title II entity preferred to use the 2010 Standards as the standard for new construction or alterations commenced within the six-month period after the effective date of the final rule, such entity would be considered in compliance with title II of the ADA.

The Department received a number of comments about the proposed six-month effective date for the title II regulation that were similar in content to those received on this issue for the proposed title III regulation. Several commenters supported the six-month effective date. One commenter stated that any revisions to its State building code becomes effective six months after adoption and that this has worked well. In addition, this commenter stated that since 2004 ADAAG is similar to IBC 2006 and ICC/ANSI A117.1-2003, the transition should be easy. By contrast, another commenter advocated for a minimum 12-month effective date, arguing that a shorter effective date could cause substantial economic hardships to many cities and towns because of the lengthy lead time necessary for construction projects. This commenter was concerned that a six-month effective date could lead to projects having to be completely redrawn, rebid, and rescheduled to ensure compliance with the new standards. Other commenters advocated that the effective date be extended to at least 18 months after the publication of the rule. One of these commenters expressed concern that the kinds of bureaucratic organizations subject to the title II regulations lack the internal resources to quickly evaluate the regulatory changes, determine whether they are currently compliant with the 1991 standards, and determine what they have to do to comply with the new standards. The other commenter argued that 18 months is the minimum amount of time necessary to ensure that projects that have already been designed and approved do not have to undergo costly design revisions at taxpayer expense.

The Department is persuaded by the concerns raised by commenters for both the title II and III regulations that the six-month compliance date proposed in the NPRM for application of the 2010 Standards may be too short for certain projects that are already in the midst of the design and permitting process. The Department has determined that for new construction and alterations, compliance with the 2010 Standards will not be required until 18 months from the date the final rule is published. Until the time compliance with the 2010 Standards is required, public entities will have the option of complying with the 2010 Standards, the UFAS, or the 1991 Standards. However, public entities that choose to comply with the 2010 Standards in lieu of the 1991 Standards or UFAS prior to the compliance date described in this rule must choose one of the three standards, and may not rely on some of the requirements contained in one standard and some of the requirements contained in the other standards.

Triggering event. In Sec. 35.151(c)(2) of the NPRM, the Department proposed that the commencement of construction serve as the triggering event for applying the proposed standards to new construction and alterations under title II. This language is consistent with the triggering event set forth in Sec. 35.151(a) of the 1991 title II regulation. The Department received only four comments on this section of the title II rule. Three commenters supported the use of "start of construction" as the triggering event. One commenter argued that the Department should use the "last building permit or start of physical construction, whichever comes first," stating that "altering a design after a building permit has been issued can be an undue burden."

After considering these comments, the Department has decided to continue to use the commencement of physical construction as the triggering event for application of the 2010 Standards for entities covered by title II. The Department has also added clarifying language at Sec. 35.151(c)(4) to the regulation to make it clear that the date of ceremonial groundbreaking or the date a structure is razed to make it possible for construction of a facility to take place does not qualify as the commencement of physical construction.

Section 234 of the 2010 Standards provides accessibility guidelines for newly designed and constructed amusement rides. The amusement ride provisions do not provide a "triggering event" for new construction or alteration of an amusement ride. An industry commenter requested that the triggering event of "first use," as noted in the Advisory note to section 234.1 of the 2004 ADAAG, be included in the final rule. The Advisory note provides that "[a] custom designed and constructed ride is new upon its first use, which is the first time amusement park patrons take the ride." The Department declines to treat amusement rides differently than other types of new construction and alterations. Under the final rule, they are subject to Sec. 35.151(c). Thus, newly constructed and altered amusement rides shall comply with the 2010 Standards if the sta0rt of physical construction or the alteration is on or after 18 months from the publication date of this rule. The Department also notes that section 234.4.2 of the 2010 Standards only applies where the structural or operational characteristics of an amusement ride are altered. It does not apply in cases where the only change to a ride is the theme.

Noncomplying new construction and alterations. The element-by- element safe harbor referenced in Sec. 35.150(b)(2) has no effect on new or altered elements in existing facilities that were subject to the 1991 Standards or UFAS on the date that they were constructed or altered, but do not comply with the technical and scoping specifications for those elements in the 1991 Standards or UFAS. Section 35.151(c)(5) of the final rule sets forth the rules for noncompliant new construction or alterations in facilities that were subject to the requirements of this part. Under those provisions, noncomplying new construction and alterations constructed or altered after the effective date of the applicable ADA requirements and before March 15, 2012 shall, before March 15, 2012, be made accessible in accordance with either the 1991 Standards, UFAS, or the 2010 Standards. Noncomplying new construction and alterations constructed or altered after the effective date of the applicable ADA requirements and before March 15, 2012, shall, on or after March 15, 2012 be made accessible in accordance with the 2010 Standards.

- **Appendix to 35.151(c)**

Compliance Date for New Construction or Alterations	Applicable Standards
Before September 15, 2010	1991 Standards or UFAS
On or after September 15, 2010, and before March 15, 2012	1991 Standards, UFAS, or 2010 Standards
On or after March 15, 2012	2010 Standards

- **(d) Scope of coverage.** The 1991 Standards and the 2010 Standards apply to fixed or built-in elements of buildings, structures, site improvements, and pedestrian routes or vehicular ways located on a site. Unless specifically stated otherwise, the advisory notes, appendix notes, and figures contained in the 1991

Standards and the 2010 Standards explain or illustrate the requirements of the rule; they do not establish enforceable requirements.

Guidance

§ 35.151(d) Scope of coverage

In the NPRM, the Department proposed a new provision, Sec. 35.151(d), to clarify that the requirements established by Sec. 35.151, including those contained in the 2004 ADAAG, prescribe what is necessary to ensure that buildings and facilities, including fixed or built-in elements in new or altered facilities, are accessible to individuals with disabilities. Once the construction or alteration of a facility has been completed, all other aspects of programs, services, and activities conducted in that facility are subject to the operational requirements established in this final rule. Although the Department may use the requirements of the 2010 Standards as a guide to determining when and how to make equipment and furnishings accessible, those determinations fall within the discretionary authority of the Department.

The Department also wishes to clarify that the advisory notes, appendix notes, and figures that accompany the 1991 and 2010 Standards do not establish separately enforceable requirements unless specifically stated otherwise in the text of the standards. This clarification has been made to address concerns expressed by ANPRM commenters who mistakenly believed that the advisory notes in the 2004 ADAAG established requirements beyond those established in the text of the guidelines (e.g., Advisory 504.4 suggests, but does not require, that covered entities provide visual contrast on stair tread nosing to make them more visible to individuals with low vision). The Department received no significant comments on this section and it is unchanged in the final rule.

Definitions of residential facilities and transient lodging. The 2010 Standards add a definition of "residential dwelling unit" and modify the current definition of "transient lodging." Under section 106.5 of the 2010 Standards, "residential dwelling unit" is defined as "[a] unit intended to be used as a residence, that is primarily long-term in nature" and does not include transient lodging, inpatient medical care, licensed long-term care, and detention or correctional facilities. Additionally, section 106.5 of the 2010 Standards changes the definition of "transient lodging" to a building or facility "containing one or more guest room(s) for sleeping that provides accommodations that are primarily short-term in nature." "Transient lodging" does not include residential dwelling units intended to be used as a residence. The references to "dwelling units" and "dormitories" that are in the definition of the 1991 Standards are omitted from the 2010 Standards.

The comments about the application of transient lodging or residential standards to social service center establishments, and housing at a place of education are addressed separately below. The Department received one additional comment on this issue from an organization representing emergency response personnel seeking an exemption from the transient lodging accessibility requirements for crew quarters and common use areas serving those crew quarters (e.g., locker rooms, exercise rooms, day room) that are used exclusively by on-duty emergency response personnel and that are not used for any public purpose. The commenter argued that since emergency response personnel must meet certain physical qualifications that have the effect of exempting persons with mobility disabilities, there is no need to build crew quarters and common use areas serving those crew quarters to meet the 2004 ADAAG. In addition, the commenter argued that applying the transient lodging standards would impose significant costs and create living space that is less usable for most emergency response personnel.

The ADA does not exempt spaces because of a belief or policy that excludes persons with disabilities from certain work. However, the Department believes that crew quarters that are used exclusively as a residence by emergency response personnel and the kitchens and bathrooms exclusively serving those quarters are more like residential dwelling units and are therefore covered by the residential dwelling standards in the 2010 Standards, not the transient lodging standards. The residential dwelling standards address most of the concerns of the commenter. For example, the commenter was concerned that sinks in kitchens and lavatories in bathrooms that are accessible under the transient lodging standards would be too low to be comfortably used by emergency response personnel. The residential dwelling standards allow such features to be adaptable so that they would not have to be lowered until accessibility was needed. Similarly, grab bars and shower seats would not have to be installed at the time of construction provided that reinforcement has been installed in walls and located so as to permit their installation at a later date.

- **(e) Social service center establishments.** Group homes, halfway houses, shelters, or similar social service center establishments that provide either temporary sleeping accommodations or residential dwelling units that are subject to this section shall comply with the provisions of the 2010 Standards applicable to residential facilities, including, but not limited to, the provisions in sections 233 and 809.
  - o (1) In sleeping rooms with more than 25 beds covered by this section, a minimum of 5% of the beds shall have clear floor space complying with section 806.2.3 of the 2010 Standards.
  - o (2) Facilities with more than 50 beds covered by this section that provide common use bathing facilities, shall provide at least one roll-in shower with a seat that complies with the relevant provisions of section 608 of the 2010 Standards. Transfer-type showers are not permitted in lieu of a roll-in shower with a seat, and the exceptions in sections 608.3 and 608.4 for residential dwelling units are not permitted. When separate shower facilities are provided for men and for women, at least one roll-in shower shall be provided for each group.

Guidance

§ 35.151(e) Social service center establishments

In the NPRM, the Department proposed a new Sec. 35.151(e) requiring group homes, halfway houses, shelters, or similar social service center establishments that provide temporary sleeping accommodations or residential dwelling units to comply with the provisions of the 2004 ADAAG that apply to residential facilities, including, but not limited to, the provisions in sections 233 and 809.

The NPRM explained that this proposal was based on two important changes in the 2004 ADAAG. First, for the first time, residential dwelling units are explicitly covered in the 2004 ADAAG in section 233. Second, the 2004 ADAAG eliminates the language contained in the 1991 Standards addressing scoping and technical requirements for homeless shelters, group homes, and similar social service center establishments. Currently, such establishments are covered in section 9.5 of the transient lodging section of the 1991 Standards. The deletion of section 9.5 creates an ambiguity of coverage that must be addressed.

The NPRM explained the Department's belief that transferring coverage of social service center establishments from the transient lodging standards to the residential facilities standards would alleviate conflicting requirements for social service center providers. The Department believes that a substantial percentage of social service center establishments are recipients of Federal financial assistance from the Department of Housing and Urban Development (HUD). The Department of Health and Human Services (HHS) also provides financial assistance for the operation of shelters through the Administration for Children and Families programs. As such, these establishments are covered both by the ADA and section 504 of the Rehabilitation Act. UFAS is currently the design standard for new construction and alterations for entities subject to section 504. The two design standards for accessibility--the 1991 Standards and UFAS--have confronted many social service providers with separate, and sometimes conflicting, requirements for design and construction of facilities. To resolve these conflicts, the residential facilities standards in the 2004 ADAAG have been coordinated with the section 504 requirements. The transient lodging standards, however, are not similarly coordinated. The deletion of section 9.5 of the 1991 Standards from the 2004 ADAAG presented two options: (1) Require coverage under the transient lodging standards, and subject such facilities to separate, conflicting requirements for design and construction; or (2) require coverage under the residential facilities standards, which would harmonize the regulatory requirements under the ADA and section 504. The Department chose the option that harmonizes the regulatory requirements: coverage under the residential facilities standards.

In the NPRM, the Department expressed concern that the residential facilities standards do not include a requirement for clear floor space next to beds similar to the requirement in the transient lodging standards and as a result, the Department proposed adding a provision that would require certain social service center establishments that provide sleeping rooms with more than 25 beds to ensure that a minimum of 5 percent of the beds have clear floor space in accordance with section 806.2.3 or 2004 ADAAG.

In the NPRM, the Department requested information from providers who operate homeless shelters, transient group homes, halfway houses, and other social service center establishments, and from the clients of these facilities who would be affected by this proposed change, asking, "[t]o what extent have conflicts between the ADA and section 504 affected these facilities? What would be the effect of applying the residential dwelling unit requirements to these facilities, rather than the requirements for transient lodging guest rooms?" 73 FR 34466, 34491 (June 17, 2008).

Many of the commenters supported applying the residential facilities requirements to social service center establishments, stating that even though the residential facilities requirements are less demanding in some instances, the existence of one clear standard will result in an overall increased level of accessibility by eliminating the confusion and inaction that are sometimes caused by the current existence of multiple requirements. One commenter also stated that "it makes sense to treat social service center establishments like residential facilities because this is how these establishments function in practice."

Two commenters agreed with applying the residential facilities requirements to social service center establishments but recommended adding a requirement for various bathing options, such as a roll-in shower (which is not required under the residential standards).

One commenter objected to the change and asked the Department to require that social service center establishments continue to comply with the transient lodging standards.

One commenter stated that it did not agree that the standards for residential coverage would serve persons with disabilities as well as the 1991 transient lodging standards. This commenter expressed concern that the Department had eliminated guidance for social service agencies and that the rule should be put on hold until those safeguards are restored. Another commenter argued that the rule that would provide the greatest access for persons with disabilities should prevail.

Several commenters argued for the application of the transient lodging standards to all social service center establishments except those that were "intended as a person's place of abode," referencing the Department's question related to the definition of "place of lodging" in the title III NPRM. One commenter stated that the International Building Code requires accessible units in all transient facilities. The commenter expressed concern that group homes should be built to be accessible, rather than adaptable.

The Department continues to be concerned about alleviating the challenges for social service providers that are also subject to section 504 and would likely be subject to conflicting requirements if the transient lodging standards were applied. Thus, the Department has retained the requirement that social service center establishments comply with the residential dwelling standards. The Department believes, however, that social service center establishments that provide emergency shelter to large transient populations should be able to provide bathing facilities that are accessible to persons with mobility disabilities who need roll-in showers. Because of the transient nature of the population of these large shelters, it will not be feasible to modify bathing facilities in a timely manner when faced with a need to provide a roll-in shower with a seat when requested by an overnight visitor. As a result, the Department has added a requirement that social service center establishments with sleeping accommodations for more than 50 individuals must provide at least one roll-in shower with a seat that complies with the relevant provisions of section 608 of the 2010 Standards. Transfer-type showers are not permitted in lieu of a roll-in shower with a seat and the exceptions in sections 608.3 and 608.4 for residential dwelling units are not permitted. When separate shower facilities are provided for men and for women, at least one roll-in shower shall be provided for each group. This supplemental requirement to the residential facilities standards is in addition to the supplemental requirement that was proposed in the NPRM for clear floor space in sleeping rooms with more than 25 beds.

The Department also notes that while dwelling units at some social service center establishments are also subject to the Fair Housing Act (FHAct) design and construction requirements that require certain features of adaptable and accessible design, FHAct units do not provide the same level of accessibility that is required for residential facilities under the 2010 Standards. The FHAct requirements, where also applicable, should not be considered a substitute for the 2010 Standards. Rather, the 2010 Standards must be followed in addition to the FHAct requirements.

The Department also notes that whereas the NPRM used the term "social service establishment," the final rule uses the term "social service center establishment." The Department has made this editorial change so that the final rule is consistent with the terminology used in the ADA. See 42 U.S.C. 12181(7)(k).

- **(f) Housing at a place of education.** Housing at a place of education that is subject to this section shall comply with the provisions of the 2010 Standards applicable to transient lodging, including, but not limited to, the requirements for transient lodging guest rooms in sections 224 and 806 subject to the following exceptions. For the purposes of the application of this section, the term "sleeping room" is intended to be used interchangeably with the term "guest room" as it is used in the transient lodging standards.
  - (1) Kitchens within housing units containing accessible sleeping rooms with mobility features (including suites and clustered sleeping rooms) or on floors containing accessible sleeping rooms with mobility features shall provide turning spaces that comply with section 809.2.2 of the 2010 Standards and kitchen work surfaces that comply with section 804.3 of the 2010 Standards.
  - (2) Multi-bedroom housing units containing accessible sleeping rooms with mobility features shall have an accessible route throughout the unit in accordance with section 809.2 of the 2010 Standards.
  - (3) Apartments or townhouse facilities that are provided by or on behalf of a place of education, which are leased on a year-round basis exclusively to graduate students or faculty, and do not contain any public use or common use areas available for educational programming, are not subject to the transient lodging standards and shall comply with the requirements for residential facilities in sections 233 and 809 of the 2010 Standards.

Guidance

§ 35.151(f) Housing at a place of education

The Department of Justice and the Department of Education share responsibility for regulation and enforcement of the ADA in postsecondary educational settings, including its requirements for architectural features. In addition, the Department of Housing and Urban Development (HUD) has enforcement responsibility for housing subject to title II of the ADA. Housing facilities in educational settings range from traditional residence halls and dormitories to apartment or townhouse-style residences. In addition to title II of the ADA, public universities and schools that receive Federal financial assistance are also subject to section 504, which contains its own accessibility requirements through the application of UFAS. Residential housing in an educational setting is also covered by the FHAct, which requires newly constructed multifamily housing to include certain features of accessible and adaptable design. Covered entities subject to the ADA must always be aware of, and comply with, any other Federal statutes or regulations that govern the operation of residential properties.

Although the 1991 Standards mention dormitories as a form of transient lodging, they do not specifically address how the ADA applies to dormitories or other types of residential housing provided in an educational setting. The 1991 Standards also do not contain any specific provisions for residential facilities, allowing covered entities to elect to follow the residential standards contained in UFAS. Although the 2004 ADAAG contains provisions for both residential facilities and transient lodging, the guidelines do not indicate which requirements apply to housing provided in an educational setting, leaving it to the adopting agencies to make that choice. After evaluating both sets of standards, the Department concluded that the benefits of applying the transient lodging standards outweighed the benefits of applying the residential facilities standards. Consequently, in the NPRM, the Department proposed a new Sec. 35.151(f) that provided that residence halls or dormitories operated by or on behalf of places of education shall comply with the provisions of the proposed standards for transient lodging, including, but not limited to, the provisions in sections 224 and 806 of the 2004 ADAAG.

Both public and private school housing facilities have varied characteristics. College and university housing facilities typically provide housing for up to one academic year, but may be closed during school vacation periods. In the summer, they are often used for short-term stays of one to three days, a week, or several months. Graduate and faculty housing is often provided year-round in the form of apartments, which may serve individuals or families with children. These housing facilities are diverse in their layout. Some are double-occupancy rooms with a shared toilet and bathing room, which may be inside or outside the unit. Others may contain cluster, suite, or group arrangements where several rooms are located inside a defined unit with bathing, kitchen, and similar common facilities. In some cases, these suites are indistinguishable in features from traditional apartments. Universities may build their own housing facilities or enter into agreements with private developers to build, own, or lease housing to the educational institution or to its students. Academic housing may be located on the campus of the university or may be located in nearby neighborhoods.

Throughout the school year and the summer, academic housing can become program areas in which small groups meet, receptions and educational sessions are held, and social activities occur. The ability to move between rooms--both accessible rooms and standard rooms--in order to socialize, to study, and to use all public use and common use areas is an essential part of having access to these educational programs and activities. Academic housing is also used for short-term transient educational programs during the time students are not in regular residence and may be rented out to transient visitors in a manner similar to a hotel for special university functions.

The Department was concerned that applying the new construction requirements for residential facilities to educational housing facilities could hinder access to educational programs for students with disabilities. Elevators are not generally required under the 2004 ADAAG residential facilities standards unless they are needed to provide an accessible route from accessible units to public use and common use areas, while under the 2004 ADAAG as it applies to other types of facilities, multistory public facilities must have elevators unless they meet very specific exceptions. In addition, the residential facilities standards do not require accessible roll- in showers in bathrooms, while the transient lodging requirements require some of the accessible units to be served by bathrooms with roll-in showers. The transient lodging standards also require that a greater number of units have accessible features for persons with communication disabilities. The transient lodging standards provide for installation of the required accessible features so that they are available immediately, but the residential facilities standards allow for certain features of the unit to be adaptable. For example, only reinforcements for grab bars need to be provided in residential dwellings, but the actual grab bars must be installed under the transient lodging standards. By contrast, the residential facilities standards do require certain features that provide greater accessibility within units, such as more usable kitchens, and an accessible route throughout the dwelling. The residential facilities standards also require 5 percent of the units to be accessible to persons with mobility disabilities, which is a continuation of the same scoping that is currently required under UFAS, and is therefore applicable to any educational institution that is covered by section 504. The transient lodging standards require a lower percentage of accessible sleeping rooms for facilities with large numbers of rooms than is required by UFAS. For example, if a dormitory had 150 rooms, the transient lodging standards would require seven accessible rooms while the residential standards would require eight. In a large dormitory with 500 rooms, the transient lodging standards would require 13 accessible rooms and the residential facilities standards would require 25. There are other differences between the two sets of standards as well with respect to requirements for accessible windows, alterations, kitchens, accessible route throughout a unit, and clear floor space in bathrooms allowing for a side transfer.

In the NPRM, the Department requested public comment on how to scope educational housing facilities, asking, "[w]ould the residential facility requirements or the transient lodging requirements in the 2004 ADAAG be more appropriate for housing at places of education? How would the different requirements affect the cost when building new dormitories and other student housing?" 73 FR 34466, 34492 (June 17, 2008).

The vast majority of the comments received by the Department advocated using the residential facilities standards for housing at a place of education instead of the transient lodging standards, arguing that housing at places of public education are in fact homes for the students who live in them. These commenters argued, however, that the Department should impose a requirement for a variety of options for accessible bathing and should ensure that all floors of dormitories be accessible so that students with disabilities have the same opportunities to participate in the life of the dormitory community that are provided to students without disabilities. Commenters representing persons with disabilities and several individuals argued that, although the transient lodging standards may provide a few more accessible features (such as roll-in showers), the residential facilities standards would ensure that students with disabilities have access to all rooms in their assigned unit, not just to the sleeping room, kitchenette, and wet bar. One commenter stated that, in its view, the residential facilities standards were congruent with overlapping requirements from HUD, and that access provided by the residential facilities requirements within alterations would ensure dispersion of accessible features more effectively. This commenter also argued that while the increased number of required accessible units for residential facilities as compared to transient lodging may increase the cost of construction or alteration, this cost would be offset by a reduced need to adapt rooms later if the demand for accessible rooms exceeds the supply. The commenter also encouraged the Department to impose a visitability (accessible doorways and necessary clear floor space for turning radius) requirement for both the residential facilities and transient lodging requirements to allow students with mobility impairments to interact and socialize in a fully integrated fashion.

Two commenters supported the Department's proposed approach. One commenter argued that the transient lodging requirements in the 2004 ADAAG would provide greater accessibility and increase the opportunity of students with disabilities to participate fully in campus life. A second commenter generally supported the provision of accessible dwelling units at places of education, and pointed out that the relevant scoping in the International Building Code requires accessible units "consistent with hotel accommodations."

The Department has considered the comments recommending the use of the residential facilities standards and acknowledges that they require certain features that are not included in the transient lodging standards and that should be required for housing provided at a place of education. In addition, the Department notes that since educational institutions often use their academic housing facilities as short-term transient lodging in the summers, it is important that accessible features be installed at the outset. It is not realistic to expect that the educational institution will be able to adapt a unit in a timely manner in order to provide accessible accommodations to someone attending a one-week program during the summer.

The Department has determined that the best approach to this type of housing is to continue to require the application of transient lodging standards, but at the same time to add several requirements drawn from the residential facilities standards related to accessible turning spaces and work surfaces in kitchens, and the accessible route throughout the unit. This will ensure the maintenance of the transient lodging standard requirements related to access to all floors of the facility, roll-in showers in facilities with more than 50 sleeping rooms, and other important accessibility features not found in the residential facilities standards, but will also ensure usable kitchens and access to all the rooms in a suite or apartment.

The Department has added a new definition to Sec. 35.104, "Housing at a Place of Education," and has revised Sec. 35.151(f) to reflect the accessible features that now will be required in addition to the requirements set forth under the transient lodging standards. The Department also recognizes that some educational institutions provide some residential housing on a year-round basis to graduate students and staff which is comparable to private rental housing, and which contains no facilities for educational programming. Section 35.151(f)(3) exempts from the transient lodging standards apartments or townhouse facilities provided by or on behalf of a place of education that are leased on a year-round basis exclusively to graduate students or faculty, and do not contain any public use or common use areas available for educational programming; instead, such housing shall comply with the requirements for residential facilities in sections 233 and 809 of the 2010 Standards.

Section 35.151(f) uses the term "sleeping room" in lieu of the term "guest room," which is the term used in the transient lodging standards. The Department is using this term because it believes that, for the most part, it provides a better description of the sleeping facilities used in a place of education than "guest room." The final rule states that the Department intends the terms to be used interchangeably in the application of the transient lodging standards to housing at a place of education.

- **(g) Assembly areas**. Assembly areas subject to this section shall comply with the provisions of the 2010 Standards applicable to assembly areas, including, but not limited to, sections 221 and 802. In addition, assembly areas shall ensure that—
  - (1) In stadiums, arenas, and grandstands, wheelchair spaces and companion seats are dispersed to all levels that include seating served by an accessible route;
  - (2) Assembly areas that are required to horizontally disperse wheelchair spaces and companion seats by section 221.2.3.1 of the 2010 Standards and have seating encircling, in whole or in part, a field of play or performance area shall disperse wheelchair spaces and companion seats around that field of play or performance area;
  - (3) Wheelchair spaces and companion seats are not located on (or obstructed by) temporary platforms or other movable structures, except that when an entire seating section is placed on temporary platforms or other movable structures in an area where fixed seating is not provided, in order to increase seating for an event, wheelchair spaces and companion seats may be placed in that section. When wheelchair spaces and companion seats are not required to accommodate persons eligible for those spaces and seats, individual, removable seats may be placed in those spaces and seats;
  - (4) Stadium-style movie theaters shall locate wheelchair spaces and companion seats on a riser or cross-aisle in the stadium section that satisfies at least one of the following criteria—
    - (i) It is located within the rear 60% of the seats provided in an auditorium; or
    - (ii) It is located within the area of an auditorium in which the vertical viewing angles (as measured to the top of the screen) are from the 40th to the 100th percentile of vertical viewing angles for all seats as ranked from the seats in the first row (1st percentile) to seats in the back row (100th percentile).

Guidance

§ 35.151(g) Assembly areas

In the NPRM, the Department proposed Sec. 35.151(g) to supplement the assembly area requirements of the 2004 ADAAG, which the Department is adopting as part of the 2010 Standards. The NPRM proposed at Sec. 35.151(g)(1) to require wheelchair spaces and companion seating locations to be dispersed to all levels of the facility and are served by an accessible route. The Department received no significant comments on this paragraph and has decided to adopt the proposed language with minor modifications. The Department has retained the substance of this section in the final rule but has clarified that the requirement applies to stadiums, arenas, and grandstands. In addition, the Department has revised the phrase "wheelchair and companion seating locations" to "wheelchair spaces and companion seats."

Section 35.151(g)(1) ensures that there is greater dispersion of wheelchair spaces and companion seats throughout stadiums, arenas, and grandstands than would otherwise be required by sections 221 and 802 of the 2004 ADAAG. In some cases, the accessible route may not be the same route that other individuals use to reach their seats. For example, if other patrons reach their seats on the field by an inaccessible route (e.g., by stairs), but there is an accessible route that complies with section 206.3 of the 2010 Standards that could be connected to seats on the field, wheelchair spaces and companion seats must be placed on the field even if that route is not generally available to the public.

Regulatory language that was included in the 2004 ADAAG advisory, but that did not appear in the NPRM, has been added by the Department in Sec. 35.151(g)(2). Section 35.151(g)(2) now requires an assembly area that has seating encircling, in whole or in part, a field of play or performance area such as an arena or stadium, to place wheelchair spaces and companion seats around the entire facility. This rule, which is designed to prevent a public entity from placing wheelchair spaces and companion seats on one side of the facility only, is consistent with the Department's enforcement practices and reflects its interpretation of section 4.33.3 of the 1991 Standards.

In the NPRM, the Department proposed Sec. 35.151(g)(2) which prohibits wheelchair spaces and companion seating locations from being "located on, (or obstructed by) temporary platforms or other moveable structures." Through its enforcement actions, the Department discovered that some venues place wheelchair spaces and companion seats on temporary platforms that, when removed, reveal conventional seating underneath, or cover the wheelchair spaces and companion seats with temporary platforms on top of which they place risers of conventional seating. These platforms cover groups of conventional seats and are used to provide groups of wheelchair seats and companion seats.

Several commenters requested an exception to the prohibition of the use of temporary platforms for public entities that sell most of their tickets on a season-ticket or other multi-event basis. Such commenters argued that they should be able to use temporary platforms because they know, in advance, that the patrons sitting in certain areas for the whole season do not need wheelchair spaces and companion seats. The Department declines to adopt such an exception. As it explained in detail in the NPRM, the Department believes that permitting the use of movable platforms that seat four or more wheelchair users and their companions have the potential to reduce the number of available wheelchair seating spaces below the level required, thus reducing the opportunities for persons who need accessible seating to have the same choice of ticket prices and amenities that are available to other patrons in the facility. In addition, use of removable platforms may result in instances where last minute requests for wheelchair and companion seating cannot be met because entire sections of accessible seating will be lost when a platform is removed. See 73 FR 34466, 34493 (June 17, 2008). Further, use of temporary platforms allows facilities to limit persons who need accessible seating to certain seating areas, and to relegate accessible seating to less desirable locations. The use of temporary platforms has the effect of neutralizing dispersion and other seating requirements (e.g., line of sight) for wheelchair spaces and companion seats. Cf. Independent Living Resources v. Oregon Arena Corp., 1 F. Supp. 2d 1159, 1171 (D. Or. 1998) (holding that while a public accommodation may "infill" wheelchair spaces with removable seats when the wheelchair spaces are not needed to accommodate individuals with disabilities, under certain circumstances "[s]uch a practice might well violate the rule that wheelchair spaces must be dispersed throughout the arena in a manner that is roughly proportionate to the overall distribution of seating"). In addition, using temporary platforms to convert unsold wheelchair spaces to conventional seating undermines the flexibility facilities need to accommodate secondary ticket markets exchanges as required by Sec. 35.138(g) of the final rule.

As the Department explained in the NPRM, however, this provision was not designed to prohibit temporary seating that increases seating for events (e.g., placing temporary seating on the floor of a basketball court for a concert). Consequently, the final rule, at Sec. 35.151(g)(3), has been amended to clarify that if an entire seating section is on a temporary platform for a particular event, then wheelchair spaces and companion seats may be in that seating section. However, adding a temporary platform to create wheelchair spaces and companion seats that are otherwise dissimilar from nearby fixed seating and then simply adding a small number of additional seats to the platform would not qualify as an "entire seating section" on the platform. In addition, Sec. 35.151(g)(3) clarifies that facilities may fill in wheelchair spaces with removable seats when the wheelchair spaces are not needed by persons who use wheelchairs.

The Department has been responsive to assembly areas' concerns about reduced revenues due to unused accessible seating. Accordingly, the Department has reduced scoping requirements significantly--by almost half in large assembly areas--and determined that allowing assembly areas to infill unsold wheelchair spaces with readily removable temporary individual seats appropriately balances their economic concerns with the rights of individuals with disabilities. See section 221.2 of the 2010 Standards.

For stadium-style movie theaters, in Sec. 35.151(g)(4) of the NPRM the Department proposed requiring placement of wheelchair seating spaces and companion seats on a riser or cross-aisle in the stadium section of the theater and placement of such seating so that it satisfies at least one of the following criteria: (1) It is located within the rear 60 percent of the seats provided in the auditorium; or (2) it is located within the area of the auditorium where the vertical viewing angles are between the 40th to 100th percentile of vertical viewing angles for all seats in that theater as ranked from the first row (1st percentile) to the back row (100th percentile). The vertical viewing angle is the angle between a horizontal line perpendicular to the seated viewer's eye to the screen and a line from the seated viewer's eye to the top of the screen.

The Department proposed this bright-line rule for two reasons: (1) The movie theater industry petitioned for such a rule; and (2) the Department has acquired expertise on the design of stadium style theaters from litigation against several major movie theater chains. See U.S. v. AMC Entertainment, 232 F. Supp. 2d 1092 (C.D. Ca. 2002), rev'd in part, 549 F. 3d 760 (9th Cir. 2008); U.S. v. Cinemark USA, Inc., 348 F. 3d 569 (6th Cir. 2003), cert. denied, 542 U.S. 937 (2004). Two industry commenters--at least one of whom otherwise supported this rule--requested that the Department explicitly state that this rule does not apply retroactively to existing theaters. Although this rule on its face applies to new construction and alterations, these commenters were concerned that the rule could be interpreted to apply retroactively because of the Department's statement in the ANPRM that this bright-line rule, although newly- articulated, does not represent a "substantive change from the existing line-of-sight requirements" of section 4.33.3 of the 1991 Standards. See 69 FR 58768, 58776 (Sept. 30, 2004).

Although the Department intends for Sec. 35.151(g)(4) of this rule to apply prospectively to new construction and alterations, this rule is not a departure from, and is consistent with, the line- of-sight requirements in the 1991 Standards. The Department has always interpreted the line-of-sight requirements in the 1991 Standards to require viewing angles provided to patrons who use wheelchairs to be comparable to those afforded to other spectators. Section 35.151(g)(4) merely represents the application of these requirements to stadium-style movie theaters.

One commenter from a trade association sought clarification whether Sec. 35.151(g)(4) applies to stadium-style theaters with more than 300 seats, and argued that it should not since dispersion requirements apply in those theaters. The Department declines to limit this rule to stadium-style theaters with 300 or fewer seats; stadium-style theaters of all sizes must comply with this rule. So, for example, stadium-style theaters that must vertically disperse wheelchair and companion seats must do so within the parameters of this rule.

The NPRM included a provision that required assembly areas with more than 5,000 seats to provide at least five wheelchair spaces with at least three companion seats for each of those five wheelchair spaces. The Department agrees with commenters who asserted that group seating is better addressed through ticketing policies rather than design and has deleted that provision from this section of the final rule.

- **(h) Medical care facilities.** Medical care facilities that are subject to this section shall comply with the provisions of the 2010 Standards applicable to medical care facilities, including, but not limited to, sections 223 and 805. In addition, medical care facilities that do not specialize in the treatment of conditions that affect mobility shall disperse the accessible patient bedrooms required by section 223.2.1 of the 2010 Standards in a manner that is proportionate by type of medical specialty.

Guidance

§ 35.151(h) Medical care facilities

In the 1991 title II regulation, there was no provision addressing the dispersion of accessible sleeping rooms in medical care facilities. The Department is aware, however, of problems that individuals with disabilities face in receiving full and equal medical care when accessible sleeping rooms are not adequately dispersed. When accessible rooms are not fully dispersed, a person with a disability is often placed in an accessible room in an area that is not medically appropriate for his or her condition, and is thus denied quick access to staff with expertise in that medical specialty and specialized equipment. While the Access Board did not establish specific design requirements for dispersion in the 2004 ADAAG, in response to extensive comments in support of dispersion it added an advisory note, Advisory 223.1 General, encouraging dispersion of accessible rooms within the facility so that accessible rooms are more likely to be proximate to appropriate qualified staff and resources.

In the NPRM, the Department sought additional comment on the issue, asking whether it should require medical care facilities, such as hospitals, to disperse their accessible sleeping rooms, and if so, by what method (by specialty area, floor, or other criteria). All of the comments the Department received on this issue supported dispersing accessible sleeping rooms proportionally by specialty area. These comments, from individuals, organizations, and a building code association, argued that it would not be difficult for hospitals to disperse rooms by specialty area, given the high level of regulation to which hospitals are subject and the planning that hospitals do based on utilization trends. Further, commenters suggested that without a requirement, it is unlikely that hospitals would disperse the rooms. In addition, concentrating accessible rooms in one area perpetuates segregation of individuals with disabilities, which is counter to the purpose of the ADA.

The Department has decided to require medical care facilities to disperse their accessible sleeping rooms in a manner that is proportionate by type of medical specialty. This does not require exact mathematical proportionality, which at times would be impossible. However, it does require that medical care facilities disperse their accessible rooms by medical specialty so that persons with disabilities can, to the extent practical, stay in an accessible room within the wing or ward that is appropriate for their medical needs. The language used in this rule ("in a manner that is proportionate by type of medical specialty") is more specific than that used in the NPRM ("in a manner that enables patients with disabilities to have access to appropriate specialty services") and adopts the concept of proportionality proposed by the commenters. Accessible rooms should be dispersed throughout all medical specialties, such as obstetrics, orthopedics, pediatrics, and cardiac care.

- **(i) Curb ramps.**
  - (1) Newly constructed or altered streets, roads, and highways must contain curb ramps or other sloped areas at any intersection having curbs or other barriers to entry from a street level pedestrian walkway.
  - (2) Newly constructed or altered street level pedestrian walkways must contain curb ramps or other sloped areas at intersections to streets, roads, or highways.

Guidance

§ 35.151(i) Curb ramps

Section 35.151(e) on curb ramps in the 1991 rule has been redesignated as Sec. 35.151(i). In the NPRM, the Department proposed making a minor editorial change to this section, deleting the phrase "other sloped areas" from the two places in which it appears in the 1991 title II regulation. In the NPRM, the Department stated that the phrase "other sloped areas" lacks technical precision. The Department received no significant public comments on this proposal. Upon further consideration, however, the Department has concluded that the regulation should acknowledge that there are times when there are transitions from sidewalk to road surface that do not technically qualify as "curb ramps" (sloped surfaces that have a running slope that exceed 5 percent). Therefore, the Department has decided not to delete the phrase "other sloped areas."

- **(j) Facilities with residential dwelling units for sale to individual owners.**
  - (1) Residential dwelling units designed and constructed or altered by public entities that will be offered for sale to individuals shall comply with the requirements for residential facilities in the 2010 Standards including sections 233 and 809.
  - (2) The requirements of paragraph (1) also apply to housing programs that are operated by public entities where design and construction of particular residential dwelling units take place only after a specific buyer has been identified. In such programs, the covered entity must provide the units that comply with the requirements for accessible features to those pre-identified buyers with disabilities who have requested such a unit.

Guidance

§ 35.151(j) Facilities with residential housing for sale to individual owners

Although public entities that operate residential housing programs are subject to title II of the ADA, and therefore must provide accessible residential housing, the 1991 Standards did not contain scoping or technical standards that specifically applied to residential housing units. As a result, under the Department's title II regulation, these agencies had the choice of complying with UFAS, which contains specific scoping and technical standards for residential housing units, or applying the ADAAG transient lodging standards to their housing. Neither UFAS nor the 1991 Standards distinguish between residential housing provided for rent and those provided for sale to individual owners. Thus, under the 1991 title II regulation, public entities that construct residential housing units to be sold to individual owners must ensure that some of those units are accessible. This requirement is in addition to any accessibility requirements imposed on housing programs operated by public entities that receive Federal financial assistance from Federal agencies such as HUD.

The 2010 Standards contain scoping and technical standards for residential dwelling units. However, section 233.3.2 of the 2010 Standards specifically defers to the Department and to HUD, the standard-setting agency under the ABA, to decide the appropriate scoping for those residential dwelling units built by or on behalf of public entities with the intent that the finished units will be sold to individual owners. These programs include, for example, HUD's public housing and HOME programs as well as State-funded programs to construct units for sale to individuals. In the NPRM, the Department did not make a specific proposal for this scoping. Instead, the Department stated that after consultation and coordination with HUD, the Department would make a determination in the final rule. The Department also sought public comment on this issue stating that "[t]he Department would welcome recommendations from individuals with disabilities, public housing authorities, and other interested parties that have experience with these programs. Please comment on the appropriate scoping for residential dwelling units built by or on behalf of public entities with the intent that the finished units will be sold to individual owners." 73 FR 34466, 34492 (June 17, 2008).

All of the public comments received by the Department in response to this question were supportive of the Department's ensuring that the residential standards apply to housing built on behalf of public entities with the intent that the finished units would be sold to individual owners. The vast majority of commenters recommended that the Department require that projects consisting of five or more units, whether or not the units are located on one or multiple locations, comply with the 2004 ADAAG requirements for scoping of residential units, which require that 5 percent, and no fewer than one, of the dwelling units provide mobility features, and that 2 percent, and no fewer than one, of the dwelling units provide communication features. See 2004 ADAAG Section 233.3. These commenters argued that the Department should not defer to HUD because HUD has not yet adopted the 2004 ADAAG and there is ambiguity on the scope of coverage of pre-built for sale units under HUD's current section 504 regulations. In addition, these commenters expressed concern that HUD's current regulation, 24 CFR 8.29, presumes that a prospective buyer is identified before design and construction begins so that disability features can be incorporated prior to construction. These commenters stated that State and Federally funded homeownership programs typically do not identify prospective buyers before construction has commenced. One commenter stated that, in its experience, when public entities build accessible for-sale units, they often sell these units through a lottery system that does not make any effort to match persons who need the accessible features with the units that have those features. Thus, accessible units are often sold to persons without disabilities. This commenter encouraged the Department to make sure that accessible for-sale units built or funded by public entities are placed in a separate lottery restricted to income-eligible persons with disabilities.

Two commenters recommended that the Department develop rules for four types of for-sale projects: single family pre-built (where buyer selects the unit after construction), single family post-built (where the buyer chooses the model prior to its construction), multi-family pre-built, and multi-family post-built. These commenters recommended that the Department require pre-built units to comply with the 2004 ADAAG 233.1 scoping requirements. For post- built units, the commenters recommended that the Department require all models to have an alternate design with mobility features and an alternate design with communications features in compliance with 2004 ADAAG. Accessible models should be available at no extra cost to the buyer. One commenter recommended that, in addition to required fully accessible units, all ground floor units should be readily convertible for accessibility or for sensory impairments technology enhancements.

The Department believes that consistent with existing requirements under title II, housing programs operated by public entities that design and construct or alter residential units for sale to individual owners should comply with the 2010 Standards, including the requirements for residential facilities in sections 233 and 809. These requirements will ensure that a minimum of 5 percent of the units, but no fewer than one unit, of the total number of residential dwelling units will be designed and constructed to be accessible for persons with mobility disabilities. At least 2 percent, but no fewer than one unit, of the total number of residential dwelling units shall provide communication features.

The Department recognizes that there are some programs (such as the one identified by the commenter), in which units are not designed and constructed until an individual buyer is identified. In such cases, the public entity is still obligated to comply with the 2010 Standards. In addition, the public entity must ensure that pre- identified buyers with mobility disabilities and visual and hearing disabilities are afforded the opportunity to buy the accessible units. Once the program has identified buyers who need the number of accessible units mandated by the 2010 Standards, it may have to make reasonable modifications to its policies, practices, and procedures in order to provide accessible units to other buyers with disabilities who request such units.

The Department notes that the residential facilities standards allow for construction of units with certain features of adaptability. Public entities that are concerned that fully accessible units are less marketable may choose to build these units to include the allowable adaptable features, and then adapt them at their own expense for buyers with mobility disabilities who need accessible units. For example, features such as grab bars are not required but may be added by the public entity if needed by the buyer at the time of purchase and cabinets under sinks may be designed to be removable to allow access to the required knee space for a forward approach.

The Department agrees with the commenters that covered entities may have to make reasonable modifications to their policies, practices, and procedures in order to ensure that when they offer pre-built accessible residential units for sale, the units are offered in a manner that gives access to those units to persons with disabilities who need the features of the units and who are otherwise eligible for the housing program. This may be accomplished, for example, by adopting preferences for accessible units for persons who need the features of the units, holding separate lotteries for accessible units, or other suitable methods that result in the sale of accessible units to persons who need the features of such units. In addition, the Department believes that units designed and constructed or altered that comply with the requirements for residential facilities and are offered for sale to individuals must be provided at the same price as units without such features.

- **(k) Detention and correctional facilities.**
  - (1) New construction of jails, prisons, and other detention and correctional facilities shall comply with the 2010 Standards except that public entities shall provide accessible mobility features complying with section 807.2 of the 2010 Standards for a minimum of 3%, but no fewer than one, of the total number of cells in a facility. Cells with mobility features shall be provided in each classification level.
  - (2) Alterations to detention and correctional facilities. Alterations to jails, prisons, and other detention and correctional facilities shall comply with the 2010 Standards except that public entities shall provide accessible mobility features complying with section 807.2 of the 2010 Standards for a minimum of 3%, but no fewer than one, of the total number of cells being altered until at least 3%, but no fewer than one, of the total number of cells in a facility shall provide mobility features complying with section 807.2. Altered cells with mobility features shall be provided in each classification level. However, when alterations are made to specific cells, detention and correctional facility operators may satisfy their obligation to provide the required number of cells with mobility features by providing the required

mobility features in substitute cells (cells other than those where alterations are originally planned), provided that each substitute cell—

- (i) Is located within the same prison site;
- (ii) Is integrated with other cells to the maximum extent feasible;
- (iii) Has, at a minimum, equal physical access as the altered cells to areas used by inmates or detainees for visitation, dining, recreation, educational programs, medical services, work programs, religious services, and participation in other programs that the facility offers to inmates or detainees; and,
- (iv) If it is technically infeasible to locate a substitute cell within the same prison site, a substitute cell must be provided at another prison site within the corrections system.
  - ○ (3) With respect to medical and long-term care facilities in jails, prisons, and other detention and correctional facilities, public entities shall apply the 2010 Standards technical and scoping requirements for those facilities irrespective of whether those facilities are licensed.

Guidance

§ 35.151(k) Detention and correctional facilities

The 1991 Standards did not contain specific accessibility standards applicable to cells in correctional facilities. However, correctional and detention facilities operated by or on behalf of public entities have always been subject to the nondiscrimination and program accessibility requirements of title II of the ADA. The 2004 ADAAG established specific requirements for the design and construction and alterations of cells in correctional facilities for the first time.

Based on complaints received by the Department, investigations, and compliance reviews of jails, prisons, and other detention and correctional facilities, the Department has determined that many detention and correctional facilities do not have enough accessible cells, toilets, and shower facilities to meet the needs of their inmates with mobility disabilities and some do not have any at all. Inmates are sometimes housed in medical units or infirmaries separate from the general population simply because there are no accessible cells. In addition, some inmates have alleged that they are housed at a more restrictive classification level simply because no accessible housing exists at the appropriate classification level. The Department's compliance reviews and investigations have substantiated certain of these allegations.

The Department believes that the insufficient number of accessible cells is, in part, due to the fact that most jails and prisons were built long before the ADA became law and, since then, have undergone few alterations that would trigger the obligation to provide accessible features in accordance with UFAS or the 1991 Standards. In addition, the Department has found that even some new correctional facilities lack accessible features. The Department believes that the unmet demand for accessible cells is also due to the changing demographics of the inmate population. With thousands of prisoners serving life sentences without eligibility for parole, prisoners are aging, and the prison population of individuals with disabilities and elderly individuals is growing. A Bureau of Justice Statistics study of State and Federal sentenced inmates (those sentenced to more than one year) shows the total estimated count of State and Federal prisoners aged 55 and older grew by 36,000 inmates from 2000 (44,200) to 2006 (80,200). William J. Sabol et al., Prisoners in 2006, Bureau of Justice Statistics Bulletin, Dec. 2007, at 23 (app. table 7), available at http://bjs.ojp.usdoj.gov/ index.cfm?ty=pbdetail&iid=908 (last visited July 16, 2008); Allen J. Beck et al., Prisoners in 2000, Bureau of Justice Statistics Bulletin, Aug. 2001, at 10 (Aug. 2001) (Table 14), available at bjs.ojp.usdoj.gov/index.cfm?ty=pbdetail&iid=927 (last visited July 16, 2008). This jump constitutes an increase of 81 percent in prisoners aged 55 and older during this period.

In the NPRM, the Department proposed a new section, Sec. 35.152, which combined a range of provisions relating to both program accessibility and application of the proposed standards to detention and correctional facilities. In the final rule, the Department is placing those provisions that refer to design, construction, and alteration of detention and correction facilities in a new paragraph (k) of Sec. 35.151, the section of the rule that addresses new construction and alterations for covered entities. Those portions of the final rule that address other issues, such as placement policies and program accessibility, are placed in the new Sec. 35.152.

In the NPRM, the Department also sought input on how best to meet the needs of inmates with mobility disabilities in the design, construction, and alteration of detention and correctional facilities. The Department received a number of comments in response to this question.

New Construction. The NPRM did not expressly propose that new construction of correctional and detention facilities shall comply with the proposed standards because the Department assumed it would be clear that the requirements of Sec. 35.151 would apply to new construction of correctional and detention facilities in the same manner that they apply to other facilities constructed by covered entities. The Department has decided to create a new section, Sec. 35.151(k)(1), which clarifies that new construction of jails, prisons, and other detention facilities shall comply with the requirements of 2010 Standards. Section 35.151(k)(1) also increases the scoping for accessible cells from the 2 percent specified in the 2004 ADAAG to 3 percent.

Alterations. Although the 2010 Standards contain specifications for alterations in existing detention and correctional facilities, section 232.2 defers to the Attorney General the decision as to the extent these requirements will apply to alterations of cells. The NPRM proposed at Sec. 35.152(c) that "[a]lterations to jails, prisons, and other detention and correctional facilities will comply with the requirements of Sec. 35.151(b)." 73 FR 34466, 34507 (June 17, 2008). The final rule retains that requirement at Sec. 35.151(k)(2), but increases the scoping for accessible cells from the 2 percent specified in the 2004 ADAAG to 3 percent.

Substitute cells. In the ANPRM, the Department sought public comment about the most effective means to ensure that existing correctional facilities are made accessible to prisoners with disabilities and presented three options: (1) Require all altered elements to be accessible, which would maintain the current policy that applies to other ADA alteration requirements; (2) permit substitute cells to be made accessible within the same facility, which would permit correctional authorities to meet their obligation by providing the required accessible features in cells within the same facility, other than those specific cells in which alterations are planned; or (3) permit substitute cells to be made accessible within a prison system, which would focus on ensuring that prisoners with disabilities are housed in facilities that best meet their needs, as alterations within a prison environment often result in piecemeal accessibility.

In Sec. 35.152(c) of the NPRM, the Department proposed language based on Option 2, providing that when cells are altered, a covered entity may satisfy its obligation to provide the required number of cells with mobility features by providing the required mobility features in substitute cells (i.e., cells other than those where alterations are originally planned), provided that each substitute cell is located within the same facility, is integrated with other cells to the maximum extent feasible, and has, at a minimum, physical access equal to that of the original cells to areas used by inmates or detainees for visitation, dining, recreation, educational programs, medical services, work programs, religious services, and participation in other programs that the facility offers to inmates or detainees.

The Department received few comments on this proposal. The majority who chose to comment supported an approach that allowed substitute cells to be made accessible within the same facility. In their view, such an approach balanced administrators' needs, cost considerations, and the needs of inmates with disabilities. One commenter noted, however, that with older facilities, required modifications may be inordinately costly and technically infeasible. A large county jail system supported the proposed approach as the most viable option allowing modification or alteration of existing cells based on need and providing a flexible approach to provide program and mobility accessibility. It noted, as an alternative, that permitting substitute cells to be made accessible within a prison system would also be a viable option since such an approach could create a centralized location for accessibility needs and, because that jail system's facilities were in close proximity, it would have little impact on families for visitation or on accessible programming.

A large State department of corrections objected to the Department's proposal. The commenter stated that some very old prison buildings have thick walls of concrete and reinforced steel that are difficult, if not impossible to retrofit, and to do so would be very expensive. This State system approaches accessibility by looking at its system as a whole and providing access to programs for inmates with disabilities at selected prisons. This commenter explained that not all of its facilities offer the same programs or the same levels of medical or mental health services. An inmate, for example, who needs education, substance abuse treatment, and sex offender counseling may be transferred between facilities in order to meet his needs. The inmate population is always in flux and there are not always beds or program availability for every inmate at his security level. This commenter stated that the Department's proposed language would put the State in the position of choosing between adding accessible cells and modifying paths of travel to programs and services at great expense or not altering old facilities, causing them to become in states of disrepair and obsolescent, which would be fiscally irresponsible.

The Department is persuaded by these comments and has modified the alterations requirement in Sec. 35.151(k)(2)(iv) in the final rule to allow that if it is technically infeasible to provide substitute cells in the same facility, cells can be provided elsewhere within the corrections system.

Number of accessible cells. Section 232.2.1 of the 2004 ADAAG requires at least 2 percent, but no fewer than one, of the cells in newly constructed detention and correctional facilities to have accessibility features for individuals with mobility disabilities. Section 232.3 provides that, where special holding cells or special housing cells are provided, at least one cell serving each purpose shall have mobility features. The Department sought input on whether these 2004 ADAAG requirements are sufficient to meet the needs of inmates with mobility disabilities. A major association representing county jails throughout the country stated that the 2004 ADAAG 2 percent requirement for accessible cells is sufficient to meet the needs of county jails.

Similarly, a large county sheriff's department advised that the 2 percent requirement far exceeds the need at its detention facility, where the average age of the population is 32. This commenter stressed that the regulations need to address the differences between a local detention facility with low average lengths of stay as opposed to a State prison housing inmates for lengthy periods. This commenter asserted that more stringent requirements will raise construction costs by requiring modifications that are not needed. If more stringent requirements are adopted, the commenter suggested that they apply only to State and Federal prisons that house prisoners sentenced to long terms. The Department notes that a prisoner with a mobility disability needs a cell with mobility features regardless of the length of incarceration. However, the length of incarceration is most relevant in addressing the needs of an aging population.

The overwhelming majority of commenters responded that the 2 percent ADAAG requirement is inadequate to meet the needs of the incarcerated. Many commenters suggested that the requirement be expanded to apply to each area, type, use, and class of cells in a facility. They asserted that if a facility has separate areas for specific programs, such as a dog training program or a substance abuse unit, each of these areas should also have 2 percent accessible cells but not less than one. These same commenters suggested that 5-7 percent of cells should be accessible to meet the needs of both an aging population and the larger number of inmates with mobility disabilities. One organization recommended that the requirement be increased to 5 percent overall, and that at least 2 percent of each type and use of cell be accessible. Another commenter recommended that 10 percent of cells be accessible. An organization with extensive corrections experience noted that the integration mandate requires a sufficient number and distribution of accessible cells so as to provide distribution of locations relevant to programs to ensure that persons with disabilities have access to the programs.

Through its investigations and compliance reviews, the Department has found that in most detention and correctional facilities, a 2 percent accessible cell requirement is inadequate to meet the needs of the inmate population with disabilities. That finding is supported by the majority of the commenters that recommended a 5-7 percent requirement. Indeed, the Department itself requires more than 2 percent of the cells to be accessible at its own corrections facilities. The Federal Bureau of Prisons is subject to the requirements of the 2004 ADAAG through the General Services Administration's adoption of the 2004 ADAAG as the enforceable accessibility standard for Federal facilities under the Architectural Barriers Act of 1968. 70 FR 67786, 67846-47 (Nov. 8, 2005). However, in order to meet the needs of inmates with mobility disabilities, the Bureau of Prisons has elected to increase that percentage and require that 3 percent of inmate housing at its facilities be accessible. Bureau of Prisons, Design Construction Branch, Design Guidelines, Attachment A: Accessibility Guidelines for Design, Construction, and Alteration of Federal Bureau of Prisons (Oct. 31, 2006).

The Department believes that a 3 percent accessible requirement is reasonable. Moreover, it does not believe it should impose a higher percentage on detention and corrections facilities than it utilizes for its own facilities. Thus, the Department has adopted a 3 percent requirement in Sec. 35.151(k) for both new construction and alterations. The Department notes that the 3 percent requirement is a minimum. As corrections systems plan for new facilities or alterations, the Department urges planners to include numbers of inmates with disabilities in their population projections in order to take the necessary steps to provide a sufficient number of accessible cells to meet inmate needs.

Dispersion of Cells. The NPRM did not contain express language addressing dispersion of cells in a facility. However, Advisory 232.2 of the 2004 ADAAG recommends that "[a]ccessible cells or rooms should be dispersed among different levels of security, housing categories, and holding classifications (e.g., male/female and adult/juvenile) to facilitate access." In explaining the basis for recommending, but not requiring, this type of dispersal, the Access Board stated that "[m]any detention and correctional facilities are designed so that certain areas (e.g., `shift' areas) can be adapted to serve as different types of housing according to need" and that "[p]lacement of accessible cells or rooms in shift areas may allow additional flexibility in meeting requirements for dispersion of accessible cells or rooms."

The Department notes that inmates are typically housed in separate areas of detention and correctional facilities based on a number of factors, including their classification level. In many instances, detention and correctional facilities have housed inmates in inaccessible cells, even though accessible cells were available elsewhere in the facility, because there were no cells in the areas where they needed to be housed, such as in administrative or disciplinary segregation, the women's section of the facility, or in a particular security classification area.

The Department received a number of comments stating that dispersal of accessible cells together with an adequate number of accessible cells is necessary to prevent inmates with disabilities from placement in improper security classification and to ensure integration. Commenters recommended modification of the scoping requirements to require a percentage of accessible cells in each program, classification, use or service area. The Department is persuaded by these comments. Accordingly, Sec. 35.151(k)(1) and (k)(2) of the final rule require accessible cells in each classification area.

Medical facilities. The NPRM also did not propose language addressing the application of the 2004 ADAAG to medical and long- term care facilities in correctional and detention facilities. The provisions of the 2004 ADAAG contain requirements for licensed medical and long-term care facilities, but not those that are unlicensed. A disability advocacy group and a number of other commenters recommended that the Department expand the application of section 232.4 to apply to all such facilities in detention and correctional facilities, regardless of licensure. They recommended that whenever a correctional facility has a program that is addressed specifically in the 2004 ADAAG, such as a long-term care facility, the 2004 ADAAG scoping and design features should apply for those elements. Similarly, a building code organization noted that its percentage requirements for accessible units is based on what occurs in the space, not on the building type.

The Department is persuaded by these comments and has added Sec. 35.151(k)(3), which states that "[w]ith respect to medical and long-term care facilities in jails, prisons, and other detention and correctional facilities, public entities shall apply the 2010 Standards technical and scoping requirements for those facilities irrespective of whether those facilities are licensed."

The remaining text of the 2010 Standards for Title III – the 2004 ADAAG – can be found at <u>2010 Standards for Titles II and III: 2004 ADAAG</u>

Title III
2010 Standards for Public Accommodations and Commercial Facilities

Public accommodations and commercial facilities must follow the requirements of the 2010 Standards, including both the Title III regulations at 28 CFR part 36, subpart D; and the 2004 ADAAG at 36 CFR part 1191, appendices B and D.

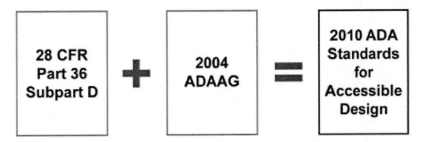

In the few places where requirements between the two differ, the requirements of 28 CFR part 36, subpart D prevail.

Compliance Date for Title III

The compliance date for the 2010 Standards for new construction and alterations is determined by:

- the date the last application for a building permit or permit extension is certified to be complete by a State, county, or local government;
- the date the last application for a building permit or permit extension is received by a State, county, or local government, where the government does not certify the completion of applications; or
- the start of physical construction or alteration, if no permit is required.

If that date is on or after March 15, 2012, then new construction and alterations must comply with the 2010 Standards. If that date is on or after September 15, 2010, and before March 15, 2012, then new construction and alterations must comply with either the 1991 or the 2010 Standards.

CONTENTS

28 CFR part 36, subpart D – New Construction and Alterations

> **Guidance on the Revisions to 28 CFR part 36, subpart D**
> Subpart D establishes the title III requirements applicable to new construction and alterations. The Department has amended this subpart to adopt the 2004 ADAAG, set forth the effective dates for implementation of the 2010 Standards, and make related revisions as described below.

§36.401 New construction.

- **(a) General.**
  - o (1) Except as provided in paragraphs (b) and (c) of this section, discrimination for purposes of this part includes a failure to design and construct facilities for first occupancy after January 26, 1993, that are readily accessible to and usable by individuals with disabilities.
  - o (2) For purposes of this section, a facility is designed and constructed for first occupancy after January 26, 1993, only –
    - ▪ (i) If the last application for a building permit or permit extension for the facility is certified to be complete, by a State, County, or local government after January 26, 1992 (or, in those jurisdictions where the government does not certify completion of applications, if the last application for a building permit or permit extension for the facility is received by the State, County, or local government after January 26, 1992); and
    - ▪ (ii) If the first certificate of occupancy for the facility is issued after January 26, 1993.
- **(b) Commercial facilities located in private residences.**
  - o (1) When a commercial facility is located in a private residence, the portion of the residence used exclusively as a residence is not covered by this subpart, but that portion used exclusively in the operation of the commercial facility or that portion used both for the commercial facility and for residential purposes is covered by the new construction and alterations requirements of this subpart.
  - o (2) The portion of the residence covered under paragraph (b)(1) of this section extends to those elements used to enter the commercial facility, including the homeowner's front sidewalk, if any, the door or entryway, and hallways; and those portions of the residence, interior or exterior, available to or used by employees or visitors of the commercial facility, including restrooms.
- **(c) Exception for structural impracticability.**
  - o (1) Full compliance with the requirements of this section is not required where an entity can demonstrate that it is structurally impracticable to meet the requirements. Full compliance will be considered structurally impracticable only in those rare circumstances when the unique characteristics of terrain prevent the incorporation of accessibility features.
  - o (2) If full compliance with this section would be structurally impracticable, compliance with this section is required to the extent that it is not structurally impracticable. In that case, any portion of the facility that can be made accessible shall be made accessible to the extent that it is not structurally impracticable.
  - o (3) If providing accessibility in conformance with this section to individuals with certain disabilities (e.g., those who use wheelchairs) would be structurally impracticable, accessibility shall nonetheless be ensured to persons with other types of disabilities (e.g., those who use crutches or who have sight, hearing, or mental impairments) in accordance with this section.

- **(d) Elevator exemption.**
  - (1) For purposes of this paragraph (d) –
    - (i) Professional office of a health care provider means a location where a person or entity regulated by a State to provide professional services related to the physical or mental health of an individual makes such services available to the public. The facility housing the "professional office of a health care provider" only includes floor levels housing at least one health care provider, or any floor level designed or intended for use by at least one health care provider.
    - (ii) Shopping center or shopping mall means –
      - (A) A building housing five or more sales or rental establishments; or
      - (B) A series of buildings on a common site, either under common ownership or common control or developed either as one project or as a series of related projects, housing five or more sales or rental establishments. For purposes of this section, places of public accommodation of the types listed in paragraph (5) of the definition of "place of public accommodation" in section § 36.104 are considered sales or rental establishments. The facility housing a "shopping center or shopping mall" only includes floor levels housing at least one sales or rental establishment, or any floor level designed or intended for use by at least one sales or rental establishment.
  - (2) This section does not require the installation of an elevator in a facility that is less than three stories or has less than 3000 square feet per story, except with respect to any facility that houses one or more of the following:
    - (i) A shopping center or shopping mall, or a professional office of a health care provider.
    - (ii) A terminal, depot, or other station used for specified public transportation, or an airport passenger terminal. In such a facility, any area housing passenger services, including boarding and debarking, loading and unloading, baggage claim, dining facilities, and other common areas open to the public, must be on an accessible route from an accessible entrance.
  - (3) The elevator exemption set forth in this paragraph (d) does not obviate or limit, in any way the obligation to comply with the other accessibility requirements established in paragraph (a) of this section. For example, in a facility that houses a shopping center or shopping mall, or a professional office of a health care provider, the floors that are above or below an accessible ground floor and that do not house sales or rental establishments or a professional office of a health care provider, must meet the requirements of this section but for the elevator.

§36.402 Alterations.
- **(a) General.**
  - (1) Any alteration to a place of public accommodation or a commercial facility, after January 26, 1992, shall be made so as to ensure that, to the maximum extent feasible, the altered portions of the facility are readily accessible to and usable by individuals with disabilities, including individuals who use wheelchairs.
  - (2) An alteration is deemed to be undertaken after January 26, 1992, if the physical alteration of the property begins after that date.
- **(b) Alteration.** For the purposes of this part, an alteration is a change to a place of public accommodation or a commercial facility that affects or could affect the usability of the building or facility or any part thereof.
  - (1) Alterations include, but are not limited to, remodeling, renovation, rehabilitation, reconstruction, historic restoration, changes or rearrangement in structural parts or elements, and changes or rearrangement in the plan configuration of walls and full-height partitions. Normal maintenance, reroofing, painting or wallpapering, asbestos removal, or changes to mechanical and electrical systems are not alterations unless they affect the usability of the building or facility.
  - (2) If existing elements, spaces, or common areas are altered, then each such altered element, space, or area shall comply with the applicable provisions of appendix A to this part.

- **(c) To the maximum extent feasible.** The phrase "to the maximum extent feasible," as used in this section, applies to the occasional case where the nature of an existing facility makes it virtually impossible to comply fully with applicable accessibility standards through a planned alteration. In these circumstances, the alteration shall provide the maximum physical accessibility feasible. Any altered features of the facility that can be made accessible shall be made accessible. If providing accessibility in conformance with this section to individuals with certain disabilities (e.g., those who use wheelchairs) would not be feasible, the facility shall be made accessible to persons with other types of disabilities (e.g., those who use crutches, those who have impaired vision or hearing, or those who have other impairments).

§36.403 Alterations: Path of travel.

- **(a) General.**
  - (1) An alteration that affects or could affect the usability of or access to an area of a facility that contains a primary function shall be made so as to ensure that, to the maximum extent feasible, the path of travel to the altered area and the restrooms, telephones, and drinking fountains serving the altered area, are readily accessible to and usable by individuals with disabilities, including individuals who use wheelchairs, unless the cost and scope of such alterations is disproportionate to the cost of the overall alteration.
  - (2) If a private entity has constructed or altered required elements of a path of travel at a place of public accommodation or commercial facility in accordance with the specifications in the 1991 Standards, the private entity is not required to retrofit such elements to reflect the incremental changes in the 2010 Standards solely because of an alteration to a primary function area served by that path of travel.
- **(b) Primary function.** A "primary function" is a major activity for which the facility is intended. Areas that contain a primary function include, but are not limited to, the customer services lobby of a bank, the dining area of a cafeteria, the meeting rooms in a conference center, as well as offices and other work areas in which the activities of the public accommodation or other private entity using the facility are carried out. Mechanical rooms, boiler rooms, supply storage rooms, employee lounges or locker rooms, janitorial closets, entrances, corridors, and restrooms are not areas containing a primary function.
- **(c) Alterations to an area containing a primary function.**
  - (1) Alterations that affect the usability of or access to an area containing a primary function include, but are not limited to –
    - (i) Remodeling merchandise display areas or employee work areas in a department store;
    - (ii) Replacing an inaccessible floor surface in the customer service or employee work areas of a bank;
    - (iii) Redesigning the assembly line area of a factory; or
    - (iv) Installing a computer center in an accounting firm.
  - (2) For the purposes of this section, alterations to windows, hardware, controls, electrical outlets, and signage shall not be deemed to be alterations that affect the usability of or access to an area containing a primary function.
- **(d) Landlord/tenant:** If a tenant is making alterations as defined in § 36.402 that would trigger the requirements of this section, those alterations by the tenant in areas that only the tenant occupies do not trigger a path of travel obligation upon the landlord with respect to areas of the facility under the landlord's authority, if those areas are not otherwise being altered.
- **(e) Path of travel.**
  - (1) A "path of travel" includes a continuous, unobstructed way of pedestrian passage by means of which the altered area may be approached, entered, and exited, and which connects the altered area with an exterior approach (including sidewalks, streets, and parking areas), an entrance to the facility, and other parts of the facility.
  - (2) An accessible path of travel may consist of walks and sidewalks, curb ramps and other interior or exterior pedestrian ramps; clear floor paths through lobbies, corridors, rooms, and other improved areas; parking access aisles; elevators and lifts; or a combination of these elements.

o (3) For the purposes of this part, the term "path of travel" also includes the restrooms, telephones, and drinking fountains serving the altered area.

- **(f) Disproportionality.**
  o (1) Alterations made to provide an accessible path of travel to the altered area will be deemed disproportionate to the overall alteration when the cost exceeds 20% of the cost of the alteration to the primary function area.
  o (2) Costs that may be counted as expenditures required to provide an accessible path of travel may include:
    - (i) Costs associated with providing an accessible entrance and an accessible route to the altered area, for example, the cost of widening doorways or installing ramps;
    - (ii) Costs associated with making restrooms accessible, such as installing grab bars, enlarging toilet stalls, insulating pipes, or installing accessible faucet controls;
    - (iii) Costs associated with providing accessible telephones, such as relocating the telephone to an accessible height, installing amplification devices, or installing a text telephone (TTY);
    - (iv) Costs associated with relocating an inaccessible drinking fountain.
- **(g) Duty to provide accessible features in the event of disproportionality.**
  o (1) When the cost of alterations necessary to make the path of travel to the altered area fully accessible is disproportionate to the cost of the overall alteration, the path of travel shall be made accessible to the extent that it can be made accessible without incurring disproportionate costs.
  o (2) In choosing which accessible elements to provide, priority should be given to those elements that will provide the greatest access, in the following order:
    - (i) An accessible entrance;
    - (ii) An accessible route to the altered area;
    - (iii) At least one accessible restroom for each sex or a single unisex restroom;
    - (iv) Accessible telephones;
    - (v) Accessible drinking fountains; and
    - (vi) When possible, additional accessible elements such as parking, storage, and alarms.
- **(h) Series of smaller alterations.**
  o (1) The obligation to provide an accessible path of travel may not be evaded by performing a series of small alterations to the area served by a single path of travel if those alterations could have been performed as a single undertaking.
  o (2)
    - (i) If an area containing a primary function has been altered without providing an accessible path of travel to that area, and subsequent alterations of that area, or a different area on the same path of travel, are undertaken within three years of the original alteration, the total cost of alterations to the primary function areas on that path of travel during the preceding three year period shall be considered in determining whether the cost of making that path of travel accessible is disproportionate.
    - (ii) Only alterations undertaken after January 26, 1992, shall be considered in determining if the cost of providing an accessible path of travel is disproportionate to the overall cost of the alterations.

Guidance

§ 36.403 Alterations: Path of Travel

In the NPRM, the Department proposed one change to Sec. 36.403 on alterations and path of travel by adding a path of travel safe harbor. Proposed Sec. 36.403(a)(1) stated that if a private entity has constructed or altered required elements of a path of travel in accordance with the 1991 Standards, the private entity is not required to retrofit such elements to reflect incremental changes in the 2010 Standards solely because of an alteration to a primary function area served by that path of travel.

A substantial number of commenters objected to the Department's creation of a safe harbor for alterations to required elements of a path of travel that comply with the current 1991 Standards. These commenters argued that if a public accommodation already is in the process of altering its facility, there should be a legal requirement that individuals with disabilities are entitled to increased accessibility provided by the 2004 ADAAG for path of travel work. These commenters also stated that they did not believe there was a statutory basis for "grandfathering" facilities that comply with the 1991 Standards. Another commenter argued that the updates incorporated into the 2004 ADAAG provide very substantial improvements for access, and that since there already is a 20 percent cost limit on the amount that can be expended on path of travel alterations, there is no need for a further limitation.

Some commenters supported the safe harbor as lessening the economic costs of implementing the 2004 ADAAG for existing facilities. One commenter also stated that without the safe harbor, entities that already have complied with the 1991 Standards will have to make and pay for compliance twice, as compared to those entities that made no effort to comply in the first place. Another commenter asked that the safe harbor be revised to include pre-ADA facilities that have been made compliant with the 1991 Standards to the extent "readily achievable" or, in the case of alterations, "to the maximum extent feasible," but that are not in full compliance with the 1991 Standards.

The final rule retains the safe harbor for required elements of a path of travel to altered primary function areas for private entities that already have complied with the 1991 Standards with respect to those required elements. As discussed with respect to Sec. 36.304, the Department believes that this safe harbor strikes an appropriate balance between ensuring that individuals with disabilities are provided access to buildings and facilities and mitigating potential financial burdens on existing places of public accommodation that are undertaking alterations subject to the 2010 Standards. This safe harbor is not a blanket exemption for facilities. If a private entity undertakes an alteration to a primary function area, only the required elements of a path of travel to that area that already comply with the 1991 Standards are subject to the safe harbor. If a private entity undertakes an alteration to a primary function area and the required elements of a path of travel to the altered area do not comply with the 1991 Standards, then the private entity must bring those elements into compliance with the 2010 Standards.

§36.404 Alterations: Elevator exemption

- (a) This section does not require the installation of an elevator in an altered facility that is less than three stories or has less than 3,000 square feet per story, except with respect to any facility that houses a shopping center, a shopping mall, the professional office of a health care provider, a terminal, depot, or other station used for specified public transportation, or an airport passenger terminal.
  - o (1) For the purposes of this section, professional office of a health care provider means a location where a person or entity regulated by a State to provide professional services related to the physical or mental health of an individual makes such services available to the public. The facility that houses a professional office of a health care provider only includes floor levels housing by at least one health care provider, or any floor level designed or intended for use by at least one health care provider.
  - o (2) For the purposes of this section, shopping center or shopping mall means –
    - (i) A building housing five or more sales or rental establishments; or

- ▪ (ii) A series of buildings on a common site, connected by a common pedestrian access route above or below the ground floor, that is either under common ownership or common control or developed either as one project or as a series of related projects, housing five or more sales or rental establishments. For purposes of this section, places of public accommodation of the types listed in paragraph (5) of the definition of place of public accommodation in § 36.104 are considered sales or rental establishments. The facility housing a "shopping center or shopping mall" only includes floor levels housing at least one sales or rental establishment, or any floor level designed or intended for use by at least one sales or rental establishment.

- (b) The exemption provided in paragraph (a) of this section does not obviate or limit in any way the obligation to comply with the other accessibility requirements established in this subpart. For example, alterations to floors above or below the accessible ground floor must be accessible regardless of whether the altered facility has an elevator.

§36.405 Alterations: Historic preservation.

- (a) Alterations to buildings or facilities that are eligible for listing in the National Register of Historic Places under the National Historic Preservation Act (16 U.S.C. 470 *et seq.*) or are designated as historic under State or local law, shall comply to the maximum extent feasible with this part.

- (b) If it is determined that it is not feasible to provide physical access to an historic property that is a place of public accommodation in a manner that will not threaten or destroy the historic significance of the building or the facility, alternative methods of access shall be provided pursuant to the requirements of subpart C of this part.

Guidance

§ 36.405 Alterations: Historic Preservation

In the 1991 rule, the Department provided guidance on making alterations to buildings or facilities that are eligible for listing in the National Register of Historic Places under the National Historic Preservation Act or that are designated as historic under State or local law. That provision referenced the 1991 Standards. Because those cross-references to the 1991 Standards are no longer applicable, it is necessary in this final rule to provide new regulatory text. No substantive change in the Department's approach in this area is intended by this revision.

---

§36.406 Standards for new construction and alterations.

- **(a) Accessibility standards and compliance date.**

  - o (1) New construction and alterations subject to §§ 36.401 or 36.402 shall comply with the 1991 Standards if the date when the last application for a building permit or permit extension is certified to be complete by a State, county, or local government (or, in those jurisdictions where the government does not certify completion of applications, if the date when the last application for a building permit or permit extension is received by the State, county, or local government) is before September 15, 2010, or if no permit is required, if the start of physical construction or alterations occurs before September 15, 2010.

  - o (2) New construction and alterations subject to §§ 36.401 or 36.402 shall comply either with the 1991 Standards or with the 2010 Standards if the date when the last application for a building permit or permit extension is certified to be complete by a State, county, or local government (or, in those jurisdictions where the government does not certify completion of applications, if the date when the last application for a building permit or permit extension is received by the State, county, or local government) is on or after September 15, 2010, and before March 15, 2012, or if no permit is required, if the start of physical construction or alterations occurs on or after September 15, 2010, and before March 15, 2012.

  - o (3) New construction and alterations subject to §§ 36.401 or 36.402 shall comply with the 2010 Standards if the date when the last application for a building permit or permit extension is certified to be complete by a State, county, or local government (or, in those jurisdictions where the government does not certify completion of applications, if the date when the last application for a building permit or permit extension is received by the State, county, or local government) is on or after March 15, 2012, or if no permit is required, if the start of physical construction or alterations occurs on or after March 15, 2012.

o (4) For the purposes of this section, "start of physical construction or alterations" does not mean ceremonial groundbreaking or razing of structures prior to site preparation.

o **(5) Noncomplying new construction and alterations.**

- (i) Newly constructed or altered facilities or elements covered by §§ 36.401 or 36.402 that were constructed or altered before March 15, 2012, and that do not comply with the 1991 Standards shall, before March 15, 2012, be made accessible in accordance with either the 1991 Standards or the 2010 Standards.

- (ii) Newly constructed or altered facilities or elements covered by §§ 36.401 or 36.402 that are constructed or altered on or after March 15, 2012, that do not comply with the 1991 Standards shall, on or after March 15, 2012, be made accessible in accordance with the 2010 Standards.

Appendix to 36.406(a)

Compliance Dates for New Construction and Alterations	Applicable Standards
On or after January 26, 1993 and before September 15, 2010	1991 Standards
On or after September 15, 2010, and before March 15, 2012	1991 Standards or 2010 Standards
On or after March 15, 2012	2010 Standards

Guidance

§ 36.406 Standards for New Construction and Alterations

Applicable standards. Section 306 of the ADA, 42 U.S.C. 12186, directs the Attorney General to issue regulations to implement title III that are consistent with the guidelines published by the Access Board. As described in greater detail elsewhere in this Appendix, the Department is a statutory member of the Access Board and was involved significantly in the development of the 2004 ADAAG. Nonetheless, the Department has reviewed the standards and has determined that additional regulatory provisions are necessary to clarify how the Department will apply the 2010 Standards to places of lodging, social service center establishments, housing at a place of education, assembly areas, and medical care facilities. Those provisions are contained in Sec. 36.406(c)-(g). Each of these provisions is discussed below.

Section 36.406(a) adopts the 2004 ADAAG as part of the 2010 Standards and establishes the compliance date and triggering events for the application of those standards to both new construction and alterations. Appendix B of this final rule (Analysis and Commentary on the 2010 ADA Standards for Accessible Design) provides a description of the major changes in the 2010 Standards (as compared to the 1991 ADAAG) and a discussion of the public comments that the Department received on specific sections of the 2004 ADAAG. A number of commenters asked the Department to revise certain provisions in the 2004 ADAAG in a manner that would reduce either the required scoping or specific technical accessibility requirements. As previously stated, the ADA requires the Department to adopt standards consistent with the guidelines adopted by the Access Board. The Department will not adopt any standards that provide less accessibility than is provided under the guidelines contained in the 2004 ADAAG because the guidelines adopted by the Access Board are "minimum guidelines." 42 U.S.C. 12186(c).

In the NPRM, the Department specifically proposed amending Sec. 36.406(a) by dividing it into two sections. Proposed Sec. 36.406(a)(1) specified that new construction and alterations subject to this part shall comply with the 1991 Standards if physical construction of the property commences less than six months after the effective date of the rule. Proposed Sec. 36.406(a)(2) specified that new construction and alterations subject to this part shall comply with the proposed standards if physical construction of the property commences six months or more after the effective date of the rule. The Department also proposed deleting the advisory information now published in a table at Sec. 36.406(b).

Compliance date. When the ADA was enacted, the compliance dates for various provisions were delayed in order to provide time for covered entities to become familiar with their new obligations. Titles II and III of the ADA generally became effective on January 26, 1992, six months after the regulations were published. See 42 U.S.C. 12131 note; 42 U.S.C. 12181 note. New construction under title II and alterations under either title II or title III had to comply with the design standards on that date. See 42 U.S.C. 12131 note; 42 U.S.C. 12183(a)(2). For new construction under title III, the requirements applied to facilities designed and constructed for first occupancy after January 26, 1993--18 months after the 1991 Standards were published by the Department. See 42 U.S.C. 12183(a)(1).

The Department received numerous comments on the issue of effective date, many of them similar to those received in response to the ANPRM. A substantial number of commenters advocated a minimum of 18 months from publication of the final rule to the effective date for application of the standards to new construction, consistent with the time period used for implementation of the 1991 Standards. Many of these commenters argued that the 18-month period was necessary to minimize the likelihood of having to redesign projects already in the design and permitting stages at the time that the final rule is published. According to these commenters, large projects take several years from design to occupancy, and can be subject to delays from obtaining zoning, site approval, third- party design approval (i.e., architectural review), and governmental permits. To the extent the new standards necessitate changes in any previous submissions or permits already issued, businesses might have to expend significant funds and incur delays due to redesign and resubmission.

Some commenters also expressed concern that a six-month period would be hard to implement given that many renovations are planned around retail selling periods, holidays, and other seasonal concerns. For example, hotels plan renovations during their slow periods, retail establishments avoid renovations during the major holiday selling periods, and businesses in certain parts of the country cannot do any major construction during parts of the winter.

Some commenters argued that chain establishments need additional time to redesign their "master facility" designs for replication at multiple locations, taking into account both the new standards and applicable State and local accessibility requirements.

Other commenters argued for extending the effective date from six months to a minimum of 12 months for many of the same reasons, and one commenter argued that there should be a tolling of the effective date for those businesses that are in the midst of the permitting process if the necessary permits are delayed due to legal challenges or other circumstances outside the business's control.

Several commenters took issue with the Department's characterization of the 2004 ADAAG and the 1991 Standards as two similar rules. These commenters argued that many provisions in the 2004 ADAAG represent a "substantial and significant" departure from the 1991 Standards and that it will take a great deal of time and money to identify all the changes and implement them. In particular, they were concerned that small businesses lacked the internal resources to respond quickly to the new changes and that they would have to hire outside experts to assist them. One commenter expressed concern that regardless of familiarity with the 2004 ADAAG, since the 2004 ADAAG standards are organized in an entirely different manner from the 1991 Standards, and contain, in the commenter's view, extensive changes, it will make the shift from the old to the new standards quite complicated.

Several commenters also took issue with the Department's proffered rationale that by adopting a six-month effective date, the Department was following the precedent of other Federal agencies that have adopted the 2004 ADAAG for facilities whose accessibility they regulate. These commenters argued that the Department's title III regulation applies to a much broader range and number of facilities and programs than the other Federal agencies (i.e., Department of Transportation and the General Services Administration) and that those agencies regulate accessibility primarily in either governmental facilities or facilities operated by quasi-governmental authorities.

Several commenters representing the travel, vacation, and golf industries argued that the Department should adopt a two-year effective date for new construction. In addition to many of the arguments made by commenters in support of an 18-month effective date, these commenters also argued that a two-year time frame would allow States with DOJ-certified building codes to have the time to amend their codes to meet the 2004 ADAAG so that design professionals can work from compatible codes and standards.

Several commenters recommended treating alterations differently than new construction, arguing for a one-year effective date for alterations. Another commenter representing building officials argued that a minimum of a six-month phase-in for alterations was sufficient, since a very large percentage of alteration projects "are of a scale that they should be able to accommodate the phase- in."

In contrast, many commenters argued that the proposed six-month effective date should be retained in the final rule.

The Department has been persuaded by concerns raised by some of the commenters that the six month compliance date proposed in the NPRM for application of the 2010 Standards may be too short for certain projects that are already in the midst of the design and permitting process. The Department has determined that for new construction and alterations, compliance with the 2010 Standards will not be required until 18 months from the date the final rule is published. This is consistent with the amount of time given when the 1991 regulation was published. Since many State and local building codes contain provisions that are consistent with 2004 ADAAG, the Department has decided that public accommodations that choose to comply with the 2010 Standards as defined in Sec. 36.104 before the compliance date will still be considered in compliance with the ADA. However, public accommodations that choose to comply with the 2010 Standards in lieu of the 1991 Standards prior to the compliance date described in this rule must choose one or the other standard, and may not rely on some of the requirements contained in one standard and some of the requirements contained in the other standard.

Triggering event. In the NPRM, the Department proposed using the start of physical construction as the triggering event for applying the proposed standards to new construction under title III. This triggering event parallels that for the alterations provisions (i.e., the date on which construction begins), and would apply clearly across all types of covered public accommodations. The Department also proposed that for prefabricated elements, such as modular buildings and amusement park rides and attractions, or installed equipment, such as ATMs, the start of construction means the date on which the site preparation begins. Site preparation includes providing an accessible route to the element.

The Department's NPRM sought public comment on how to define the start of construction and the practicality of applying commencement of construction as a triggering event. The Department also requested input on whether the proposed definition of the start of construction was sufficiently clear and inclusive of different types of facilities. The Department also sought input about facilities subject to title III for which commencement of construction would be ambiguous or problematic.

The Department received numerous comments recommending that the Department adopt a two-pronged approach to defining the triggering event. In those cases where permits are required, the Department should use "date of permit application" as the effective date triggering event, and if no permit is required, the Department should use "start of construction." A number of these commenters argued that the date of permit application is appropriate because the applicant would have to consider the applicable State and Federal accessibility standards in order to submit the designs usually required with the application. Moreover, the date of permit application is a typical triggering event in other code contexts, such as when jurisdictions introduce an updated building code. Some commenters expressed concern that using the date of "start of construction" was problematic because the date can be affected by factors that are outside the control of the owner. For example, an owner can plan construction to start before the new standards take effect and therefore use the 1991 Standards in the design. If permits are not issued in a timely manner, then the construction could be delayed until after the effective date, and then the project would have to be redesigned. This problem would be avoided if the permit application date was the triggering event. Two commenters expressed concern that the term "start of construction" is ambiguous, because it is unclear whether start of construction means the razing of structures on the site to make way for a new facility or means site preparation, such as regrading or laying the foundation.

One commenter recommended using the "signing date of a construction contract," and an additional commenter recommended that the new standards apply only to "buildings permitted after the effective date of the regulations."

One commenter stated that for facilities that fall outside the building permit requirements (ATMs, prefabricated saunas, small sheds), the triggering event should be the date of installation, rather than the date the space for the facility is constructed.

The Department is persuaded by the comments to adopt a two- pronged approach to defining the triggering event for new construction and alterations. The final rule states that in those cases where permits are required, the triggering event shall be the date when the last application for a building permit application or permit extension is certified to be complete by a State, county, or local government, or in those jurisdictions where the government does not certify completion of applications, the date when the last application for a building permit or permit extension is received by the State, county, or local government. If no permits are required, then the triggering event shall be the "start of physical construction or alterations." The Department has also added clarifying language related to the term "start of physical construction or alterations" to make it clear that "start of physical construction or alterations" is not intended to mean the date of ceremonial groundbreaking or the date a structure is razed to make it possible for construction of a facility to take place.

Amusement rides. Section 234 of the 2010 Standards provides accessibility guidelines for newly designed and constructed amusement rides. The amusement ride provisions do not provide a "triggering event" for new construction or alteration of an amusement ride. An industry commenter requested that the triggering event of "first use" as noted in the Advisory note to section 234.1 of the 2004 ADAAG be included in the final rule. The Advisory note provides that "[a] custom designed and constructed ride is new upon its first use, which is the first time amusement park patrons take the ride." The Department declines to treat amusement rides differently than other types of new construction and alterations and under the final rule, they are subject to Sec. 36.406(a)(3). Thus, newly constructed and altered amusement rides shall comply with the 2010 Standards if the start of physical construction or the alteration is on or after 18 months from the publication date of this rule. The Department also notes that section 234.4.2 of the 2010 Standards only applies where the structural or operational characteristics of an amusement ride are altered. It does not apply in cases where the only change to a ride is the theme.

Noncomplying new construction and alterations. The element-by- element safe harbor referenced in Sec. 36.304(d)(2) has no effect on new or altered elements in existing facilities that were subject to the 1991 Standards on the date that they were constructed or altered, but do not comply with the technical and scoping specifications for those elements in the 1991 Standards. Section 36.406(a)(5) of the final rule sets forth the rules for noncompliant new construction or alterations in facilities that were subject to the requirements of this part. Under those provisions, noncomplying new construction and alterations constructed or altered after the effective date of the applicable ADA requirements and before March 15, 2012 shall, before March 15, 2012, be made accessible in accordance with either the 1991 Standards or the 2010 Standards. Noncomplying new construction and alterations constructed or altered after the effective date of the applicable ADA requirements and before March 15, 2012, shall, on or after March 15, 2012, be made accessible in accordance with the 2010 Standards.

- **(b) Scope of coverage.** The 1991 Standards and the 2010 Standards apply to fixed or built-in elements of buildings, structures, site improvements, and pedestrian routes or vehicular ways located on a site. Unless specifically stated otherwise, advisory notes, appendix notes, and figures contained in the 1991 Standards and 2010 Standards explain or illustrate the requirements of the rule; they do not establish enforceable requirements.

Guidance

§ 36.406(b) Scope of coverage: Application of Standards to Fixed Elements

The final rule contains a new Sec. 36.406(b) that clarifies that the requirements established by this section, including those contained in the 2004 ADAAG, prescribe the requirements necessary to ensure that fixed or built-in elements in new or altered facilities are accessible to individuals with disabilities. Once the construction or alteration of a facility has been completed, all other aspects of programs, services, and activities conducted in that facility are subject to the operational requirements established elsewhere in this final rule. Although the Department has often chosen to use the requirements of the 1991 Standards as a guide to determining when and how to make equipment and furnishings accessible, those coverage determinations fall within the discretionary authority of the Department.

The Department is also clarifying that the advisory notes, appendix notes, and figures that accompany the 1991 and 2010 Standards do not establish separately enforceable requirements unless otherwise specified in the text of the standards. This clarification has been made to address concerns expressed by ANPRM commenters who mistakenly believed that the advisory notes in the 2004 ADAAG established requirements beyond those established in the text of the guidelines (e.g., Advisory 504.4 suggests, but does not require, that covered entities provide visual contrast on stair tread nosings to make them more visible to individuals with low vision). The Department received no comments on this provision in the NPRM.

- **(c) Places of lodging.** Places of lodging subject to this part shall comply with the provisions of the 2010 Standards applicable to transient lodging, including, but not limited to, the requirements for transient lodging guest rooms in sections 224 and 806 of the 2010 Standards.
  - ○ **(1) Guest rooms.** Guest rooms with mobility features in places of lodging subject to the transient lodging requirements of 2010 Standards shall be provided as follows –
    - ▪ (i) Facilities that are subject to the same permit application on a common site that each have 50 or fewer guest rooms may be combined for the purposes of determining the required number of accessible rooms and type of accessible bathing facility in accordance with table 224.2 to section 224.2 of the 2010 Standards.
    - ▪ (ii) Facilities with more than 50 guest rooms shall be treated separately for the purposes of determining the required number of accessible rooms and type of accessible bathing facility in accordance with table 224.2 to section 224.2 of the 2010 Standards.
  - ○ **(2) Exception.** Alterations to guest rooms in places of lodging where the guest rooms are not owned or substantially controlled by the entity that owns, leases, or operates the overall facility and the physical features of the guest room interiors are controlled by their individual owners are not required to comply with § 36.402 or the alterations requirements in section 224.1.1 of the 2010 Standards.
  - ○ **(3) Facilities with residential units and transient lodging units.** Residential dwelling units that are designed and constructed for residential use exclusively are not subject to the transient lodging standards.

Guidance

§ 36.406(c) Places of Lodging

In the NPRM, the Department proposed a new definition for public accommodations that are "places of lodging" and a new Sec. 36.406(c) to clarify the scope of coverage for places of public accommodation that meet this definition. For many years the Department has received inquiries from members of the public seeking clarification of ADA coverage of rental accommodations in timeshares, condominium hotels, and mixed-use and corporate hotel facilities that operate as places of public accommodation (as that term is now defined in Sec. 36.104). These facilities, which have attributes of both residential dwellings and transient lodging facilities, have become increasingly popular since the ADA's enactment in 1990 and make up the majority of new hotel construction in some vacation destinations. The hybrid residential and lodging characteristics of these new types of facilities, as well as their ownership characteristics, complicate determinations of ADA coverage, prompting questions from both industry and individuals with disabilities. While the Department has interpreted the ADA to encompass these hotel-like facilities when they are used to provide transient lodging, the regulation previously has specifically not addressed them. In the NPRM, the Department proposed a new Sec. 36.406(c), entitled "Places of Lodging," which was intended to clarify that places of lodging, including certain timeshares, condominium hotels, and mixed-use and corporate hotel facilities, shall comply with the provisions of the proposed standards, including, but not limited to, the requirements for transient lodging in sections 224 and 806 of the 2004 ADAAG.

The Department's NPRM sought public input on this proposal. The Department received a substantial number of comments on these issues from industry representatives, advocates for persons with disabilities, and individuals. A significant focus of these comments was on how the Department should define and regulate vacation rental units in timeshares, vacation communities, and condo-hotels where the units are owned and controlled by individual owners and rented out some portion of time to the public, as compared to traditional hotels and motels that are owned, controlled, and rented to the public by one entity.

Scoping and technical requirements applicable to "places of lodging." In the NPRM, the Department asked for public comment on its proposal in Sec. 36.406(c) to apply to places of lodging the scoping and technical requirements for transient lodging, rather than the scoping and technical requirements for residential dwelling units.

Commenters generally agreed that the transient lodging requirements should apply to places of lodging. Several commenters stated that the determination as to which requirements apply should be made based on the intention for use at the time of design and construction. According to these commenters, if units are intended for transient rentals, then the transient lodging standards should apply, and if they are intended to be used for residential purposes, the residential standards should apply. Some commenters agreed with the application of transient lodging standards to places of lodging in general, but disagreed about the characterization of certain types of facilities as covered places of lodging.

The Department agrees that the scoping and technical standards applicable to transient lodging should apply to facilities that contain units that meet the definition of "places of lodging."

Scoping for timeshare or condominium hotels. In the NPRM, the Department sought comment on the appropriate basis for determining scoping for a timeshare or condominium-hotel. A number of commenters indicated that scoping should be based on the usage of the facility. Only those units used for short-term stays should be counted for application of the transient lodging standards, while units sold as residential properties should be treated as residential units not subject to the ADA. One commenter stated that scoping should be based on the maximum number of sleeping units available for public rental. Another commenter pointed out that unlike traditional hotels and motels, the number of units available for rental in a facility or development containing individually owned units is not fixed over time. Owners have the right to participate in a public rental program some, all, or none of the time, and individual owner participation changes from year to year.

The Department believes that the determination for scoping should be based on the number of units in the project that are designed and constructed with the intention that their owners may participate in a transient lodging rental program. The Department cautions that it is not the number of owners that actually exercise their right to participate in the program that determines the scoping. Rather it is the units that could be placed into an on-site or off-site transient lodging rental program. In the final rule, the Department has added a provision to Sec. 36.406(c)(3), which states that units intended to be used exclusively for residential purposes that are contained in facilities that also meet the definition of place of lodging are not covered by the transient lodging standards. Title III of the ADA does not apply to units designed and constructed with the intention that they be rented or sold as exclusively residential units. Such units are covered by the Fair Housing Act (FHAct), which contains requirements for certain features of accessible and adaptable design both for units and for public and common use areas. All units designed and constructed with the intention that they may be used for both residential and transient lodging purposes are covered by the ADA and must be counted for determining the required number of units that must meet the transient lodging standards in the 2010 Standards. Public use and common use areas in facilities containing units subject to the ADA also must meet the 2010 Standards. In some developments, units that may serve as residential units some of the time and rental units some of the time will have to meet both the FHAct and the ADA requirements. For example, all of the units in a vacation condominium facility whose owners choose to rent to the public when they are not using the units themselves would be counted for the purposes of determining the appropriate number of units that must comply with the 2010 Standards. In a newly constructed condominium that has three floors with units dedicated to be sold solely as residential housing and three floors with units that may be used as residences or hotel units, only the units on the three latter floors would be counted for applying the 2010 Standards. In a newly constructed timeshare development containing 100 units, all of which may be made available to the public through an exchange or rental program, all 100 units would be counted for purposes of applying the 2010 Standards.

One commenter also asked the Department for clarification of how to count individually owned "lock-off units." Lock-off units are units that are multi-bedroom but can be "locked off" into two separate units, each having individual external access. This commenter requested that the Department state in the final rule that individually owned lock-off units do not constitute multiple guest rooms for purposes of calculating compliance with the scoping requirements for accessible units, since for the most part the lock- off units are used as part of a larger accessible unit, and portions of a unit not locked off would constitute both an accessible one- bedroom unit or an accessible two-bedroom unit with the lock-off unit.

It is the Department's view that lock-off units that are individually owned that can be temporarily converted into two units do not constitute two separate guest rooms for purposes of calculating compliance with the scoping requirements.

One commenter asked the Department how developers should scope units where buildings are constructed in phases over a span of years, recommending that the scoping be based on the total number of units expected to be constructed at the project and not on a building-by-building basis or on a phase-by-phase basis. The Department does not think scoping should be based on planned number of units, which may or may not be actually constructed over a period of years. However, the Department recognizes that resort developments may contain buildings and facilities that are of all sizes from single-unit cottages to facilities with hundreds of units. The Department believes it would be appropriate to allow designers, builders, and developers to aggregate the units in facilities with 50 or fewer units that are subject to a single permit application and that are on a common site or that are constructed at the same time for the purposes of applying the scoping requirements in table 224.2. Facilities with more than 50 units should be scoped individually in accordance with the table. The regulation has been revised to reflect this application of the scoping requirements.

One commenter also asked the Department to use the title III regulation to declare that timeshares subject to the transient lodging standards are exempt from the design and construction requirements of the FHAct. The coverage of the FHAct is set by Congress and interpreted by regulations issued by the Department of Housing and Urban Development. The Department has no authority to exempt anyone from coverage of the FHAct.

Application of ADA to places of lodging that contain individually owned units. The Department believes that regardless of ownership structure for individual units, rental programs (whether they are on- or off-site) that make transient lodging guest rooms available to the public must comply with the general nondiscrimination requirements of the ADA. In addition, as provided in Sec. 36.406(c), newly constructed facilities that contain accommodations intended to be used for transient lodging purposes must comply with the 2010 Standards.

In the NPRM, the Department asked for public comment on several issues related to ensuring the availability of accessible units in a rental program operated by a place of lodging. The Department sought input on how it could address a situation in which a new or converted facility constructs the required number of accessible units, but the owners of those units choose not to participate in the rental program; whether the facility has an obligation to encourage or require owners of accessible units to participate in the rental program; and whether the facility developer, the condominium association, or the hotel operator has an obligation to retain ownership or control over a certain number of accessible units to avoid this problem.

In the NPRM, the Department sought public input on how to regulate scoping for a timeshare or condominium-rental facility that decides, after the sale of units to individual owners, to begin a rental program that qualifies the facility as a place of lodging, and how the condominium association, operator, or developer should determine which units to make accessible.

A number of commenters expressed concerns about the ability of the Department to require owners of accessible units to participate in the rental program, to require developers, condo associations, or homeowners associations to retain ownership of accessible units, and to impose accessibility requirements on individual owners who choose to place inaccessible units into a rental program after purchase. These commenters stated that individuals who purchase accessible vacation units in condominiums, individual vacation homes, and timeshares have ownership rights in their units and may choose lawfully to make their units available to the public some, all, or none of the time. Commenters advised the Department that the Securities and Exchange Commission takes the position that if condominium units are offered in connection with participation in a required rental program for any part of the year, require the use of an exclusive rental agent, or impose conditions otherwise restricting the occupancy or rental of the unit, then that offering will be viewed as an offering of securities in the form of an investment (rather than a real estate offering). SEC Release No. 33-5347, Guidelines as to the Applicability of the Federal Securities Laws to Offers and Sales of Condominiums or Units in a Real Estate Development (Jan. 4, 1973). Consequently, most condominium developers do not impose such restrictions at the time of sale. Moreover, owners who choose to rent their units as a short-term vacation rental can select any rental or management company to lease and manage their unit, or they may rent them out on their own. They also may choose never to lease those units. Thus, there are no guarantees that at any particular time, accessible units will be available for rental by the public. According to this commenter, providing incentives for owners of accessible units to place their units in the rental program will not work, because it does not guarantee the availability of the requisite number of rooms dispersed across the development, and there is not any reasonable, identifiable source of funds to cover the costs of such incentives.

A number of commenters also indicated that it potentially is discriminatory as well as economically infeasible to require that a developer hold back the accessible units so that the units can be maintained in the rental program year-round. One commenter pointed out that if a developer did not sell the accessible condominiums or timeshares in the building inventory, the developer would be subject to a potential ADA or FHAct complaint because persons with disabilities who wanted to buy accessible units rather than rent them each year would not have the option to purchase them. In addition, if a developer held back accessible units, the cost of those units would have to be spread across all the buyers of the inaccessible units, and in many cases would make the project financially infeasible. This would be especially true for smaller projects. Finally, this commenter argued that requiring units to be part of the common elements that are owned by all of the individual unit owners is infeasible because the common ownership would result in pooled rental income, which would transform the owners into participants in a rental pool, and thus turn the sale of the condominiums into the sale of securities under SEC Release 33-5347.

Several commenters noted that requiring the operator of the rental program to own the accessible units is not feasible either because the operator of the rental program would have to have the funds to invest in the purchase of all of the accessible units, and it would not have a means of recouping its investment. One commenter stated that in Texas, it is illegal for on-site rental programs to own condominium units. Another commenter noted that such a requirement might lead to the loss of on-site rental programs, leaving owners to use individual third-party brokers, or rent the units privately. One commenter acknowledged that individual owners cannot be required to place their units in a rental pool simply to offer an accessible unit to the public, since the owners may be purchasing units for their own use. However, this commenter recommended that owners who choose to place their units in a rental pool be required to contribute to a fund that would be used to renovate units that are placed in the rental pool to increase the availability of accessible units. One commenter argued that the legal entity running the place of lodging has an obligation to retain control over the required number of accessible units to ensure that they are available in accordance with title III.

A number of commenters also argued that the Department has no legal authority to require individual owners to engage in barrier removal where an existing development adds a rental program. One commenter stated that Texas law prohibits the operator of on-site rental program from demanding that alterations be made to a particular unit. In addition, under Texas law, condominium declarations may not require some units and not others to make changes, because that would lead to unequal treatment of units and owners, which is not permissible.

One commenter stated that since it was not possible for operators of rental programs offering privately owned condominiums to comply with accessible scoping, the Department should create exemptions from the accessible scoping, especially for existing facilities. In addition, this commenter stated that if an operator of an on-site rental program were to require renovations as a condition of participation in the rental program, unit owners might just rent their units through a different broker or on their own, in which case such requirements would not apply.

A number of commenters argued that if a development decides to create a rental program, it must provide accessible units. Otherwise the development would have to ensure that units are retrofitted. A commenter argued that if an existing building is being converted, the Department should require that if alterations of the units are performed by an owner or developer prior to sale of the units, then the alterations requirements should apply, in order to ensure that there are some accessible units in the rental pool. This commenter stated that because of the proliferation of these type of developments in Hawaii, mandatory alteration is the only way to guarantee the availability of accessible units in the long run. In this commenter's view, since conversions almost always require makeover of existing buildings, this will not lead to a significant expense.

The Department agrees with the commenters that it would not be feasible to require developers to hold back or purchase accessible units for the purposes of making them available to the public in a transient lodging rental program, nor would it be feasible to require individual owners of accessible units to participate in transient lodging rental programs.

The Department recognizes that places of lodging are developed and financed under myriad ownership and management structures and agrees that there will be circumstances where there are legal barriers to requiring compliance with either the alterations requirements or the requirements related to barrier removal. The Department has added an exception to Sec. 36.406(c), providing that in existing facilities that meet the definition of places of lodging, where the guest rooms are not owned or substantially controlled by the entity that owns, leases, or operates the overall facility and the physical features of the guest room interiors are controlled by their individual owners, the units are not subject to the alterations requirement, even where the owner rents the unit out to the public through a transient lodging rental program. In addition, the Department has added an exception to the barrier removal requirements at Sec. 36.304(g) providing that in existing facilities that meet the definition of places of lodging, where the guest rooms are not owned or substantially controlled by the entity that owns, leases, or operates the overall facility and the physical features of the guest room interiors are controlled by their individual owners, the units are not subject to the barrier removal requirement. The Department notes, however, that there are legal relationships for some timeshares and cooperatives where the ownership interests do not convey control over the physical features of units. In those cases, it may be the case that the facility has an obligation to meet the alterations or barrier removal requirements or to maintain accessible features.

- **(d) Social service center establishments**. Group homes, halfway houses, shelters, or similar social service center establishments that provide either temporary sleeping accommodations or residential dwelling units that are subject to this part shall comply with the provisions of the 2010 Standards applicable to residential facilities, including, but not limited to, the provisions in sections 233 and 809.

  o (1) In sleeping rooms with more than 25 beds covered by this part, a minimum of 5% of the beds shall have clear floor space complying with section 806.2.3 of the 2010 Standards.

  o (2) Facilities with more than 50 beds covered by this part that provide common use bathing facilities shall provide at least one roll-in shower with a seat that complies with the relevant provisions of section 608 of the 2010 Standards. Transfer-type showers are not permitted in lieu of a roll-in shower with a seat, and the exceptions in sections 608.3 and 608.4 for residential dwelling units are not permitted. When separate shower facilities are provided for men and for women, at least one roll-in shower shall be provided for each group.

Guidance

§ 36.406(d) Social Service Center Establishments

In the NPRM, the Department proposed a new Sec. 36.406(d) requiring group homes, halfway houses, shelters, or similar social service center establishments that provide temporary sleeping accommodations or residential dwelling units to comply with the provisions of the 2004 ADAAG that apply to residential facilities, including, but not limited to, the provisions in sections 233 and 809.

The NPRM explained that this proposal was based on two important changes in the 2004 ADAAG. First, for the first time, residential dwelling units are explicitly covered in the 2004 ADAAG in section 233. Second, the 2004 ADAAG eliminates the language contained in the 1991 Standards addressing scoping and technical requirements for homeless shelters, group homes, and similar social service center establishments. Currently, such establishments are covered in section 9.5 of the transient lodging section of the 1991 Standards. The deletion of section 9.5 creates an ambiguity of coverage that must be addressed.

The NPRM explained the Department's belief that transferring coverage of social service center establishments from the transient lodging standards to the residential facilities standards would alleviate conflicting requirements for social service providers. The Department believes that a substantial percentage of social service providers are recipients of Federal financial assistance from the Department of Housing and Urban Development (HUD). The Department of Health and Human Services (HHS) also provides financial assistance for the operation of shelters through the Administration for Children and Families programs. As such, they are covered both by the ADA and section 504. UFAS is currently the design standard for new construction and alterations for entities subject to section 504. The two design standards for accessibility--the 1991 Standards and UFAS--have confronted many social service providers with separate, and sometimes conflicting, requirements for design and construction of facilities. To resolve these conflicts, the residential facilities standards in the 2004 ADAAG have been coordinated with the section 504 requirements. The transient lodging standards, however, are not similarly coordinated. The deletion of section 9.5 of the 1991 Standards from the 2004 ADAAG presented two options: (1) Require coverage under the transient lodging standards, and subject such facilities to separate, conflicting requirements for design and construction; or (2) require coverage under the residential facilities standards, which would harmonizes the regulatory requirements under the ADA and section 504. The Department chose the option that harmonizes the regulatory requirements: coverage under the residential facilities standards.

In the NPRM, the Department expressed concern that the residential facilities standards do not include a requirement for clear floor space next to beds similar to the requirement in the transient lodging standards; as a result, the Department proposed adding a provision that would require certain social service center establishments that provide sleeping rooms with more than 25 beds to ensure that a minimum of 5 percent of the beds have clear floor space in accordance with section 806.2.3 of the 2004 ADAAG.

The Department requested information from providers who operate homeless shelters, transient group homes, halfway houses, and other social service center establishments, and from the clients of these facilities who would be affected by this proposed change. In the NPRM, the Department asked to what extent conflicts between the ADA and section 504 have affected these facilities and what the effect would be of applying the residential dwelling unit requirements to these facilities, rather than the requirements for transient lodging guest rooms.

Many of the commenters supported applying the residential facilities requirements to social service center establishments stating that even though the residential facilities requirements are less demanding, in some instances, the existence of one clear standard will result in an overall increased level of accessibility by eliminating the confusion and inaction that are sometimes caused by the current existence of multiple requirements. One commenter stated that the residential facilities guidelines were more appropriate because individuals housed in social service center establishments typically stay for a prolonged period of time, and guests of a transient lodging facility typically are not housed to participate in a program or receive services.

One commenter opposed to the proposed section argued for the application of the transient lodging standards to all social service center establishments except those that were "intended as a person's place of abode," referencing the Department's question related to the definition of place of lodging in the title III NPRM. A second commenter stated that the use of transient lodging guidelines would lead to greater accessibility.

The Department continues to be concerned about alleviating the challenges for social service providers that are also subject to section 504 and that would likely be subject to conflicting requirements if the transient lodging standard were applied. Thus, the Department has retained the requirement that social service center establishments comply with the residential dwelling standards. The Department did not receive comments regarding adding a requirement for bathing options, such as a roll-in shower, in social service center establishments operated by public accommodations. The Department did, however, receive comments in support of adding such a requirement regarding public entities under title II. The Department believes that social service center establishments that provide emergency shelter to large transient populations should be able to provide bathing facilities that are accessible to persons with mobility disabilities who need roll-in showers. Because of the transient nature of the population of these large shelters, it will not be feasible to modify bathing facilities in a timely manner when faced with a need to provide a roll-in shower with a seat when requested by an overnight visitor. As a result, the Department has added a requirement that social service center establishments with sleeping accommodations for more than 50 individuals must provide at least one roll-in shower with a seat that complies with the relevant provisions of section 608 of the 2010 Standards. Transfer-type showers are not permitted in lieu of a roll-in shower with a seat, and the exceptions in sections 608.3 and 608.4 for residential dwelling units are not permitted. When separate shower facilities are provided for men and for women, at least one roll-in shower must be provided for each group. This supplemental requirement to the residential facilities standards is in addition to the supplemental requirement that was proposed in the NPRM for clear floor space in sleeping rooms with more than 25 beds.

The Department also notes that while dwelling units at some social service center establishments are also subject to FHAct design and construction requirements that require certain features of adaptable and accessible design, FHAct units do not provide the same level of accessibility that is required for residential facilities under the 2010 Standards. The FHAct requirements, where also applicable, should not be considered a substitute for the 2010 Standards. Rather, the 2010 Standards must be followed in addition to the FHAct requirements.

The Department also notes that while in the NPRM the Department used the term "social service establishment," the final rule uses the term "social service center establishment." The Department has made this editorial change so that the final rule is consistent with the terminology used in the ADA. See 42 U.S.C. 12181(7)(K).

- **(e) Housing at a place of education.** Housing at a place of education that is subject to this part shall comply with the provisions of the 2010 Standards applicable to transient lodging, including, but not limited to, the requirements for transient lodging guest rooms in sections 224 and 806, subject to the following exceptions. For the purposes of the application of this section, the term "sleeping room" is intended to be used interchangeably with the term "guest room" as it is used in the transient lodging standards.
  - (1) Kitchens within housing units containing accessible sleeping rooms with mobility features (including suites and clustered sleeping rooms) or on floors containing accessible sleeping rooms with mobility features shall provide turning spaces that comply with section 809.2.2 of the 2010 Standards and kitchen work surfaces that comply with section 804.3 of the 2010 Standards.
  - (2) Multi-bedroom housing units containing accessible sleeping rooms with mobility features shall have an accessible route throughout the unit in accordance with section 809.2 of the 2010 Standards.
  - (3) Apartments or townhouse facilities that are provided by or on behalf of a place of education, which are leased on a year-round basis exclusively to graduate students or faculty and do not contain any public use or common use areas available for educational programming, are not subject to the transient lodging standards and shall comply with the requirements for residential facilities in sections 233 and 809 of the 2010 Standards.

Guidance

§ 36.406(e) Housing at a Place of Education

The Department of Justice and the Department of Education share responsibility for regulation and enforcement of the ADA in postsecondary educational settings, including architectural features. Housing types in educational settings range from traditional residence halls and dormitories to apartment or townhouse-style residences. In addition to title III of the ADA, universities and schools that are recipients of Federal financial assistance also are subject to section 504, which contains its own accessibility requirements currently through the application of UFAS. Residential housing, including housing in an educational setting, is also covered by the FHAct, which requires newly constructed multifamily housing to include certain features of accessible and adaptable design. Covered entities subject to the ADA must always be aware of, and comply with, any other Federal statutes or regulations that govern the operation of residential properties.

Although the 1991 Standards mention dormitories as a form of transient lodging, they do not specifically address how the ADA applies to dormitories and other types of residential housing provided in an educational setting. The 1991 Standards also do not contain any specific provisions for residential facilities, allowing covered entities to elect to follow the residential standards contained in UFAS. Although the 2004 ADAAG contains provisions for both residential facilities and transient lodging, the guidelines do not indicate which requirements apply to housing provided in an educational setting, leaving it to the adopting agencies to make that choice. After evaluating both sets of standards, the Department concluded that the benefits of applying the transient lodging standards outweighed the benefits of applying the residential facilities standards. Consequently, in the NPRM, the Department proposed a new Sec. 36.406(e) that provided that residence halls or dormitories operated by or on behalf of places of education shall comply with the provisions of the proposed standards for transient lodging, including, but not limited to, the provisions in sections 224 and 806 of the 2004 ADAAG.

Private universities and schools covered by title III as public accommodations are required to make their programs and activities accessible to persons with disabilities. The housing facilities that they provide have varied characteristics. College and university housing facilities typically provide housing for up to one academic year, but may be closed during school vacation periods. In the summer, they often are used for short-term stays of one to three days, a week, or several months. Graduate and faculty housing often is provided year-round in the form of apartments, which may serve individuals or families with children. These housing facilities are diverse in their layout. Some are double-occupancy rooms with a shared toilet and bathing room, which may be inside or outside the unit. Others may contain cluster, suite, or group arrangements where several rooms are located inside a defined unit with bathing, kitchen, and similar common facilities. In some cases, these suites are indistinguishable in features from traditional apartments. Universities may build their own housing facilities or enter into agreements with private developers to build, own, or lease housing to the educational institution or to its students. Academic housing may be located on the campus of the university or may be located in nearby neighborhoods.

Throughout the school year and the summer, academic housing can become program areas in which small groups meet, receptions and educational sessions are held, and social activities occur. The ability to move between rooms--both accessible rooms and standard rooms--in order to socialize, to study, and to use all public use and common use areas is an essential part of having access to these educational programs and activities. Academic housing also is used for short-term transient educational programs during the time students are not in regular residence and may be rented out to transient visitors in a manner similar to a hotel for special university functions.

The Department was concerned that applying the new construction requirements for residential facilities to educational housing facilities could hinder access to educational programs for students with disabilities. Elevators generally are not required under the 2004 ADAAG residential facilities standards unless they are needed to provide an accessible route from accessible units to public use and common use areas, while under the 2004 ADAAG as it applies to other types of facilities, multistory private facilities must have elevators unless they meet very specific exceptions. In addition, the residential facilities standards do not require accessible roll- in showers in bathrooms, while the transient lodging requirements require some of the accessible units to be served by bathrooms with roll-in showers. The transient lodging standards also require that a greater number of units have accessible features for persons with communication disabilities. The transient lodging standards provide for installation of the required accessible features so that they are available immediately, but the residential facilities standards allow for certain features of the unit to be adaptable. For example, only reinforcements for grab bars need to be provided in residential dwellings, but the actual grab bars must be installed under the transient lodging standards. By contrast, the residential facilities standards do require certain features that provide greater accessibility within units, such as usable kitchens and an accessible route throughout the dwelling. The residential facilities standards also require 5 percent of the units to be accessible to persons with mobility disabilities, which is a continuation of the same scoping that is currently required under UFAS and is therefore applicable to any educational institution that is covered by section 504. The transient lodging standards require a lower percentage of accessible sleeping rooms for facilities with large numbers of rooms than is required by UFAS. For example, if a dormitory has 150 rooms, the transient lodging standards would require 7 accessible rooms, while the residential standards would require 8. In a large dormitory with 500 rooms, the transient lodging standards would require 13 accessible rooms, and the residential facilities standards would require 25. There are other differences between the two sets of standards, including requirements for accessible windows, alterations, kitchens, an accessible route throughout a unit, and clear floor space in bathrooms allowing for a side transfer.

In the NPRM, the Department requested public comment on how to scope educational housing facilities, and it asked whether the residential facilities requirements or the transient lodging requirements in the 2004 ADAAG would be more appropriate for housing at places of education and asked how the different requirements would affect the cost of building new dormitories and other student housing. See 73 FR 34508, 34545 (June 17, 2008).

The Department received several comments on this issue under title III. One commenter stated that the Department should adopt the residential facilities standards for housing at a place of education. In the commenter's view, the residential facilities standards are congruent with overlapping requirements imposed by HUD, and the residential facilities requirements would ensure dispersion of accessible features more effectively. This commenter also argued that while the increased number of required accessible units for residential facilities as compared to transient lodging may increase the cost of construction or alteration, this cost would be offset by a reduced need later to adapt rooms if the demand for accessible rooms exceeds the supply. The commenter also encouraged the Department to impose a visitability (accessible doorways and necessary clear floor space for turning radius) requirement for both the residential facilities and transient lodging requirements to allow students with mobility impairments to interact and socialize in a fully integrated fashion. Another commenter stated that while dormitories should be treated like residences as opposed to transient lodging, the Department should ensure that "all floors are accessible," thus ensuring community integration and visitability. Another commenter argued that housing at a place of education is comparable to residential housing, and that most of the housing types used by schools do not have the same amenities and services or function like transient lodging and should not be treated as such.

Several commenters focused on the length of stay at this type of housing and suggested that if the facilities are subject to occupancy for greater than 30 days, the residential standards should apply. Another commenter supported the Department's adoption of the transient lodging standards, arguing this will provide greater accessibility and therefore increase opportunities for students with disabilities to participate. One commenter, while supporting the use of transient lodging standards in this area, argued that the Department also should develop regulations relating to the usability of equipment in housing facilities by persons who are blind or visually impaired. Another commenter argued that the Department should not impose the transient lodging requirements on K-12 schools because the cost of adding elevators can be prohibitive, and because there are safety concerns related to evacuating students in wheelchairs living on floors above the ground floor in emergencies causing elevator failures.

The Department has considered the comments recommending the use of the residential facilities standards and acknowledges that they require certain features that are not included in the transient lodging standards and that should be required for housing provided at a place of education. In addition, the Department notes that since educational institutions often use their academic housing facilities as short-term transient lodging in the summers, it is important that accessible features be installed at the outset. It is not realistic to expect that the educational institution will be able to adapt a unit in a timely manner in order to provide accessible accommodations to someone attending a one-week program during the summer.

The Department has determined that the best approach to this type of housing is to continue to require the application of transient lodging standards but, at the same time, to add several requirements drawn from the residential facilities standards related to accessible turning spaces and work surfaces in kitchens, and the accessible route throughout the unit. This will ensure the maintenance of the transient lodging standard requirements related to access to all floors of the facility, roll-in showers in facilities with more than 50 sleeping rooms, and other important accessibility features not found in the residential facilities standards, but also will ensure usable kitchens and access to all the rooms in a suite or apartment.

The Department has added a new definition to Sec. 36.104, "Housing at a Place of Education," and has revised Sec. 36.406(e) to reflect the accessible features that now will be required in addition to the requirements set forth under the transient lodging standards. The Department also recognizes that some educational institutions provide some residential housing on a year-round basis to graduate students and staff that is comparable to private rental housing but contains no facilities for educational programming. Section 36.406(e)(3) exempts from the transient lodging standards apartments or townhouse facilities that are provided with a lease on a year-round basis exclusively to graduate students or faculty and that do not contain any public use or common use areas available for educational programming; instead, such housing must comply with the requirements for residential facilities in sections 233 and 809 of the 2010 Standards.

The regulatory text uses the term "sleeping room" in lieu of the term "guest room," which is the term used in the transient lodging standards. The Department is using this term because it believes that for the most part, it provides a better description of the sleeping facilities used in a place of education than "guest room." The final rule states in Sec. 36.406(e) that the Department intends the terms to be used interchangeably in the application of the transient lodging standards to housing at a place of education.

- **(f) Assembly areas.** Assembly areas that are subject to this part shall comply with the provisions of the 2010 Standards applicable to assembly areas, including, but not limited to, sections 221 and 802. In addition, assembly areas shall ensure that –
  - o (1) In stadiums, arenas, and grandstands, wheelchair spaces and companion seats are dispersed to all levels that include seating served by an accessible route;
  - o (2) In assembly areas that are required to horizontally disperse wheelchair spaces and companion seats by section 221.2.3.1 of the 2010 Standards and that have seating encircling, in whole or in part, a field of play or performance, wheelchair spaces and companion seats are dispersed around that field of play or performance area;
  - o (3) Wheelchair spaces and companion seats are not located on (or obstructed by) temporary platforms or other movable structures, except that when an entire seating section is placed on temporary platforms or other movable structures in an area where fixed seating is not provided, in order to increase seating for an event, wheelchair spaces and companion seats may be placed in that section. When wheelchair spaces and companion seats are not required to accommodate persons eligible for those spaces and seats, individual, removable seats may be placed in those spaces and seats;
  - o (4) In stadium-style movie theaters, wheelchair spaces and companion seats are located on a riser or cross-aisle in the stadium section that satisfies at least one of the following criteria –
    - ▪ (i) It is located within the rear 60% of the seats provided in an auditorium; or
    - ▪ (ii) It is located within the area of an auditorium in which the vertical viewing angles (as measured to the top of the screen) are from the 40th to the 100th percentile of vertical viewing angles for all seats as ranked from the seats in the first row (1st percentile) to seats in the back row (100th percentile).

Guidance

§ 36.406(f) Assembly Areas

In the NPRM, the Department proposed Sec. 36.406(f) to supplement the assembly area requirements of the 2004 ADAAG, which the Department is adopting as part of the 2010 Standards. The NPRM proposed at Sec. 36.406(f)(1) to require wheelchair spaces and companion seating locations to be dispersed to all levels of the facility that are served by an accessible route. The Department received no significant comments on this paragraph and has decided to adopt the proposed language with minor modifications.

Section 36.406(f)(1) ensures that there is greater dispersion of wheelchair spaces and companion seats throughout stadiums, arenas, and grandstands than would otherwise be required by sections 221 and 802 of the 2004 ADAAG. In some cases, the accessible route may not be the same route that other individuals use to reach their seats. For example, if other patrons reach their seats on the field by an inaccessible route (e.g., by stairs), but there is an accessible route that complies with section 206.3 of the 2004 ADAAG that could be connected to seats on the field, wheelchair spaces and companion seats must be placed on the field even if that route is not generally available to the public.

Regulatory language that was included in the 2004 ADAAG advisory, but that did not appear in the NPRM, has been added by the Department in Sec. 36.406(f)(2). Section 36.406(f)(2) now requires an assembly area that has seating encircling, in whole or in part, a field of play or performance area, such as an arena or stadium, to place wheelchair spaces and companion seats around the entire facility. This rule, which is designed to prevent a public accommodation from placing wheelchair spaces and companion seats on one side of the facility only, is consistent with the Department's enforcement practices and reflects its interpretation of section 4.33.3 of the 1991 Standards.

In the NPRM, the Department proposed Sec. 36.406(f)(2), which prohibits wheelchair spaces and companion seating locations from being "located on (or obstructed by) temporary platforms * * *." 73 FR 34508, 34557 (June 17, 2008). Through its enforcement actions, the Department discovered that some venues place wheelchair spaces and companion seats on temporary platforms that, when removed, reveal conventional seating underneath, or cover the wheelchair spaces and companion seats with temporary platforms on top of which they place risers of conventional seating. These platforms cover groups of conventional seats and are used to provide groups of wheelchair seats and companion seats.

Several commenters requested an exception to the prohibition of the use of temporary platforms for public accommodations that sell most of their tickets on a season-ticket or other multi-event basis. Such commenters argued that they should be able to use temporary platforms because they know, in advance, that the patrons sitting in certain areas for the whole season do not need wheelchair spaces and companion seats. The Department declines to adopt such an exception. As it explained in detail in the NPRM, the Department believes that permitting the use of movable platforms that seat four or more wheelchair users and their companions have the potential to reduce the number of available wheelchair seating spaces below the level required, thus reducing the opportunities for persons who need accessible seating to have the same choice of ticket prices and amenities that are available to other patrons in the facility. In addition, use of removable platforms may result in instances where last minute requests for wheelchair and companion seating cannot be met because entire sections of accessible seating will be lost when a platform is removed. See 73 FR 34508, 34546 (June 17, 2008). Further, use of temporary platforms allows facilities to limit persons who need accessible seating to certain seating areas, and to relegate accessible seating to less desirable locations. The use of temporary platforms has the effect of neutralizing dispersion and other seating requirements (e.g., line of sight) for wheelchair spaces and companion seats. Cf. Independent Living Resources v. Oregon Arena Corp., 1 F. Supp. 2d 1159, 1171 (D. Or. 1998) (holding that while a public accommodation may "infill" wheelchair spaces with removable seats when the wheelchair spaces are not needed to accommodate individuals with disabilities, under certain circumstances "[s]uch a practice might well violate the rule that wheelchair spaces must be dispersed throughout the arena in a manner that is roughly proportionate to the overall distribution of seating"). In addition, using temporary platforms to convert unsold wheelchair spaces to conventional seating undermines the flexibility facilities need to accommodate secondary ticket market exchanges as required by Sec. 36.302(f)(7) of the final rule.

As the Department explained in the NPRM, however, this provision was not designed to prohibit temporary seating that increases seating for events (e.g., placing temporary seating on the floor of a basketball court for a concert). Consequently, the final rule, at Sec. 36.406(f)(3), has been amended to clarify that if an entire seating section is on a temporary platform for a particular event, then wheelchair spaces and companion seats may also be in that seating section. However, adding a temporary platform to create wheelchair spaces and companion seats that are otherwise dissimilar from nearby fixed seating and then simply adding a small number of additional seats to the platform would not qualify as an "entire seating section" on the platform. In addition, Sec. 36.406(f)(3) clarifies that facilities may fill in wheelchair spaces with removable seats when the wheelchair spaces are not needed by persons who use wheelchairs.

The Department has been responsive to assembly areas' concerns about reduced revenues due to unused accessible seating. Accordingly, the Department has reduced scoping requirements significantly--by almost half in large assembly areas--and determined that allowing assembly areas to in-fill unsold wheelchair spaces with readily removable temporary individual seats appropriately balances their economic concerns with the rights of individuals with disabilities. See section 221.1 of the 2010 Standards.

For stadium-style movie theaters, in Sec. 36.406(f)(4) of the NPRM the Department proposed requiring placement of wheelchair seating spaces and companion seats on a riser or cross-aisle in the stadium section of the theater that satisfies at least one of the following criteria: (1) It is located within the rear 60 percent of the seats provided in the auditorium; or (2) It is located within the area of the auditorium where the vertical viewing angles are between the 40th and 100th percentile of vertical viewing angles for all seats in that theater as ranked from the first row (1st percentile) to the back row (100th percentile). The vertical viewing angle is the angle between a horizontal line perpendicular to the seated viewer's eye to the screen and a line from the seated viewer's eye to the top of the screen.

The Department proposed this bright-line rule for two reasons: (1) the movie theater industry petitioned for such a rule; and (2) the Department has acquired expertise in the design of stadium-style theaters during its litigation with several major movie theater chains. See United States. v. AMC Entertainment, Inc., 232 F. Supp.2d 1092 (C.D. Cal. 2002), rev'd in part, 549 F.3d 760 (9th Cir. 2008); United States v. Cinemark USA,

Inc., 348 F.3d 569 (6th Cir. 2003). Two industry commenters--at least one of whom otherwise supported this rule--requested that the Department explicitly state that this rule does not apply retroactively to existing theaters. Although this provision on its face applies to new construction and alterations, these commenters were concerned that the rule could be interpreted to apply retroactively because of the Department's statements in the NPRM and ANPRM that this bright line rule, although newly articulated, is not a new standard but "merely codifi[es] longstanding Department requirement[s]," 73 FR 34508, 34534 (June 17, 2008), and does not represent a "substantive change from the existing line-of-sight requirements" of section 4.33.3 of the 1991 Standards, 69 FR 58768, 58776 (Sept. 30, 2004). Although the Department intends for Sec. 36.406(f)(4) of this rule to apply prospectively to new construction and alterations, this rule is not a departure from, and is consistent with, the line- of-sight requirements in the 1991 Standards. The Department has always interpreted the line-of-sight requirements in the 1991 Standards to require viewing angles provided to patrons who use wheelchairs to be comparable to those afforded to other spectators. Section 36.406(f)(4) merely represents the application of these requirements to stadium-style movie theaters.

One commenter from a trade association sought clarification whether Sec. 36.406(f)(4) applies to stadium-style theaters with more than 300 seats, and argued that it should not since dispersion requirements apply in those theaters. The Department declines to limit this rule to stadium-style theaters with 300 or fewer seats; stadium-style theaters of all sizes must comply with this rule. So, for example, stadium-style theaters that must vertically disperse wheelchair spaces and companion seats must do so within the parameters of this rule.

The NPRM included a provision that required assembly areas with more than 5,000 seats to provide at least five wheelchair spaces with at least three companion seats for each of those five wheelchair spaces. The Department agrees with commenters who asserted that group seating is better addressed through ticketing policies rather than design and has deleted that provision from this section of the final rule.

- **(g) Medical care facilities**. Medical care facilities that are subject to this part shall comply with the provisions of the 2010 Standards applicable to medical care facilities, including, but not limited to, sections 223 and 805. In addition, medical care facilities that do not specialize in the treatment of conditions that affect mobility shall disperse the accessible patient bedrooms required by section 223.2.1 of the 2010 Standards in a manner that is proportionate by type of medical specialty.

Guidance

§ 36.406(g) Medical Care Facilities

In the 1991 title III regulation, there was no provision addressing the dispersion of accessible sleeping rooms in medical care facilities. The Department is aware, however, of problems that individuals with disabilities face in receiving full and equal medical care when accessible sleeping rooms are not adequately dispersed. When accessible rooms are not fully dispersed, a person with a disability is often placed in an accessible room in an area that is not medically appropriate for his or her condition, and is thus denied quick access to staff with expertise in that medical specialty and specialized equipment. While the Access Board did not establish specific design requirements for dispersion in the 2004 ADAAG, in response to extensive comments in support of dispersion it added an advisory note, Advisory 223.1 General, encouraging dispersion of accessible rooms within the facility so that accessible rooms are more likely to be proximate to appropriate qualified staff and resources.

In the NPRM, the Department sought additional comment on the issue, asking whether it should require medical care facilities, such as hospitals, to disperse their accessible sleeping rooms, and if so, by what method (by specialty area, floor, or other criteria). All of the comments the Department received on this issue supported dispersing accessible sleeping rooms proportionally by specialty area. These comments from individuals, organizations, and a building code association, argued that it would not be difficult for hospitals to disperse rooms by specialty area, given the high level of regulation to which hospitals are subject and the planning that hospitals do based on utilization trends. Further, comments suggest that without a requirement, it is unlikely that hospitals would disperse the rooms. In addition, concentrating accessible rooms in one area perpetuates segregation of individuals with disabilities, which is counter to the purpose of the ADA.

The Department has decided to require medical care facilities to disperse their accessible sleeping rooms in a manner that is proportionate by type of medical specialty. This does not require exact mathematical proportionality, which at times would be impossible. However, it does require that medical care facilities disperse their accessible rooms by medical specialty so that persons with disabilities can, to the extent practical, stay in an accessible room within the wing or ward that is appropriate for their medical needs. The language used in this rule ("in a manner that is proportionate by type of medical specialty") is more specific than that used in the NPRM ("in a manner that enables patients with disabilities to have access to appropriate specialty services") and adopts the concept of proportionality proposed by the commenters. Accessible rooms should be dispersed throughout all medical specialties, such as obstetrics, orthopedics, pediatrics, and cardiac care.

§36.407 – 36.499 [Reserved]

**The remaining text of the 2010 Standards for Title II – the 2004 ADAAG – can be found at
2010 Standards for Titles II and III: 2004 ADAAG**

2004 ADAAG
2010 Standards for
Titles II and III Facilities

The following section applies to *both* State and local government facilities (Title II) and public accommodations and commercial facilities (Title III). The section consists of (ADA) Chapters 1 and 2 and Chapters 3 through 10, of the 2004 ADAAG (36 CFR part 1191, appendices B and D, adopted as part of both the Title II and Title III 2010 Standards).

State and local government facilities must follow the requirements of the 2010 Standards, including both the Title II regulations at 28 CFR 35.151; and the 2004 ADAAG at 36 CFR part 1191, appendices B and D.

Public accommodations and commercial facilities must follow the requirements of the 2010 Standards, including both the Title III regulations at 28 CFR part 36, subpart D; and the 2004 ADAAG at 36 CFR part 1191, appendices B and D.

In the few places where requirements between the regulation and the 2004 ADAAG differ, the requirements of 28 CFR 35.151 or 28 CFR part 36, subpart D, prevail.

Guidance

Appendix B to part 36: Analysis and Commentary on the 2010 ADA Standards for Accessible Design

The following is a discussion of substantive changes in the scoping and technical requirements for new construction and alterations resulting from the adoption of new ADA Standards for Accessible Design (2010 Standards) in the final rules for title II (28 CFR part 35) and title III (28 CFR part 36) of the Americans with Disabilities Act (ADA). The full text of the 2010 Standards is available for review at www.ada.gov.

In the Department's revised ADA title II regulation, 28 CFR 35.104 Definitions, the Department defines the term "2010 Standards" to mean the 2010 ADA Standards for Accessible Design. The 2010 Standards consist of the 2004 ADA Accessibility Guidelines (ADAAG) and the requirements contained in 28 CFR 35.151.

In the Department's revised ADA title III regulation, 28 CFR 36.104 Definitions, the Department defines the term "2010 Standards" to mean the 2010 ADA Standards for Accessible Design. The 2010 Standards consist of the 2004 ADA Accessibility Guidelines (ADAAG) and the requirements contained in 28 CFR part 36 subpart D.

This summary addresses selected substantive changes between the 1991 ADA Standards for Accessible Design (1991 Standards) codified at 28 CFR part 36, app. A (2009) and the 2010 Standards. Editorial changes are not discussed. Scoping and technical requirements are discussed together, where appropriate, for ease of understanding the requirements. In addition, this document addresses selected public comments received by the Department in response to its September 2004 Advance Notice of Proposed Rulemaking (ANPRM) and its June 2008 Notice of Proposed Rulemaking (NPRM).

The ANPRM and NPRM issued by the Department concerning the proposed 2010 Standards stated that comments received by the Access Board in response to its development of the ADAAG upon which the 2010 Standards are based would be considered in the development of the final Standards. Therefore, the Department will not restate here all of the comments and responses to them issued by the Access Board. The Department is supplementing the Access Board's comments and responses with substantive comments and responses here. Comments and responses addressed by the Access Board that also were separately submitted to the Department will not be restated in their entirety here.

CONTENTS

ADA CHAPTER 1: APPLICATION AND ADMINISTRATION

101 Purpose

101.1 General. This document contains scoping and technical requirements for accessibility to sites, facilities, buildings, and elements by individuals with disabilities. The requirements are to be applied during the design, construction, additions to, and alteration of sites, facilities, buildings, and elements to the extent required by regulations issued by Federal agencies under the Americans with Disabilities Act of 1990 (ADA).

Advisory

101.1 General. In addition to these requirements, covered entities must comply with the regulations issued by the Department of Justice and the Department of Transportation under the Americans with Disabilities Act. There are issues affecting individuals with disabilities which are not addressed by these requirements, but which are covered by the Department of Justice and the Department of Transportation regulations.

101.2 Effect on Removal of Barriers in Existing Facilities. This document does not address existing facilities unless altered at the discretion of a covered entity. The Department of Justice has authority over existing facilities that are subject to the requirement for removal of barriers under Title III of the ADA. Any determination that this document applies to existing facilities subject to the barrier removal requirement is solely within the discretion of the Department of Justice and is effective only to the extent required by regulations issued by the Department of Justice.

102 Dimensions for Adults and Children

The technical requirements are based on adult dimensions and anthropometrics. In addition, this document includes technical requirements based on children's dimensions and anthropometrics for drinking fountains, water closets, toilet compartments, lavatories and sinks, dining surfaces, and work surfaces.

Guidance

Section 2.1 of the 1991 Standards stated that the specifications were based upon adult dimensions and anthropometrics. The 1991 Standards did not provide specific requirements for children's elements or facilities.

Section 102 of the 2010 Standards states that the technical requirements are based on adult dimensions and anthropometrics. In addition, technical requirements are also provided based on children's dimensions and anthropometrics for drinking fountains, water closets and other elements located in toilet compartments, lavatories and sinks, dining surfaces, and work surfaces.

---

103 Equivalent Facilitation

Nothing in these requirements prevents the use of designs, products, or technologies as alternatives to those prescribed, provided they result in substantially equivalent or greater accessibility and usability.

Advisory

103 Equivalent Facilitation. The responsibility for demonstrating equivalent facilitation in the event of a challenge rests with the covered entity. With the exception of transit facilities, which are covered by regulations issued by the Department of Transportation, there is no process for certifying that an alternative design provides equivalent facilitation.

Guidance

This section acknowledges that nothing in these requirements prevents the use of designs, products, or technologies as alternatives to those prescribed, provided that the alternatives result in substantially equivalent or greater accessibility and usability.

A commenter encouraged the Department to include a procedure for determining equivalent facilitation. The Department believes that the responsibility for determining and demonstrating equivalent facilitation properly rests with the covered entity. The purpose of allowing for equivalent facilitation is to encourage flexibility and innovation while still ensuring access. The Department believes that establishing potentially cumbersome bureaucratic provisions for reviewing requests for equivalent facilitation is inappropriate.

104 Conventions

104.1 Dimensions. Dimensions that are not stated as "maximum" or "minimum" are absolute.

104.1.1 Construction and Manufacturing Tolerances. All dimensions are subject to conventional industry tolerances except where the requirement is stated as a range with specific minimum and maximum end points.

Advisory

104.1.1 Construction and Manufacturing Tolerances. Conventional industry tolerances recognized by this provision include those for field conditions and those that may be a necessary consequence of a particular manufacturing process. Recognized tolerances are not intended to apply to design work.

It is good practice when specifying dimensions to avoid specifying a tolerance where dimensions are absolute. For example, if this document requires "1 inches," avoid specifying "1 inches plus or minus X inches."

Where the requirement states a specified range, such as in Section 609.4 where grab bars must be installed between 33 inches and 36 inches above the floor, the range provides an adequate tolerance and therefore no tolerance outside of the range at either end point is permitted.

Where a requirement is a minimum or a maximum dimension that does not have two specific minimum and maximum end points, tolerances may apply. Where an element is to be installed at the minimum or maximum permitted dimension, such as "15 inches minimum" or "5 pounds maximum", it would not be good practice to specify "5 pounds (plus X pounds) or 15 inches (minus X inches)." Rather, it would be good practice to specify a dimension less than the required maximum (or more than the required minimum) by the amount of the expected field or manufacturing tolerance and not to state any tolerance in conjunction with the specified dimension.

Specifying dimensions in design in the manner described above will better ensure that facilities and elements accomplish the level of accessibility intended by these requirements. It will also more often produce an end result of strict and literal compliance with the stated requirements and eliminate enforcement difficulties and issues that might otherwise arise. Information on specific tolerances may be available from industry or trade organizations, code groups and building officials, and published references.

104.2 Calculation of Percentages. Where the required number of elements or facilities to be provided is determined by calculations of ratios or percentages and remainders or fractions result, the next greater whole number of such elements or facilities shall be provided. Where the determination of the required size or dimension of an element or facility involves ratios or percentages, rounding down for values less than one half shall be permitted.

104.3 Figures. Unless specifically stated otherwise, figures are provided for informational purposes only.

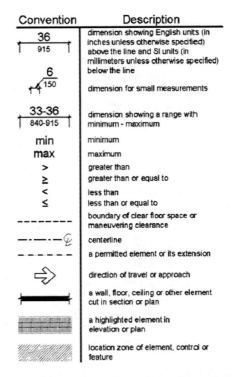

Convention	Description
36 / 915	dimension showing English units (in inches unless otherwise specified) above the line and SI units (in millimeters unless otherwise specified) below the line
6 / 150	dimension for small measurements
33-36 / 840-915	dimension showing a range with minimum - maximum
min	minimum
max	maximum
>	greater than
≥	greater than or equal to
<	less than
≤	less than or equal to
- - - - - - -	boundary of clear floor space or maneuvering clearance
— · — · — ℄	centerline
– – – – – –	a permitted element or its extension
⇨	direction of travel or approach
▬▬▬	a wall, floor, ceiling or other element cut in section or plan
(shaded)	a highlighted element in elevation or plan
(hatched)	location zone of element, control or feature

Figure 104 Graphic Convention for Figures

Guidance

Dimensions. Section 104.1 of the 2010 Standards notes that dimensions not stated as a "maximum" or "minimum" are absolute. Section 104.1.1 of the 2010 Standards provides that all dimensions are subject to conventional industry tolerances except where the requirement is stated as a range with specific minimum and maximum end points. A commenter stated that the 2010 Standards restrict the application of construction tolerances only to those few requirements that are expressed as an absolute dimension.

This is an incorrect interpretation of sections 104.1 and 104.1.1 of the 2010 Standards. Construction and manufacturing tolerances apply to absolute dimensions as well as to dimensions expressed as a maximum or minimum. When the requirement states a specified range, such as in section 609.4 where grab bars must be installed between 33 inches and 36 inches above the finished floor, that range provides an adequate tolerance. Advisory 104.1.1 gives further guidance about tolerances.

Section 104.2 of the 2010 Standards provides that where the required number of elements or facilities to be provided is determined by calculations of ratios or percentages and remainders or fractions result, the next greater whole number of such elements or facilities shall be provided. Where the determination of the required size or dimension of an element or facility involves ratios or percentages, rounding down for values less than one-half is permissible.

A commenter stated that it is customary in the building code industry to round up rather than down for values less than one-half. As noted here, where the 2010 Standards provide for scoping, any resulting fractional calculations will be rounded to the next whole number. The Department is retaining the portion of section 104.2 that permits rounding down for values less than one-half where the determination of the required size or dimension of an element or facility involves ratios or percentages. Such practice is standard with the industry, and is in keeping with model building codes.

105 Referenced Standards

105.1 General. The standards listed in 105.2 are incorporated by reference in this document and are part of the requirements to the prescribed extent of each such reference. The Director of the Federal Register has approved these standards for incorporation by reference in accordance with 5 U.S.C. 552(a) and 1 CFR part 51. Copies of the referenced standards may be inspected at the Architectural and Transportation Barriers Compliance Board, 1331 F Street, NW, Suite 1000, Washington, DC 20004; at the Department of Justice, Civil Rights Division, Disability Rights Section, 1425 New York Avenue, NW, Washington, DC; at the Department of Transportation, 400 Seventh Street, SW, Room 10424, Washington DC; or at the National Archives and Records Administration (NARA). For information on the availability of this material at NARA, call (202) 741-6030, or go to http://www.archives.gov/federal_register/code_of_federal_regulations/ibr_locations.html.

105.2 Referenced Standards. The specific edition of the standards listed below are referenced in this document. Where differences occur between this document and the referenced standards, this document applies.

105.2.1 ANSI/BHMA. Copies of the referenced standards may be obtained from the Builders Hardware Manufacturers Association, 355 Lexington Avenue, 17th floor, New York, NY 10017 (http://www.buildershardware.com).

ANSI/BHMA A156.10-1999 American National Standard for Power Operated Pedestrian Doors (see 404.3).

ANSI/BHMA A156.19-1997 American National Standard for Power Assist and Low Energy Power Operated Doors (see 404.3, 408.3.2.1, and 409.3.1).

ANSI/BHMA A156.19-2002 American National Standard for Power Assist and Low Energy Power Operated Doors (see 404.3, 408.3.2.1, and 409.3.1).

Advisory

105.2.1 ANSI/BHMA. ANSI/BHMA A156.10-1999 applies to power operated doors for pedestrian use which open automatically when approached by pedestrians. Included are provisions intended to reduce the chance of user injury or entrapment.

ANSI/BHMA A156.19-1997 and A156.19-2002 applies to power assist doors, low energy power operated doors or low energy power open doors for pedestrian use not provided for in ANSI/BHMA A156.10 for Power Operated Pedestrian Doors. Included are provisions intended to reduce the chance of user injury or entrapment.

105.2.2 ASME. Copies of the referenced standards may be obtained from the American Society of Mechanical Engineers, Three Park Avenue, New York, New York 10016 (http://www.asme.org).

ASME A17.1- 2000 Safety Code for Elevators and Escalators, including ASME A17.1a-2002 Addenda and ASME A17.1b-2003 Addenda (see 407.1, 408.1, 409.1, and 810.9).

ASME A18.1-1999 Safety Standard for Platform Lifts and Stairway Chairlifts, including ASME A18.1a-2001 Addenda and ASME A18.1b-2001 Addenda (see 410.1).

ASME A18.1-2003 Safety Standard for Platform Lifts and Stairway Chairlifts, (see 410.1).

Advisory

105.2.2 ASME. ASME A17.1-2000 is used by local jurisdictions throughout the United States for the design, construction, installation, operation, inspection, testing, maintenance, alteration, and repair of elevators and escalators. The majority of the requirements apply to the operational machinery not seen or used by elevator passengers. ASME A17.1 requires a two-way means of emergency communications in passenger elevators. This means of communication must connect with emergency or authorized personnel and not an automated answering system. The communication system must be push button activated. The activation button must be permanently identified with the word "HELP." A visual indication acknowledging the establishment of a communications link to authorized personnel must be provided. The visual indication must remain on until the call is terminated by authorized personnel. The building location, the elevator car number, and the need for assistance must be provided to authorized personnel answering the emergency call. The use of a handset by the communications system is prohibited. Only the authorized personnel answering the call can terminate the call. Operating instructions for the communications system must be provided in the elevator car.

The provisions for escalators require that at least two flat steps be provided at the entrance and exit of every escalator and that steps on escalators be demarcated by yellow lines 2 inches wide maximum along the back and sides of steps.

ASME A18.1-1999 and ASME A18.1-2003 address the design, construction, installation, operation, inspection, testing, maintenance and repair of lifts that are intended for transportation of persons with disabilities. Lifts are classified as: vertical platform lifts, inclined platform lifts, inclined stairway chairlifts, private residence vertical platform lifts, private residence inclined platform lifts, and private residence inclined stairway chairlifts.

This document does not permit the use of inclined stairway chairlifts which do not provide platforms because such lifts require the user to transfer to a seat.

ASME A18.1 contains requirements for runways, which are the spaces in which platforms or seats move. The standard includes additional provisions for runway enclosures, electrical equipment and wiring, structural support, headroom clearance (which is 80 inches minimum), lower level access ramps and pits. The enclosure walls not used for entry or exit are required to have a grab bar the full length of the wall on platform lifts. Access ramps are required to meet requirements similar to those for ramps in Chapter 4 of this document.

Each of the lift types addressed in ASME A18.1 must meet requirements for capacity, load, speed, travel, operating devices, and control equipment. The maximum permitted height for operable parts is consistent with Section 308 of this document. The standard also addresses attendant operation. However, Section 410.1 of this document does not permit attendant operation.

105.2.3 ASTM. Copies of the referenced standards may be obtained from the American Society for Testing and Materials, 100 Bar Harbor Drive, West Conshohocken, Pennsylvania 19428 (http://www.astm.org).

ASTM F 1292-99 Standard Specification for Impact Attenuation of Surface Systems Under and Around Playground Equipment (see 1008.2.6.2).

ASTM F 1292-04 Standard Specification for Impact Attenuation of Surfacing Materials Within the Use Zone of Playground Equipment (see 1008.2.6.2).

ASTM F 1487-01 Standard Consumer Safety Performance Specification for Playground Equipment for Public Use (see 106.5).

ASTM F 1951-99 Standard Specification for Determination of Accessibility of Surface Systems Under and Around Playground Equipment (see 1008.2.6.1).

Advisory

105.2.3 ASTM. ASTM F 1292-99 and ASTM F 1292-04 establish a uniform means to measure and compare characteristics of surfacing materials to determine whether materials provide a safe surface under and around playground equipment. These standards are referenced in the play areas requirements of this document when an accessible surface is required inside a play area use zone where a fall attenuating surface is also required. The standards cover the minimum impact attenuation requirements, when tested in accordance with Test Method F 355, for surface systems to be used under and around any piece of playground equipment from which a person may fall.

ASTM F 1487-01 establishes a nationally recognized safety standard for public playground equipment to address injuries identified by the U.S. Consumer Product Safety Commission. It defines the use zone, which is the ground area beneath and immediately adjacent to a play structure or play equipment designed for unrestricted circulation around the equipment and on whose surface it is predicted that a user would land when falling from or exiting a play structure or equipment. The play areas requirements in this document reference the ASTM F 1487 standard when defining accessible routes that overlap use zones requiring fall attenuating surfaces. If the use zone of a playground is not entirely surfaced with an accessible material, at least one accessible route within the use zone must be provided from the perimeter to all accessible play structures or components within the playground.

ASTM F 1951-99 establishes a uniform means to measure the characteristics of surface systems in order to provide performance specifications to select materials for use as an accessible surface under and around playground equipment. Surface materials that comply with this standard and are located in the use zone must also comply with ASTM F 1292. The test methods in this standard address access for children and adults who may traverse the surfacing to aid children who are playing. When a surface is tested it must have an average work per foot value for straight propulsion and for turning less than the average work per foot values for straight propulsion and for turning, respectively, on a hard, smooth surface with a grade of 7% (1:14).

105.2.4 ICC/IBC. Copies of the referenced standard may be obtained from the International Code Council, 5203 Leesburg Pike, Suite 600, Falls Church, Virginia 22041 (www.iccsafe.org).

International Building Code, 2000 Edition (see 207.1, 207.2, 216.4.2, 216.4.3, and 1005.2.1).

International Building Code, 2001 Supplement (see 207.1 and 207.2).

International Building Code, 2003 Edition (see 207.1, 207.2, 216.4.2, 216.4.3, and 1005.2.1).

105.2.5 NFPA. Copies of the referenced standards may be obtained from the National Fire Protection Association, 1 Batterymarch Park, Quincy, Massachusetts 02169-7471, (http://www.nfpa.org).

NFPA 72 National Fire Alarm Code, 1999 Edition (see 702.1 and 809.5.2).

NFPA 72 National Fire Alarm Code, 2002 Edition (see 702.1 and 809.5.2).

Guidance

Section 105 lists the industry requirements that are referenced in the 2010 Standards. This section also clarifies that where there is a difference between a provision of the 2010 Standards and the referenced requirements, the provision of the 2010 Standards applies.

---

106 Definitions

106.1 General. For the purpose of this document, the terms defined in 106.5 have the indicated meaning.

106.2 Terms Defined in Referenced Standards. Terms not defined in 106.5 or in regulations issued by the Department of Justice and the Department of Transportation to implement the Americans with Disabilities Act, but specifically defined in a referenced standard, shall have the specified meaning from the referenced standard unless otherwise stated.

106.3 Undefined Terms. The meaning of terms not specifically defined in 106.5 or in regulations issued by the Department of Justice and the Department of Transportation to implement the Americans with Disabilities Act or in referenced standards shall be as defined by collegiate dictionaries in the sense that the context implies.

106.4 Interchangeability. Words, terms and phrases used in the singular include the plural and those used in the plural include the singular.

106.5 Defined Terms.

Accessible. A site, building, facility, or portion thereof that complies with this part.

Accessible Means of Egress. A continuous and unobstructed way of egress travel from any point in a building or facility that provides an accessible route to an area of refuge, a horizontal exit, or a public way.

Addition. An expansion, extension, or increase in the gross floor area or height of a building or facility.

Administrative Authority. A governmental agency that adopts or enforces regulations and guidelines for the design, construction, or alteration of buildings and facilities.

Alteration. A change to a building or facility that affects or could affect the usability of the building or facility or portion thereof. Alterations include, but are not limited to, remodeling, renovation, rehabilitation, reconstruction, historic restoration, resurfacing of circulation paths or vehicular ways, changes or rearrangement of the structural parts or elements, and changes or rearrangement in the plan configuration of walls and full-height partitions. Normal maintenance, reroofing, painting or wallpapering, or changes to mechanical and electrical systems are not alterations unless they affect the usability of the building or facility.

Amusement Attraction. Any facility, or portion of a facility, located within an amusement park or theme park which provides amusement without the use of an amusement device. Amusement attractions include, but are not limited to, fun houses, barrels, and other attractions without seats.

Amusement Ride. A system that moves persons through a fixed course within a defined area for the purpose of amusement.

Amusement Ride Seat. A seat that is built-in or mechanically fastened to an amusement ride intended to be occupied by one or more passengers.

Area of Sport Activity. That portion of a room or space where the play or practice of a sport occurs.

Assembly Area. A building or facility, or portion thereof, used for the purpose of entertainment, educational or civic gatherings, or similar purposes. For the purposes of these requirements, assembly areas include, but are not limited to, classrooms, lecture halls, courtrooms, public meeting rooms, public hearing rooms, legislative chambers, motion picture houses, auditoria, theaters, playhouses, dinner theaters, concert halls, centers for the performing arts, amphitheaters, arenas, stadiums, grandstands, or convention centers.

Assistive Listening System (ALS). An amplification system utilizing transmitters, receivers, and coupling devices to bypass the acoustical space between a sound source and a listener by means of induction loop, radio frequency, infrared, or direct-wired equipment.

Boarding Pier. A portion of a pier where a boat is temporarily secured for the purpose of embarking or disembarking.

Boat Launch Ramp. A sloped surface designed for launching and retrieving trailered boats and other water craft to and from a body of water.

Boat Slip. That portion of a pier, main pier, finger pier, or float where a boat is moored for the purpose of berthing, embarking, or disembarking.

Building. Any structure used or intended for supporting or sheltering any use or occupancy.

Catch Pool. A pool or designated section of a pool used as a terminus for water slide flumes.

Characters. Letters, numbers, punctuation marks and typographic symbols.

Children's Use. Describes spaces and elements specifically designed for use primarily by people 12 years old and younger.

Circulation Path. An exterior or interior way of passage provided for pedestrian travel, including but not limited to, walks, hallways, courtyards, elevators, platform lifts, ramps, stairways, and landings.

Closed-Circuit Telephone. A telephone with a dedicated line such as a house phone, courtesy phone or phone that must be used to gain entry to a facility.

Common Use. Interior or exterior circulation paths, rooms, spaces, or elements that are not for public use and are made available for the shared use of two or more people.

Cross Slope. The slope that is perpendicular to the direction of travel (see running slope).

Curb Ramp. A short ramp cutting through a curb or built up to it.

Detectable Warning. A standardized surface feature built in or applied to walking surfaces or other elements to warn of hazards on a circulation path.

Element. An architectural or mechanical component of a building, facility, space, or site.

Elevated Play Component. A play component that is approached above or below grade and that is part of a composite play structure consisting of two or more play components attached or functionally linked to create an integrated unit providing more than one play activity.

Employee Work Area. All or any portion of a space used only by employees and used only for work. Corridors, toilet rooms, kitchenettes and break rooms are not employee work areas.

Entrance. Any access point to a building or portion of a building or facility used for the purpose of entering. An entrance includes the approach walk, the vertical access leading to the entrance platform, the entrance platform itself, vestibule if provided, the entry door or gate, and the hardware of the entry door or gate.

Facility. All or any portion of buildings, structures, site improvements, elements, and pedestrian routes or vehicular ways located on a site.

Gangway. A variable-sloped pedestrian walkway that links a fixed structure or land with a floating structure. Gangways that connect to vessels are not addressed by this document.

Golf Car Passage. A continuous passage on which a motorized golf car can operate.

Ground Level Play Component. A play component that is approached and exited at the ground level.

Key Station. Rapid and light rail stations, and commuter rail stations, as defined under criteria established by the Department of Transportation in 49 CFR 37.47 and 49 CFR 37.51, respectively.

Mail Boxes. Receptacles for the receipt of documents, packages, or other deliverable matter. Mail boxes include, but are not limited to, post office boxes and receptacles provided by commercial mail-receiving agencies, apartment facilities, or schools.

Marked Crossing. A crosswalk or other identified path intended for pedestrian use in crossing a vehicular way.

Mezzanine. An intermediate level or levels between the floor and ceiling of any story with an aggregate floor area of not more than one-third of the area of the room or space in which the level or levels are located. Mezzanines have sufficient elevation that space for human occupancy can be provided on the floor below.

Occupant Load. The number of persons for which the means of egress of a building or portion of a building is designed.

Operable Part. A component of an element used to insert or withdraw objects, or to activate, deactivate, or adjust the element.

Pictogram. A pictorial symbol that represents activities, facilities, or concepts.

Play Area. A portion of a site containing play components designed and constructed for children.

Play Component. An element intended to generate specific opportunities for play, socialization, or learning. Play components are manufactured or natural; and are stand-alone or part of a composite play structure.

Private Building or Facility. A place of public accommodation or a commercial building or facility subject to Title III of the ADA and 28 CFR part 36 or a transportation building or facility subject to Title III of the ADA and 49 CFR 37.45.

Public Building or Facility. A building or facility or portion of a building or facility designed, constructed, or altered by, on behalf of, or for the use of a public entity subject to Title II of the ADA and 28 CFR part 35 or to Title II of the ADA and 49 CFR 37.41 or 37.43.

Public Entrance. An entrance that is not a service entrance or a restricted entrance.

Public Use. Interior or exterior rooms, spaces, or elements that are made available to the public. Public use may be provided at a building or facility that is privately or publicly owned.

Public Way. Any street, alley or other parcel of land open to the outside air leading to a public street, which has been deeded, dedicated or otherwise permanently appropriated to the public for public use and which has a clear width and height of not less than 10 feet (3050 mm).

Qualified Historic Building or Facility. A building or facility that is listed in or eligible for listing in the National Register of Historic Places, or designated as historic under an appropriate State or local law.

Ramp. A walking surface that has a running slope steeper than 1:20.

Residential Dwelling Unit. A unit intended to be used as a residence, that is primarily long-term in nature. Residential dwelling units do not include transient lodging, inpatient medical care, licensed long-term care, and detention or correctional facilities.

Restricted Entrance. An entrance that is made available for common use on a controlled basis but not public use and that is not a service entrance.

Running Slope. The slope that is parallel to the direction of travel (see cross slope).

Self-Service Storage. Building or facility designed and used for the purpose of renting or leasing individual storage spaces to customers for the purpose of storing and removing personal property on a self-service basis.

Service Entrance. An entrance intended primarily for delivery of goods or services.

Site. A parcel of land bounded by a property line or a designated portion of a public right-of-way.

Soft Contained Play Structure. A play structure made up of one or more play components where the user enters a fully enclosed play environment that utilizes pliable materials, such as plastic, netting, or fabric.

Space. A definable area, such as a room, toilet room, hall, assembly area, entrance, storage room, alcove, courtyard, or lobby.

Story. That portion of a building or facility designed for human occupancy included between the upper surface of a floor and upper surface of the floor or roof next above. A story containing one or more mezzanines has more than one floor level.

Structural Frame. The columns and the girders, beams, and trusses having direct connections to the columns and all other members that are essential to the stability of the building or facility as a whole.

Tactile. An object that can be perceived using the sense of touch.

Technically Infeasible. With respect to an alteration of a building or a facility, something that has little likelihood of being accomplished because existing structural conditions would require removing or altering a load-bearing member that is an essential part of the structural frame; or because other existing physical or site constraints prohibit modification or addition of elements, spaces, or features that are in full and strict compliance with the minimum requirements.

Teeing Ground. In golf, the starting place for the hole to be played.

Transfer Device. Equipment designed to facilitate the transfer of a person from a wheelchair or other mobility aid to and from an amusement ride seat.

Transient Lodging. A building or facility containing one or more guest room(s) for sleeping that provides accommodations that are primarily short-term in nature. Transient lodging does not include residential dwelling units intended to be used as a residence, inpatient medical care facilities, licensed long-term care facilities, detention or correctional facilities, or private buildings or facilities that contain not more than five rooms for rent or hire and that are actually occupied by the proprietor as the residence of such proprietor.

Transition Plate. A sloping pedestrian walking surface located at the end(s) of a gangway.

TTY. An abbreviation for teletypewriter. Machinery that employs interactive text-based communication through the transmission of coded signals across the telephone network. TTYs may include, for example, devices known as TDDs (telecommunication display devices or telecommunication devices for deaf persons) or computers with special modems. TTYs are also called text telephones.

Use Zone. The ground level area beneath and immediately adjacent to a play structure or play equipment that is designated by ASTM F 1487 (incorporated by reference, see "Referenced Standards" in Chapter 1) for unrestricted circulation around the play equipment and where it is predicted that a user would land when falling from or exiting the play equipment.

Vehicular Way. A route provided for vehicular traffic, such as in a street, driveway, or parking facility.

Walk. An exterior prepared surface for pedestrian use, including pedestrian areas such as plazas and courts.

Wheelchair Space. Space for a single wheelchair and its occupant.

Work Area Equipment. Any machine, instrument, engine, motor, pump, conveyor, or other apparatus used to perform work. As used in this document, this term shall apply only to equipment that is permanently installed or built-in in employee work areas. Work area equipment does not include passenger elevators and other accessible means of vertical transportation.

Guidance

Various definitions have been added to the 2010 Standards and some definitions have been deleted.

One commenter asked that the term public right-of-way be defined; others asked that various terms and words defined by the 1991 Standards, but which were eliminated from the 2010 Standards, plus other words and terms used in the 2010 Standards, be defined.

The Department believes that it is not necessary to add definitions to this text because section 106.3 of the 2010 Standards provides that the meanings of terms not specifically defined in the 2010 Standards, in the Department's ADA regulations, or in referenced standards are to be defined by collegiate dictionaries in the sense that the context implies. The Department believes that this provision adequately addresses these commenters' concerns.

ADA CHAPTER 2: SCOPING REQUIREMENTS

201 Application

201.1 Scope. All areas of newly designed and newly constructed buildings and facilities and altered portions of existing buildings and facilities shall comply with these requirements.

Advisory

201.1 Scope. These requirements are to be applied to all areas of a facility unless exempted, or where scoping limits the number of multiple elements required to be accessible. For example, not all medical care patient rooms are required to be accessible; those that are not required to be accessible are not required to comply with these requirements. However, common use and public use spaces such as recovery rooms, examination rooms, and cafeterias are not exempt from these requirements and must be accessible.

201.2 Application Based on Building or Facility Use. Where a site, building, facility, room, or space contains more than one use, each portion shall comply with the applicable requirements for that use.

201.3 Temporary and Permanent Structures. These requirements shall apply to temporary and permanent buildings and facilities.

Advisory

201.3 Temporary and Permanent Structures. Temporary buildings or facilities covered by these requirements include, but are not limited to, reviewing stands, temporary classrooms, bleacher areas, stages, platforms and daises, fixed furniture systems, wall systems, and exhibit areas, temporary banking facilities, and temporary health screening facilities. Structures and equipment directly associated with the actual processes of construction are not required to be accessible as permitted in 203.2.

202 Existing Buildings and Facilities

202.1 General. Additions and alterations to existing buildings or facilities shall comply with 202.

202.2 Additions. Each addition to an existing building or facility shall comply with the requirements for new construction. Each addition that affects or could affect the usability of or access to an area containing a primary function shall comply with 202.4.

202.3 Alterations. Where existing elements or spaces are altered, each altered element or space shall comply with the applicable requirements of Chapter 2.

EXCEPTIONS:

1. Unless required by 202.4, where elements or spaces are altered and the circulation path to the altered element or space is not altered, an accessible route shall not be required.

2. In alterations, where compliance with applicable requirements is technically infeasible, the alteration shall comply with the requirements to the maximum extent feasible.

3. Residential dwelling units not required to be accessible in compliance with a standard issued pursuant to the Americans with Disabilities Act or Section 504 of the Rehabilitation Act of 1973, as amended, shall not be required to comply with 202.3.

Advisory

202.3 Alterations. Although covered entities are permitted to limit the scope of an alteration to individual elements, the alteration of multiple elements within a room or space may provide a cost-effective opportunity to make the entire room or space accessible. Any elements or spaces of the building or facility that are required to comply with these requirements must be made accessible within the scope of the alteration, to the maximum extent feasible. If providing accessibility in compliance with these requirements for people with one type of disability (e.g., people who use wheelchairs) is not feasible, accessibility must still be provided in compliance with the requirements for people with other types of disabilities (e.g., people who have hearing impairments or who have vision impairments) to the extent that such accessibility is feasible.

202.3.1 Prohibited Reduction in Access. An alteration that decreases or has the effect of decreasing the accessibility of a building or facility below the requirements for new construction at the time of the alteration is prohibited.

202.3.2 Extent of Application. An alteration of an existing element, space, or area of a building or facility shall not impose a requirement for accessibility greater than required for new construction.

202.4 Alterations Affecting Primary Function Areas. In addition to the requirements of 202.3, an alteration that affects or could affect the usability of or access to an area containing a primary function shall be made so as to ensure that, to the maximum extent feasible, the path of travel to the altered area, including the rest rooms, telephones, and drinking fountains serving the altered area, are readily accessible to and usable by individuals with disabilities, unless such alterations are disproportionate to the overall alterations in terms of cost and scope as determined under criteria established by the Attorney General. In existing transportation facilities, an area of primary function shall be as defined under regulations published by the Secretary of the Department of Transportation or the Attorney General.

EXCEPTION: Residential dwelling units shall not be required to comply with 202.4.

Advisory

202.4 Alterations Affecting Primary Function Areas. An area of a building or facility containing a major activity for which the building or facility is intended is a primary function area. Department of Justice ADA regulations state, "Alterations made to provide an accessible path of travel to the altered area will be deemed disproportionate to the overall alteration when the cost exceeds 20% of the cost of the alteration to the primary function area." (28 CFR 36.403 (f)(1)). See also Department of Transportation ADA regulations, which use similar concepts in the context of public sector transportation facilities (49 CFR 37.43 (e)(1)).

There can be multiple areas containing a primary function in a single building. Primary function areas are not limited to public use areas. For example, both a bank lobby and the bank's employee areas such as the teller areas and walk-in safe are primary function areas.

Also, mixed use facilities may include numerous primary function areas for each use. Areas containing a primary function do not include: mechanical rooms, boiler rooms, supply storage rooms, employee lounges or locker rooms, janitorial closets, entrances, corridors, or restrooms.

202.5 Alterations to Qualified Historic Buildings and Facilities. Alterations to a qualified historic building or facility shall comply with 202.3 and 202.4.

EXCEPTION: Where the State Historic Preservation Officer or Advisory Council on Historic Preservation determines that compliance with the requirements for accessible routes, entrances, or toilet facilities would threaten or destroy the historic significance of the building or facility, the exceptions for alterations to qualified historic buildings or facilities for that element shall be permitted to apply.

Advisory

202.5 Alterations to Qualified Historic Buildings and Facilities Exception. State Historic Preservation Officers are State appointed officials who carry out certain responsibilities under the National Historic Preservation Act. State Historic Preservation Officers consult with Federal and State agencies, local governments, and private entities on providing access and protecting significant elements of qualified historic buildings and facilities. There are exceptions for alterations to qualified historic buildings and facilities for accessible routes (206.2.1 Exception 1 and 206.2.3 Exception 7); entrances (206.4 Exception 2); and toilet facilities (213.2 Exception 2). When an entity believes that compliance with the requirements for any of these elements would threaten or destroy the historic significance of the building or facility, the entity should consult with the State Historic Preservation Officer. If the State Historic Preservation Officer agrees that compliance with the requirements for a specific element would threaten or destroy the historic significance of the building or facility, use of the exception is permitted. Public entities have an additional obligation to achieve program accessibility under the Department of Justice ADA regulations. See 28 CFR 35.150. These regulations require public entities that operate historic preservation programs to give priority to methods that provide physical access to individuals with disabilities. If alterations to a qualified historic building or facility to achieve program accessibility would threaten or destroy the historic significance of the building or facility, fundamentally alter the program, or result in undue financial or administrative burdens, the Department of Justice ADA regulations allow alternative methods to be used to achieve program accessibility. In the case of historic preservation programs, such as an historic house museum, alternative methods include using audio-visual materials to depict portions of the house that cannot otherwise be made accessible. In the case of other qualified historic properties, such as an historic government office building, alternative methods include relocating programs and services to accessible locations. The Department of Justice ADA regulations also allow public entities to use alternative methods when altering qualified historic buildings or facilities in the rare situations where the State Historic Preservation Officer determines that it is not feasible to provide physical access using the exceptions permitted in Section 202.5 without threatening or destroying the historic significance of the building or facility. See 28 CFR 35.151(d).

The AccessAbility Office at the National Endowment for the Arts (NEA) provides a variety of resources for museum operators and historic properties including: the Design for Accessibility Guide and the Disability Symbols. Contact NEA about these and other resources at (202) 682-5532 or www.arts.gov.

Guidance

Alterations. Under section 4.1.6(1)(c) of the 1991 Standards if alterations to single elements, when considered together, amount to an alteration of a room or space in a building or facility, the entire room or space would have to be made accessible. This requirement was interpreted to mean that if a covered entity chose to alter several elements in a room there would come a point when so much work had been done that it would be considered that the entire room or space would have to be made accessible. Under section 202.3 of the 2010 Standards entities can alter as many elements within a room or space as they like without triggering a requirement to make the entire room or space accessible based on the alteration of individual elements. This does not, however, change the requirement that if the intent was to alter the entire room or space, the entire room or space must be made accessible and comply with the applicable requirements of Chapter 2 of the 2010 Standards.

Alterations to Primary Function Areas. Section 202.4 restates a current requirement under title III, and therefore represents no change for title III facilities or for those title II facilities that have elected to comply with the 1991 Standards. However, under the revised title II regulation, state and local government facilities that have previously elected to comply with the Uniform Federal Accessibility Standards (UFAS) instead of the 1991 Standards will no longer have that option, and thus will now be subject to the path of travel requirement. The path of travel requirement provides that when a primary function area of an existing facility is altered, the path of travel to that area (including restrooms, telephones, and drinking fountains serving the area) must also be made accessible, but only to the extent that the cost of doing so does not exceed twenty percent (20%) of the cost of the alterations to the primary function area. The UFAS requirements for a substantial alteration, though different, may have covered some of the items that will now be covered by the path of travel requirement.

Visible Alarms in Alterations to Existing Facilities. The 1991 Standards, at sections 4.1.3(14) and 4.1.6(1)(b), and sections 202.3 and 215.1 of the 2010 Standards require that when existing elements and spaces of a facility are altered, the alterations must comply with new construction requirements. Section 215.1 of the 2010 Standards adds a new exception to the scoping requirement for visible alarms in existing facilities so that visible alarms must be installed only when an existing fire alarm system is upgraded or replaced, or a new fire alarm system is installed.

Some commenters urged the Department not to include the exception and to make visible alarms a mandatory requirement for all spaces, both existing and new. Other commenters said that the exception will make the safety of individuals with disabilities dependent upon the varying age of existing fire alarm systems. Other commenters suggested that including this requirement, even with the exception, will result in significant cost to building owners and operators.

The Department believes that the language of the exception to section 215.1 of the 2010 Standards strikes a reasonable balance between the interests of individuals with disabilities and those of the business community. If undertaken at the time a system is installed, whether in a new facility or in a planned system upgrade, the cost of adding visible alarms is reasonable. Over time, existing facilities will become fully accessible to individuals who are deaf or hard of hearing, and will add minimal costs to owners and operators.

203 General Exceptions

203.1 General. Sites, buildings, facilities, and elements are exempt from these requirements to the extent specified by 203.

203.2 Construction Sites. Structures and sites directly associated with the actual processes of construction, including but not limited to, scaffolding, bridging, materials hoists, materials storage, and construction trailers shall not be required to comply with these requirements or to be on an accessible route. Portable toilet units provided for use exclusively by construction personnel on a construction site shall not be required to comply with 213 or to be on an accessible route.

203.3 Raised Areas. Areas raised primarily for purposes of security, life safety, or fire safety, including but not limited to, observation or lookout galleries, prison guard towers, fire towers, or life guard stands shall not be required to comply with these requirements or to be on an accessible route.

203.4 Limited Access Spaces. Spaces accessed only by ladders, catwalks, crawl spaces, or very narrow passageways shall not be required to comply with these requirements or to be on an accessible route.

203.5 Machinery Spaces. Spaces frequented only by service personnel for maintenance, repair, or occasional monitoring of equipment shall not be required to comply with these requirements or to be on an accessible route. Machinery spaces include, but are not limited to, elevator pits or elevator penthouses; mechanical, electrical or communications equipment rooms; piping or equipment catwalks; water or sewage treatment pump rooms and stations; electric substations and transformer vaults; and highway and tunnel utility facilities.

203.6 Single Occupant Structures. Single occupant structures accessed only by passageways below grade or elevated above standard curb height, including but not limited to, toll booths that are accessed only by underground tunnels, shall not be required to comply with these requirements or to be on an accessible route.

203.7 Detention and Correctional Facilities. In detention and correctional facilities, common use areas that are used only by inmates or detainees and security personnel and that do not serve holding cells or housing cells required to comply with 232, shall not be required to comply with these requirements or to be on an accessible route.

203.8 Residential Facilities. In residential facilities, common use areas that do not serve residential dwelling units required to provide mobility features complying with 809.2 through 809.4 shall not be required to comply with these requirements or to be on an accessible route.

203.9 Employee Work Areas. Spaces and elements within employee work areas shall only be required to comply with 206.2.8, 207.1, and 215.3 and shall be designed and constructed so that individuals with disabilities can approach, enter, and exit the employee work area. Employee work areas, or portions of employee work areas, other than raised courtroom stations, that are less than 300 square feet (28 m^2) and elevated 7 inches (180 mm) or more above the finish floor or ground where the elevation is essential to the function of the space shall not be required to comply with these requirements or to be on an accessible route.

Advisory

203.9 Employee Work Areas. Although areas used exclusively by employees for work are not required to be fully accessible, consider designing such areas to include non-required turning spaces, and provide accessible elements whenever possible. Under the ADA, employees with disabilities are entitled to reasonable accommodations in the workplace; accommodations can include alterations to spaces within the facility. Designing employee work areas to be more accessible at the outset will avoid more costly retrofits when current employees become temporarily or permanently disabled, or when new employees with disabilities are hired. Contact the Equal Employment Opportunity Commission (EEOC) at http://www.eeoc.gov/ for information about title I of the ADA prohibiting discrimination against people with disabilities in the workplace.

203.10 Raised Refereeing, Judging, and Scoring Areas. Raised structures used solely for refereeing, judging, or scoring a sport shall not be required to comply with these requirements or to be on an accessible route.

203.11 Water Slides. Water slides shall not be required to comply with these requirements or to be on an accessible route.

203.12 Animal Containment Areas. Animal containment areas that are not for public use shall not be required to comply with these requirements or to be on an accessible route.

Advisory

203.12 Animal Containment Areas. Public circulation routes where animals may travel, such as in petting zoos and passageways alongside animal pens in State fairs, are not eligible for the exception.

203.13 Raised Boxing or Wrestling Rings. Raised boxing or wrestling rings shall not be required to comply with these requirements or to be on an accessible route.

203.14 Raised Diving Boards and Diving Platforms. Raised diving boards and diving platforms shall not be required to comply with these requirements or to be on an accessible route.

Guidance

Limited Access Spaces and Machinery Spaces. The 1991 Standards, at section 4.1.1, contain an exception that exempts "non-occupiable" spaces that have limited means of access, such as ladders or very narrow passageways, and that are visited only by service personnel for maintenance, repair, or occasional monitoring of equipment, from all accessibility requirements. Sections 203.4 and 203.5 of the 2010 Standards expand this exception by removing the condition that the exempt spaces be "non-occupiable," and by separating the other conditions into two independent exceptions: one for spaces with limited means of access, and the other for machinery spaces. More spaces are exempted by the exception in the 2010 Standards.

203 Employee Work Areas

Common Use Circulation Paths in Employee Work Areas. The 1991 Standards at section 4.1.1(3), and the 2010 Standards at section 203.9, require employee work areas in new construction and alterations *only* to be designed and constructed so that individuals with disabilities can approach, enter, and exit the areas. Section 206.2.8 of the 2010 Standards requires accessible common use circulation paths within employee work areas unless they are subject to exceptions in sections 206.2.8, 403.5, 405.5, and 405.8. The ADA, 42 U.S.C. 12112 (b)(5)(A) and (B), requires employers to make reasonable accommodations in the workplace for individuals with disabilities, which may include modifications to work areas when needed. Providing increased access in the facility at the time of construction or alteration will simplify the process of providing reasonable accommodations when they are needed.

The requirement for accessible common use circulation paths will not apply to existing facilities pursuant to the readily achievable barrier removal requirement. The Department has consistently taken the position that barrier removal requirements do not apply to areas used exclusively by employees because the purpose of title III is to ensure that access is provided to clients and customers. See Appendix B to the 1991 regulation implementing title III, 28 CFR part 36.

Several exceptions to section 206.2.8 of the 2010 Standards exempt common use circulation paths in employee work areas from the requirements of section 402 where it may be difficult to comply with the technical requirements for accessible routes due to the size or function of the area:

• Employee work areas, or portions of employee work areas, that are less than 300 square feet and are elevated 7 inches or more above the ground or finish floor, where elevation is essential to the function of the space, are exempt.

• Common use circulation paths within employee work areas that are less than 1,000 square feet and are defined by permanently installed partitions, counters, casework, or furnishings are exempt. Kitchens in quick service restaurants, cocktail bars, and the employee side of service counters are frequently covered by this exception.

• Common use circulation paths within employee work areas that are an integral component of equipment are exempt. Common use circulation paths within large pieces of equipment in factories, electric power plants, and amusement rides are covered by this exception.

• Common use circulation paths within exterior employee work areas that are fully exposed to the weather are exempt. Farms, ranches, and outdoor maintenance facilities are covered by this exception.

The 2010 Standards in sections 403.5 and 405.8 also contain exceptions to the technical requirements for accessible routes for circulation paths in employee work areas:

• Machinery and equipment are permitted to reduce the clear width of common use circulation paths where the reduction is essential to the function of the work performed. Machinery and equipment that must be placed a certain way to work properly, or for ergonomics or to prevent workplace injuries are covered by this exception.

- Handrails are not required on ramps, provided that they can be added in the future.

Commenters stated that the requirements set out in the 2010 Standards for accessible common use circulation paths in employee work areas are inappropriate, particularly in commercial kitchens, storerooms, and behind cocktail bars where wheelchairs would not be easily accommodated. These commenters further urged the Department not to adopt a requirement that circulation paths in employee work areas be at least 36 inches wide, including those at emergency exits.

These commenters misunderstand the scope of the provision. Nothing in the 2010 Standards requires all circulation paths in non-exempt areas to be accessible. The Department recognizes that building codes and fire and life safety codes, which are adopted by all of the states, require *primary* circulation paths in facilities, including employee work areas, to be at least 36 inches wide for purposes of emergency egress. Accessible routes also are at least 36 inches wide. Therefore, the Department anticipates that covered entities will be able to satisfy the requirement to provide accessible circulation paths by ensuring that their required *primary* circulation paths are accessible.

Individual employee work stations, such as a grocery checkout counter or an automobile service bay designed for use by one person, do not contain common use circulation paths and are not required to comply. Other work areas, such as stockrooms that typically have narrow pathways between shelves, would be required to design only one accessible circulation path into the stockroom. It would not be necessary to make each circulation path in the room accessible. In alterations it may be technically infeasible to provide accessible common use circulation paths in some employee work areas. For example, in a stock room of a department store significant existing physical constraints, such as having to move walls to avoid the loss of space to store inventory, may mean that it is technically infeasible (*see* section 106.5 "Defined Terms" of the 2010 Standards) to make even the primary common use circulation path in that stock room wide enough to be accessible. In addition, the 2010 Standards include exceptions for common use circulation paths in employee work areas where it may be difficult to comply with the technical requirements for accessible routes due to the size or function of the areas. The Department believes that these exceptions will provide the flexibility necessary to ensure that this requirement does not interfere with legitimate business operations.

Visible Alarms. Section 215.3 of the 2010 Standards provides that where employee work areas in newly constructed facilities have audible alarm coverage they are required to have wiring systems that are capable of supporting visible alarms that comply with section 702 of the 2010 Standards. The 1991 Standards, at section 4.1.1(3), require visible alarms to be provided where audible fire alarm systems are provided, but do not require areas used only by employees as work areas to be equipped with accessibility features. As applied to office buildings, the 1991 Standards require visible alarms to be provided in public and common use areas such as hallways, conference rooms, break rooms, and restrooms, where audible fire alarm systems are provided.

Commenters asserted that the requirements of section 215.3 of the 2010 Standards would be burdensome to meet. These commenters also raised concerns that all employee work areas within existing buildings and facilities must be equipped with accessibility features.

The commenters' concerns about section 215.3 of the 2010 Standards represent a misunderstanding of the requirements applicable to employee work areas.

Newly constructed buildings and facilities merely are required to provide wiring so that visible alarm systems can be added as needed to accommodate employees who are deaf or hard of hearing. This is a minimal requirement without significant impact.

The other issue in the comments represents a misunderstanding of the Department's existing regulatory requirements. Employee common use areas in covered facilities (e.g., locker rooms, break rooms, cafeterias, toilet rooms, corridors to exits, and other common use spaces) were required to be accessible under the 1991 Standards; areas in which employees actually perform their jobs are required to enable a person using a wheelchair or mobility device to approach, enter, and exit the area. The 2010 Standards require increased access through the accessible *common use* circulation path requirement, but neither the 1991 Standards nor the 2010 Standards require employee work stations to be accessible. Access to specific employee *work stations* is governed by title I of the ADA.

204 Protruding Objects

204.1 General. Protruding objects on circulation paths shall comply with 307.

EXCEPTIONS:

1. Within areas of sport activity, protruding objects on circulation paths shall not be required to comply with 307.

2. Within play areas, protruding objects on circulation paths shall not be required to comply with 307 provided that ground level accessible routes provide vertical clearance in compliance with 1008.2.

205 Operable Parts

205.1 General. Operable parts on accessible elements, accessible routes, and in accessible rooms and spaces shall comply with 309.

EXCEPTIONS:

1. Operable parts that are intended for use only by service or maintenance personnel shall not be required to comply with 309.

2. Electrical or communication receptacles serving a dedicated use shall not be required to comply with 309.

3. Where two or more outlets are provided in a kitchen above a length of counter top that is uninterrupted by a sink or appliance, one outlet shall not be required to comply with 309.

4. Floor electrical receptacles shall not be required to comply with 309.

5. HVAC diffusers shall not be required to comply with 309.

6. Except for light switches, where redundant controls are provided for a single element, one control in each space shall not be required to comply with 309.

7. Cleats and other boat securement devices shall not be required to comply with 309.3.

8. Exercise machines and exercise equipment shall not be required to comply with 309.

Advisory

205.1 General. Controls covered by 205.1 include, but are not limited to, light switches, circuit breakers, duplexes and other convenience receptacles, environmental and appliance controls, plumbing fixture controls, and security and intercom systems.

Guidance

Section 4.1.3, and more specifically sections 4.1.3(13), 4.27.3, and 4.27.4 of the 1991 Standards, require operable parts on accessible elements, along accessible routes, and in accessible rooms and spaces to comply with the technical requirements for operable parts, including height and operation. The 1991 Standards, at section 4.27.3, contain an exception, " * * * where the use of special equipment dictates otherwise or where electrical and communications systems receptacles are not normally intended for use by building occupants," from the technical requirement for the height of operable parts. Section 205.1 of the 2010 Standards divides this exception into three exceptions covering operable parts intended only for use by service or maintenance personnel, electrical or communication receptacles serving a dedicated use, and floor electrical receptacles. Operable parts covered by these new exceptions are exempt from all of the technical requirements for operable parts in section 309. The 2010 Standards also add exceptions that exempt certain outlets at kitchen counters; heating, ventilating and air conditioning diffusers; redundant controls provided for a single element, other than light switches; and exercise machines and equipment from all of the technical requirements for operable parts. Exception 7, in section 205.1 of the 2010 Standards, exempts cleats and other boat securement devices from the accessible height requirement. Similarly, section 309.4 of the 2010 Standards exempts gas pump nozzles, but only from the technical requirement for activating force.

Reach Ranges. The 1991 Standards set the maximum height for side reach at 54 inches above the floor. The 2010 Standards, at section 308.3, lower that maximum height to 48 inches above the finish floor or ground. The 2010 Standards also add exceptions, as discussed above, to the scoping requirement for operable parts for certain elements that, among other things, will exempt them from the reach range requirements in section 308.

The 1991 Standards, at sections 4.1.3, 4.27.3, and 4.2.6, and the 2010 Standards, at sections 205.1, 228.1, 228.2, 308.3, and 309.3, require operable parts of accessible elements, along accessible routes, and in accessible rooms and spaces to be placed within the forward or side-reach ranges specified in section 308. The 2010 Standards also require at least five percent (5%) of mailboxes provided in an interior location and at least one of each type of depository, vending machine, change machine, and gas pump to meet the technical requirements for a forward or a side reach.

Section 4.2.6 of the 1991 Standards specifies a maximum 54-inch high side reach and a minimum 9-inch low side reach for an unobstructed reach depth of 10 inches maximum. Section 308.3.1 of the 2010 Standards specifies a maximum 48-inch high side reach and a minimum 15-inch low side reach where the element being reached for is unobstructed. Section 308.3.1, Exception 1, permits an obstruction that is no deeper than 10 inches between the edge of the clear floor or ground space and the element that the individual with a disability is trying to reach. Changes in the side-reach range for new construction and alterations in the 2010 Standards will affect a variety of building elements such as light switches, electrical outlets, thermostats, fire alarm pull stations, card readers, and keypads.

Commenters were divided in their views about the changes to the unobstructed side-reach range. Disability advocacy groups and others, including individuals of short stature, supported the modifications to the proposed reach range requirements. Other commenters stated that the new reach range requirements will be burdensome for small businesses to comply with. These comments argued that the new reach range requirements restrict design options, especially in residential housing.

The Department continues to believe that data submitted by advocacy groups and others provides compelling evidence that lowered reach range requirements will better serve significantly greater numbers of individuals with disabilities, including individuals of short stature, persons with limited upper body strength, and others with limited use of their arms and fingers. The change to the side-reach range was developed by the Access Board over a prolonged period in which there was extensive public participation. This process did not produce any significant data to indicate that applying the new unobstructed side-reach range requirement in new construction or during alterations would impose a significant burden.

206 Accessible Routes

206.1 General. Accessible routes shall be provided in accordance with 206 and shall comply with Chapter 4.

206.2 Where Required. Accessible routes shall be provided where required by 206.2.

206.2.1 Site Arrival Points. At least one accessible route shall be provided within the site from accessible parking spaces and accessible passenger loading zones; public streets and sidewalks; and public transportation stops to the accessible building or facility entrance they serve.

EXCEPTIONS:

1. Where exceptions for alterations to qualified historic buildings or facilities are permitted by 202.5, no more than one accessible route from a site arrival point to an accessible entrance shall be required.

2. An accessible route shall not be required between site arrival points and the building or facility entrance if the only means of access between them is a vehicular way not providing pedestrian access.

Advisory

206.2.1 Site Arrival Points. Each site arrival point must be connected by an accessible route to the accessible building entrance or entrances served. Where two or more similar site arrival points, such as bus stops, serve the same accessible entrance or entrances, both bus stops must be on accessible routes. In addition, the accessible routes must serve all of the accessible entrances on the site.

206.2.1 Site Arrival Points Exception 2. Access from site arrival points may include vehicular ways. Where a vehicular way, or a portion of a vehicular way, is provided for pedestrian trvel, such as within a shopping center or shopping mall parking lot, this exception does not apply.

206.2.2 Within a Site. At least one accessible route shall connect accessible buildings, accessible facilities, accessible elements, and accessible spaces that are on the same site.

> **EXCEPTION:** An accessible route shall not be required between accessible buildings, accessible facilities, accessible elements, and accessible spaces if the only means of access between them is a vehicular way not providing pedestrian access.

Advisory

206.2.2 Within a Site. An accessible route is required to connect to the boundary of each area of sport activity. Examples of areas of sport activity include: soccer fields, basketball courts, baseball fields, running tracks, skating rinks, and the area surrounding a piece of gymnastic equipment. While the size of an area of sport activity may vary from sport to sport, each includes only the space needed to play. Where multiple sports fields or courts are provided, an accessible route is required to each field or area of sport activity.

206.2.3 Multi-Story Buildings and Facilities. At least one accessible route shall connect each story and mezzanine in multi-story buildings and facilities.

EXCEPTIONS:

1. In private buildings or facilities that are less than three stories or that have less than 3000 square feet (279 m^2) per story, an accessible route shall not be required to connect stories provided that the building or facility is not a shopping center, a shopping mall, the professional office of a health care provider, a terminal, depot or other station used for specified public transportation, an airport passenger terminal, or another type of facility as determined by the Attorney General.

2. Where a two story public building or facility has one story with an occupant load of five or fewer persons that does not contain public use space, that story shall not be required to be connected to the story above or below.

3. In detention and correctional facilities, an accessible route shall not be required to connect stories where cells with mobility features required to comply with 807.2, all common use areas serving cells with mobility features required to comply with 807.2, and all public use areas are on an accessible route.

4. In residential facilities, an accessible route shall not be required to connect stories where residential dwelling units with mobility features required to comply with 809.2 through 809.4, all common use areas serving residential dwelling units with mobility features required to comply with 809.2 through 809.4, and public use areas serving residential dwelling units are on an accessible route.

5. Within multi-story transient lodging guest rooms with mobility features required to comply with 806.2, an accessible route shall not be required to connect stories provided that spaces complying with 806.2 are on an accessible route and sleeping accommodations for two persons minimum are provided on a story served by an accessible route.

6. In air traffic control towers, an accessible route shall not be required to serve the cab and the floor immediately below the cab.

7. Where exceptions for alterations to qualified historic buildings or facilities are permitted by 202.5, an accessible route shall not be required to stories located above or below the accessible story.

Advisory

206.2.3 Multi-Story Buildings and Facilities. Spaces and elements located on a level not required to be served by an accessible route must fully comply with this document. While a mezzanine may be a change in level, it is not a story. If an accessible route is required to connect stories within a building or facility, the accessible route must serve all mezzanines.

206.2.3 Multi-Story Buildings and Facilities Exception 4. Where common use areas are provided for the use of residents, it is presumed that all such common use areas "serve" accessible dwelling units unless use is restricted to residents occupying certain dwelling units. For example, if all residents are permitted to use all laundry rooms, then all laundry rooms "serve" accessible dwelling units. However, if the laundry room on the first floor is restricted to use by residents on the first floor, and the second floor laundry room is for use by occupants of the second floor, then first floor accessible units are "served" only by laundry rooms on the first floor. In this example, an accessible route is not required to the second floor provided that all accessible units and all common use areas serving them are on the first floor.

206.2.3.1 Stairs and Escalators in Existing Buildings. In alterations and additions, where an escalator or stair is provided where none existed previously and major structural modifications are necessary for the installation, an accessible route shall be provided between the levels served by the escalator or stair unless exempted by 206.2.3 Exceptions 1 through 7.

206.2.4 Spaces and Elements. At least one accessible route shall connect accessible building or facility entrances with all accessible spaces and elements within the building or facility which are otherwise connected by a circulation path unless exempted by 206.2.3 Exceptions 1 through 7.

EXCEPTIONS:

1. Raised courtroom stations, including judges' benches, clerks' stations, bailiffs' stations, deputy clerks' stations, and court reporters' stations shall not be required to provide vertical access provided that the required clear floor space, maneuvering space, and, if appropriate, electrical service are installed at the time of initial construction to allow future installation of a means of vertical access complying with 405, 407, 408, or 410 without requiring substantial reconstruction of the space.

2. In assembly areas with fixed seating required to comply with 221, an accessible route shall not be required to serve fixed seating where wheelchair spaces required to be on an accessible route are not provided.

3. Accessible routes shall not be required to connect mezzanines where buildings or facilities have no more than one story. In addition, accessible routes shall not be required to connect stories or mezzanines where multi-story buildings or facilities are exempted by 206.2.3 Exceptions 1 through 7.

Advisory

206.2.4 Spaces and Elements. Accessible routes must connect all spaces and elements required to be accessible including, but not limited to, raised areas and speaker platforms.

206.2.4 Spaces and Elements Exception 1. The exception does not apply to areas that are likely to be used by members of the public who are not employees of the court such as jury areas, attorney areas, or witness stands.

206.2.5 Restaurants and Cafeterias. In restaurants and cafeterias, an accessible route shall be provided to all dining areas, including raised or sunken dining areas, and outdoor dining areas.

EXCEPTIONS:

1. In buildings or facilities not required to provide an accessible route between stories, an accessible route shall not be required to a mezzanine dining area where the mezzanine contains less than 25 percent of the total combined area for seating and dining and where the same decor and services are provided in the accessible area.

2. In alterations, an accessible route shall not be required to existing raised or sunken dining areas, or to all parts of existing outdoor dining areas where the same services and decor are provided in an accessible space usable by the public and not restricted to use by people with disabilities.

3. In sports facilities, tiered dining areas providing seating required to comply with 221 shall be required to have accessible routes serving at least 25 percent of the dining area provided that accessible routes serve seating complying with 221 and each tier is provided with the same services.

Advisory

206.2.5 Restaurants and Cafeterias Exception 2. Examples of "same services" include, but are not limited to, bar service, rooms having smoking and non-smoking sections, lotto and other table games, carry-out, and buffet service. Examples of "same decor" include, but are not limited to, seating at or near windows and railings with views, areas designed with a certain theme, party and banquet rooms, and rooms where entertainment is provided.

206.2.6 Performance Areas. Where a circulation path directly connects a performance area to an assembly seating area, an accessible route shall directly connect the assembly seating area with the performance area. An accessible route shall be provided from performance areas to ancillary areas or facilities used by performers unless exempted by 206.2.3 Exceptions 1 through 7.

206.2.7 Press Boxes. Press boxes in assembly areas shall be on an accessible route.

EXCEPTIONS:

1. An accessible route shall not be required to press boxes in bleachers that have points of entry at only one level provided that the aggregate area of all press boxes is 500 square feet (46 m^2) maximum.

2. An accessible route shall not be required to free-standing press boxes that are elevated above grade 12 feet (3660 mm) minimum provided that the aggregate area of all press boxes is 500 square feet (46 m^2) maximum.

Advisory

206.2.7 Press Boxes Exception 2. Where a facility contains multiple assembly areas, the aggregate area of the press boxes in each assembly area is to be calculated separately. For example, if a university has a soccer stadium with three press boxes elevated 12 feet (3660 mm) or more above grade and each press box is 150 square feet (14 m^2), then the aggregate area of the soccer stadium press boxes is less than 500 square feet (46 m^2) and Exception 2 applies to the soccer stadium. If that same university also has a football stadium with two press boxes elevated 12 feet (3660 mm) or more above grade and one press box is 250 square feet (23 m^2), and the second is 275 square feet (26 m^2), then the aggregate area of the football stadium press boxes is more than 500 square feet (46 m^2) and Exception 2 does not apply to the football stadium.

206.2.8 Employee Work Areas. Common use circulation paths within employee work areas shall comply with 402.

EXCEPTIONS:

1. Common use circulation paths located within employee work areas that are less than 1000 square feet (93 m^2) and defined by permanently installed partitions, counters, casework, or furnishings shall not be required to comply with 402.

2. Common use circulation paths located within employee work areas that are an integral component of work area equipment shall not be required to comply with 402.

3. Common use circulation paths located within exterior employee work areas that are fully exposed to the weather shall not be required to comply with 402.

Advisory

206.2.8 Employee Work Areas Exception 1. Modular furniture that is not permanently installed is not directly subject to these requirements. The Department of Justice ADA regulations provide additional guidance regarding the relationship between these requirements and elements that are not part of the built environment. Additionally, the Equal Employment Opportunity Commission (EEOC) implements title I of the ADA which requires non-discrimination in the workplace. EEOC can provide guidance regarding employers' obligations to provide reasonable accommodations for employees with disabilities.

206.2.8 Employee Work Areas Exception 2. Large pieces of equipment, such as electric turbines or water pumping apparatus, may have stairs and elevated walkways used for overseeing or monitoring purposes which are physically part of the turbine or pump. However, passenger elevators used for vertical transportation between stories are not considered "work area equipment" as defined in Section 106.5.

206.2.9 Amusement Rides. Amusement rides required to comply with 234 shall provide accessible routes in accordance with 206.2.9. Accessible routes serving amusement rides shall comply with Chapter 4 except as modified by 1002.2.

206.2.9.1 Load and Unload Areas. Load and unload areas shall be on an accessible route. Where load and unload areas have more than one loading or unloading position, at least one loading and unloading position shall be on an accessible route.

206.2.9.2 Wheelchair Spaces, Ride Seats Designed for Transfer, and Transfer Devices. When amusement rides are in the load and unload position, wheelchair spaces complying with 1002.4, amusement ride seats designed for transfer complying with 1002.5, and transfer devices complying with 1002.6 shall be on an accessible route.

206.2.10 Recreational Boating Facilities. Boat slips required to comply with 235.2 and boarding piers at boat launch ramps required to comply with 235.3 shall be on an accessible route. Accessible routes serving recreational boating facilities shall comply with Chapter 4, except as modified by 1003.2.

206.2.11 Bowling Lanes. Where bowling lanes are provided, at least 5 percent, but no fewer than one of each type of bowling lane, shall be on an accessible route.

206.2.12 Court Sports. In court sports, at least one accessible route shall directly connect both sides of the court.

206.2.13 Exercise Machines and Equipment. Exercise machines and equipment required to comply with 236 shall be on an accessible route.

206.2.14 Fishing Piers and Platforms. Fishing piers and platforms shall be on an accessible route. Accessible routes serving fishing piers and platforms shall comply with Chapter 4 except as modified by 1005.1.

206.2.15 Golf Facilities. At least one accessible route shall connect accessible elements and spaces within the boundary of the golf course. In addition, accessible routes serving golf car rental areas; bag drop areas; course weather shelters complying with 238.2.3; course toilet rooms; and practice putting greens, practice teeing grounds, and teeing stations at driving ranges complying with 238.3 shall comply with Chapter 4 except as modified by 1006.2.

> **EXCEPTION:** Golf car passages complying with 1006.3 shall be permitted to be used for all or part of accessible routes required by 206.2.15.

206.2.16 Miniature Golf Facilities. Holes required to comply with 239.2, including the start of play, shall be on an accessible route. Accessible routes serving miniature golf facilities shall comply with Chapter 4 except as modified by 1007.2.

206.2.17 Play Areas. Play areas shall provide accessible routes in accordance with 206.2.17. Accessible routes serving play areas shall comply with Chapter 4 except as modified by 1008.2.

206.2.17.1 Ground Level and Elevated Play Components. At least one accessible route shall be provided within the play area. The accessible route shall connect ground level play components required to comply with 240.2.1 and elevated play components required to comply with 240.2.2, including entry and exit points of the play components.

206.2.17.2 Soft Contained Play Structures. Where three or fewer entry points are provided for soft contained play structures, at least one entry point shall be on an accessible route. Where four or more entry points are provided for soft contained play structures, at least two entry points shall be on an accessible route.

206.3 Location. Accessible routes shall coincide with or be located in the same area as general circulation paths. Where circulation paths are interior, required accessible routes shall also be interior.

Advisory

206.3 Location. The accessible route must be in the same area as the general circulation path. This means that circulation paths, such as vehicular ways designed for pedestrian traffic, walks, and unpaved paths that are designed to be routinely used by pedestrians must be accessible or have an accessible route nearby. Additionally, accessible vertical interior circulation must be in the same area as stairs and escalators, not isolated in the back of the facility.

206.4 Entrances. Entrances shall be provided in accordance with 206.4. Entrance doors, doorways, and gates shall comply with 404 and shall be on an accessible route complying with 402.

EXCEPTIONS:

1. Where an alteration includes alterations to an entrance, and the building or facility has another entrance complying with 404 that is on an accessible route, the altered entrance shall not be required to comply with 206.4 unless required by 202.4.

2. Where exceptions for alterations to qualified historic buildings or facilities are permitted by 202.5, no more than one public entrance shall be required to comply with 206.4. Where no public entrance can comply with 206.4 under criteria established in 202.5 Exception, then either an unlocked entrance not used by the public shall comply with 206.4; or a locked entrance complying with 206.4 with a notification system or remote monitoring shall be provided.

206.4.1 Public Entrances. In addition to entrances required by 206.4.2 through 206.4.9, at least 60 percent of all public entrances shall comply with 404.

206.4.2 Parking Structure Entrances. Where direct access is provided for pedestrians from a parking structure to a building or facility entrance, each direct access to the building or facility entrance shall comply with 404.

206.4.3 Entrances from Tunnels or Elevated Walkways. Where direct access is provided for pedestrians from a pedestrian tunnel or elevated walkway to a building or facility, at least one direct entrance to the building or facility from each tunnel or walkway shall comply with 404.

206.4.4 Transportation Facilities. In addition to the requirements of 206.4.2, 206.4.3, and 206.4.5 through 206.4.9, transportation facilities shall provide entrances in accordance with 206.4.4.

206.4.4.1 Location. In transportation facilities, where different entrances serve different transportation fixed routes or groups of fixed routes, at least one public entrance serving each fixed route or group of fixed routes shall comply with 404.

> **EXCEPTION:** Entrances to key stations and existing intercity rail stations retrofitted in accordance with 49 CFR 37.49 or 49 CFR 37.51 shall not be required to comply with 206.4.4.1.

206.4.4.2 Direct Connections. Direct connections to other facilities shall provide an accessible route complying with 404 from the point of connection to boarding platforms and all transportation system elements required to be accessible. Any elements provided to facilitate future direct connections shall be on an accessible route connecting boarding platforms and all transportation system elements required to be accessible.

> **EXCEPTION:** In key stations and existing intercity rail stations, existing direct connections shall not be required to comply with 404.

206.4.4.3 Key Stations and Intercity Rail Stations. Key stations and existing intercity rail stations required by Subpart C of 49 CFR part 37 to be altered, shall have at least one entrance complying with 404.

206.4.5 Tenant Spaces. At least one accessible entrance to each tenancy in a facility shall comply with 404.

> **EXCEPTION:** Self-service storage facilities not required to comply with 225.3 shall not be required to be on an accessible route.

206.4.6 Residential Dwelling Unit Primary Entrance. In residential dwelling units, at least one primary entrance shall comply with 404. The primary entrance to a residential dwelling unit shall not be to a bedroom.

206.4.7 Restricted Entrances. Where restricted entrances are provided to a building or facility, at least one restricted entrance to the building or facility shall comply with 404.

206.4.8 Service Entrances. If a service entrance is the only entrance to a building or to a tenancy in a facility, that entrance shall comply with 404.

206.4.9 Entrances for Inmates or Detainees. Where entrances used only by inmates or detainees and security personnel are provided at judicial facilities, detention facilities, or correctional facilities, at least one such entrance shall comply with 404.

206.5 Doors, Doorways, and Gates. Doors, doorways, and gates providing user passage shall be provided in accordance with 206.5.

206.5.1 Entrances. Each entrance to a building or facility required to comply with 206.4 shall have at least one door, doorway, or gate complying with 404.

206.5.2 Rooms and Spaces. Within a building or facility, at least one door, doorway, or gate serving each room or space complying with these requirements shall comply with 404.

206.5.3 Transient Lodging Facilities. In transient lodging facilities, entrances, doors, and doorways providing user passage into and within guest rooms that are not required to provide mobility features complying with 806.2 shall comply with 404.2.3.

> **EXCEPTION:** Shower and sauna doors in guest rooms that are not required to provide mobility features complying with 806.2 shall not be required to comply with 404.2.3.

206.5.4 Residential Dwelling Units. In residential dwelling units required to provide mobility features complying with 809.2 through 809.4, all doors and doorways providing user passage shall comply with 404.

206.6 Elevators. Elevators provided for passengers shall comply with 407. Where multiple elevators are provided, each elevator shall comply with 407.

EXCEPTIONS:

1. In a building or facility permitted to use the exceptions to 206.2.3 or permitted by 206.7 to use a platform lift, elevators complying with 408 shall be permitted.

2. Elevators complying with 408 or 409 shall be permitted in multi-story residential dwelling units.

206.6.1 Existing Elevators. Where elements of existing elevators are altered, the same element shall also be altered in all elevators that are programmed to respond to the same hall call control as the altered elevator and shall comply with the requirements of 407 for the altered element.

206.7 Platform Lifts. Platform lifts shall comply with 410. Platform lifts shall be permitted as a component of an accessible route in new construction in accordance with 206.7. Platform lifts shall be permitted as a component of an accessible route in an existing building or facility.

206.7.1 Performance Areas and Speakers' Platforms. Platform lifts shall be permitted to provide accessible routes to performance areas and speakers' platforms.

206.7.2 Wheelchair Spaces. Platform lifts shall be permitted to provide an accessible route to comply with the wheelchair space dispersion and line-of-sight requirements of 221and 802.

206.7.3 Incidental Spaces. Platform lifts shall be permitted to provide an accessible route to incidental spaces which are not public use spaces and which are occupied by five persons maximum.

206.7.4 Judicial Spaces. Platform lifts shall be permitted to provide an accessible route to: jury boxes and witness stands; raised courtroom stations including, judges' benches, clerks' stations, bailiffs' stations, deputy clerks' stations, and court reporters' stations; and to depressed areas such as the well of a court.

206.7.5 Existing Site Constraints. Platform lifts shall be permitted where existing exterior site constraints make use of a ramp or elevator infeasible.

Advisory

206.7.5 Existing Site Constraints. This exception applies where topography or other similar existing site constraints necessitate the use of a platform lift as the only feasible alternative. While the site constraint must reflect exterior conditions, the lift can be installed in the interior of a building. For example, a new building constructed between and connected to two existing buildings may have insufficient space to coordinate floor levels and also to provide ramped entry from the public way. In this example, an exterior or interior platform lift could be used to provide an accessible entrance or to coordinate one or more interior floor levels.

206.7.6 Guest Rooms and Residential Dwelling Units. Platform lifts shall be permitted to connect levels within transient lodging guest rooms required to provide mobility features complying with 806.2 or residential dwelling units required to provide mobility features complying with 809.2 through 809.4.

206.7.7 Amusement Rides. Platform lifts shall be permitted to provide accessible routes to load and unload areas serving amusement rides.

206.7.8 Play Areas. Platform lifts shall be permitted to provide accessible routes to play components or soft contained play structures.

206.7.9 Team or Player Seating. Platform lifts shall be permitted to provide accessible routes to team or player seating areas serving areas of sport activity.

Advisory

206.7.9 Team or Player Seating. While the use of platform lifts is allowed, ramps are recommended to provide access to player seating areas serving an area of sport activity.

206.7.10 Recreational Boating Facilities and Fishing Piers and Platforms. Platform lifts shall be permitted to be used instead of gangways that are part of accessible routes serving recreational boating facilities and fishing piers and platforms.

206.8 Security Barriers. Security barriers, including but not limited to, security bollards and security check points, shall not obstruct a required accessible route or accessible means of egress.

EXCEPTION: Where security barriers incorporate elements that cannot comply with these requirements such as certain metal detectors, fluoroscopes, or other similar devices, the accessible route shall be permitted to be located adjacent to security screening devices. The accessible route shall permit persons with disabilities passing around security barriers to maintain visual contact with their personal items to the same extent provided others passing through the security barrier.

Guidance

Common Use Circulation Paths in Employee Work Areas. The 1991 Standards at section 4.1.1(3), and the 2010 Standards at section 203.9, require employee work areas in new construction and alterations *only* to be designed and constructed so that individuals with disabilities can approach, enter, and exit the areas. Section 206.2.8 of the 2010 Standards requires accessible common use circulation paths within employee work areas unless they are subject to exceptions in sections 206.2.8, 403.5, 405.5, and 405.8. The ADA, 42 U.S.C. 12112 (b)(5)(A) and (B), requires employers to make reasonable accommodations in the workplace for individuals with disabilities, which may include modifications to work areas when needed. Providing increased access in the facility at the time of construction or alteration will simplify the process of providing reasonable accommodations when they are needed.

The requirement for accessible common use circulation paths will not apply to existing facilities pursuant to the readily achievable barrier removal requirement. The Department has consistently taken the position that barrier removal requirements do not apply to areas used exclusively by employees because the purpose of title III is to ensure that access is provided to clients and customers. See Appendix B to the 1991 regulation implementing title III, 28 CFR part 36.

Several exceptions to section 206.2.8 of the 2010 Standards exempt common use circulation paths in employee work areas from the requirements of section 402 where it may be difficult to comply with the technical requirements for accessible routes due to the size or function of the area:

• Employee work areas, or portions of employee work areas, that are less than 300 square feet and are elevated 7 inches or more above the ground or finish floor, where elevation is essential to the function of the space, are exempt.

• Common use circulation paths within employee work areas that are less than 1,000 square feet and are defined by permanently installed partitions, counters, casework, or furnishings are exempt. Kitchens in quick service restaurants, cocktail bars, and the employee side of service counters are frequently covered by this exception.

• Common use circulation paths within employee work areas that are an integral component of equipment are exempt. Common use circulation paths within large pieces of equipment in factories, electric power plants, and amusement rides are covered by this exception.

• Common use circulation paths within exterior employee work areas that are fully exposed to the weather are exempt. Farms, ranches, and outdoor maintenance facilities are covered by this exception.

The 2010 Standards in sections 403.5 and 405.8 also contain exceptions to the technical requirements for accessible routes for circulation paths in employee work areas:

• Machinery and equipment are permitted to reduce the clear width of common use circulation paths where the reduction is essential to the function of the work performed. Machinery and equipment that must be placed a certain way to work properly, or for ergonomics or to prevent workplace injuries are covered by this exception.

• Handrails are not required on ramps, provided that they can be added in the future.

Commenters stated that the requirements set out in the 2010 Standards for accessible common use circulation paths in employee work areas are inappropriate, particularly in commercial kitchens, storerooms, and behind cocktail bars where wheelchairs would not be easily accommodated. These commenters further urged the Department not to adopt a requirement that circulation paths in employee work areas be at least 36 inches wide, including those at emergency exits.

These commenters misunderstand the scope of the provision. Nothing in the 2010 Standards requires all circulation paths in non-exempt areas to be accessible. The Department recognizes that building codes and fire and life safety codes, which are adopted by all of the states, require *primary* circulation paths in facilities, including employee work areas, to be at least 36 inches wide for purposes of emergency egress. Accessible routes also are at least 36 inches wide. Therefore, the Department anticipates that covered entities will be able to satisfy the requirement to provide accessible circulation paths by ensuring that their required *primary* circulation paths are accessible.

Individual employee work stations, such as a grocery checkout counter or an automobile service bay designed for use by one person, do not contain common use circulation paths and are not required to comply. Other work areas, such as stockrooms that typically have narrow pathways between shelves, would be required to design only one accessible circulation path into the stockroom. It would not be necessary to make each circulation path in the room accessible. In alterations it may be technically infeasible to provide accessible common use circulation paths in some employee work areas. For example, in a stock room of a department store significant existing physical constraints, such as having to move walls to avoid the loss of space to store inventory, may mean that it is technically infeasible (*see* section 106.5 "Defined Terms" of the 2010 Standards) to make even the primary common use circulation path in that stock room wide enough to be accessible. In addition, the 2010 Standards include exceptions for common use circulation paths in employee work areas where it may be difficult to comply with the technical requirements for accessible routes due to the size or function of the areas. The Department believes that these exceptions will provide the flexibility necessary to ensure that this requirement does not interfere with legitimate business operations.

Visible Alarms. Section 215.3 of the 2010 Standards provides that where employee work areas in newly constructed facilities have audible alarm coverage they are required to have wiring systems that are capable of supporting visible alarms that comply with section 702 of the 2010 Standards. The 1991 Standards, at section 4.1.1(3), require visible alarms to be provided where audible fire alarm systems are provided, but do not require areas used only by employees as work areas to be equipped with accessibility features. As applied to office buildings, the 1991 Standards require visible alarms to be provided in public and common use areas such as hallways, conference rooms, break rooms, and restrooms, where audible fire alarm systems are provided.

Commenters asserted that the requirements of section 215.3 of the 2010 Standards would be burdensome to meet. These commenters also raised concerns that all employee work areas within existing buildings and facilities must be equipped with accessibility features.

The commenters' concerns about section 215.3 of the 2010 Standards represent a misunderstanding of the requirements applicable to employee work areas.

Newly constructed buildings and facilities merely are required to provide wiring so that visible alarm systems can be added as needed to accommodate employees who are deaf or hard of hearing. This is a minimal requirement without significant impact.

The other issue in the comments represents a misunderstanding of the Department's existing regulatory requirements. Employee common use areas in covered facilities (e.g., locker rooms, break rooms, cafeterias, toilet rooms, corridors to exits, and other common use spaces) were required to be accessible under the 1991 Standards; areas in which employees actually perform their jobs are required to enable a person using a wheelchair or mobility device to approach, enter, and exit the area. The 2010 Standards require increased access through the accessible *common use* circulation path requirement, but neither the 1991 Standards nor the 2010 Standards require employee work stations to be accessible. Access to specific employee *work stations* is governed by title I of the ADA.

206 4 Accessible Routes

Slope. The 2010 Standards provide, at section 403.3, that the cross slope of walking surfaces not be steeper than 1:48. The 1991 Standards' cross slope requirement was that it not exceed 1:50. A commenter recommended increasing the cross slope requirement to allow a maximum of 1/2 inch per foot (1:24) to prevent imperfections in concrete surfaces from ponding water. The Department continues to believe that the requirement that a cross slope not be steeper than 1:48 adequately provides for water drainage in most situations. The suggested changes would double the allowable cross slope and create a significant impediment for many wheelchair users and others with a mobility disability.

Accessible Routes from Site Arrival Points and Within Sites. The 1991 Standards, at sections 4.1.2(1) and (2), and the 2010 Standards, at sections 206.2.1 and 206.2.2, require that at least one accessible route be provided within the site from site arrival points to an accessible building entrance and that at least one accessible route connect accessible facilities on the same site. The 2010 Standards also add two exceptions that exempt site arrival points and accessible facilities within a site from the accessible route requirements where the only means of access between them is a vehicular way that does not provide pedestrian access.

Commenters urged the Department to eliminate the exception that exempts site arrival points and accessible facilities from the accessible route requirements where the only means of access between them is a vehicular way not providing pedestrian access. The Department declines to accept this recommendation because the Department believes that its use will be limited. If it can be reasonably anticipated that the route between the site arrival point and the accessible facilities will be used by pedestrians, regardless of whether a pedestrian route is provided, then this exception will not apply. It will apply only in the relatively rare situations where the route between the site arrival point and the accessible facility dictates vehicular access – for example, an office complex on an isolated site that has a private access road, or a self-service storage facility where all users are expected to drive to their storage units.

Another commenter suggested that the language of section 406.1 of the 2010 Standards is confusing because it states that curb ramps on accessible routes shall comply with 406, 405.2 through 405.5, and 405.10. The 1991 Standards require that curb ramps be provided wherever an accessible route crosses a curb.

The Department declines to change this language because the change is purely editorial, resulting from the overall changes in the format of the 2010 Standards. It does not change the substantive requirement. In the 2010 Standards all elements on a required accessible route must be accessible; therefore, if the accessible route crosses a curb, a curb ramp must be provided.

Areas of Sport Activity. Section 206.2.2 of the 2010 Standards requires at least one accessible route to connect accessible buildings, facilities, elements, and spaces on the same site. Advisory section 206.2.2 adds the explanation that an accessible route must connect the boundary of each area of sport activity (e.g., courts and playing fields, whether indoor or outdoor). Section 206.2.12 of the 2010 Standards further requires that in court sports the accessible route must directly connect both sides of the court.

Limited-Use/Limited-Application Elevators, Destination-Oriented Elevators and Private Residence Elevators. The 1991 Standards, at section 4.1.3(5), and the 2010 Standards, at sections 206.2 and 206.6, include exceptions to the scoping requirement for accessible routes that exempt certain facilities from connecting each story with an elevator. If a facility is exempt from the scoping requirement, but nonetheless installs an elevator, the 1991 Standards require the elevator to comply with the technical requirements for elevators. The 2010 Standards add a new exception that allows a facility that is exempt from the scoping requirement to install a limited-use/limited-application (LULA) elevator. LULA elevators are also permitted in the 1991 Standards and the 2010 Standards as an alternative to platform lifts. The 2010 Standards also add a new exception that permits private residence elevators in multi-story dwelling and transient lodging units. The 2010 Standards contain technical requirements for LULA elevators at section 408 and private residence elevators at section 409.

Section 407.2.1.4 of the 2010 Standards includes an exception to the technical requirements for locating elevator call buttons for destination-oriented elevators. The advisory at section 407.2.1.4 describes lobby controls for destination-oriented elevator systems. Many elevator manufacturers have recently developed these new "buttonless" elevator control systems. These new, more efficient elevators are usually found in high-rise buildings that have several elevators. They require passengers to enter their destination floor on an entry device, usually a keypad, in the elevator lobby. The system then sends the most efficient car available to take all of the passengers going to the sixth floor, for example, only to the sixth floor, without making stops at the third, fourth, and fifth floors on the way to the sixth floor. The challenge for individuals who are blind or have low vision is how to know which elevator car to enter, after they have entered their destination floor into the keypad.

Commenters requested that the Department impose a moratorium on the installation of destination-oriented elevators arguing that this new technology presents wayfinding challenges for persons who are blind or have low vision.

Section 407.2.1.5 of the 2010 Standards allows destination-oriented elevators to not provide call buttons with visible signals to indicate when each call is registered and when each call is answered *provided* that visible and audible signals, compliant with 407.2.2 of the 2010 Standards, indicating which elevator car to enter, are provided. This will require the responding elevator car to automatically provide audible and visible communication so that the system will always verbally and visually indicate which elevator car to enter.

As with any new technology, all users must have time to become acquainted with how to use destination-oriented elevators. The Department will monitor the use of this new technology and work with the Access Board so that there is not a decrease in accessibility as a result of permitting this new technology to be installed.

Accessible Routes to Tiered Dining Areas in Sports Facilities. The 1991 Standards, at sections 4.1.3(1) and 5.4, and section 206.2.5 of the 2010 Standards require an accessible route to be provided to all dining areas in new construction, including raised or sunken dining areas. The 2010 Standards add a new exception for tiered dining areas in sports facilities. Dining areas in sports facilities are typically integrated into the seating bowl and are tiered to provide adequate lines of sight for individuals with disabilities. The new exception requires accessible routes to be provided to at least 25 percent (25%) of the tiered dining areas in sports facilities. Each tier must have the same services and the accessible routes must serve the accessible seating.

Accessible Routes to Press Boxes. The 1991 Standards, at sections 4.1.1(1) and 4.1.3(1), cover all areas of newly constructed facilities required to be accessible, and require an accessible route to connect accessible entrances with all accessible spaces and elements within the facility. Section 201.1 of the 2010 Standards requires that all areas of newly designed and constructed buildings and facilities and altered portions of existing buildings and facilities be accessible. Sections 206.2.7(1) and (2) of the 2010 Standards add two exceptions that exempt small press boxes that are located in bleachers with entrances on only one level, and small press boxes that are free-standing structures elevated 12 feet or more above grade, from the accessible route requirement when the aggregate area of all press boxes in a sports facility does not exceed 500 square feet. The Department anticipates that this change will significantly reduce the economic impact on smaller sports facilities, such as those associated with high schools or community colleges.

Public Entrances. The 1991 Standards, at sections 4.1.3(8) and 4.1.6(1)(h), require at least fifty percent (50%) of public entrances to be accessible. Additionally, the 1991 Standards require the number of accessible public entrances to be equivalent to the number of exits required by applicable building and fire codes. With very few exceptions, building and fire codes require at least two exits to be provided from spaces within a building and from the building itself. Therefore, under the 1991 Standards where two public entrances are planned in a newly constructed facility, both entrances are required to be accessible.

Instead of requiring accessible entrances based on the number of public entrances provided or the number of exits required (whichever is greater), section 206.4.1 of the 2010 Standards requires at least sixty percent (60%) of public entrances to be accessible. The revision is intended to achieve the same result as the 1991 Standards. Thus, under the 2010 Standards where two public entrances are planned in a newly constructed facility, both entrances must be accessible.

Where multiple public entrances are planned to serve different site arrival points, the 1991 Standards, at section 4.1.2(1), and section 206.2.1 of the 2010 Standards require at least one accessible route to be provided from each type of site arrival point provided, including accessible parking spaces, accessible passenger loading zones, public streets and sidewalks, and public transportation stops, to an accessible public entrance that serves the site arrival point.

Commenters representing small businesses recommended retaining the 1991 requirement for fifty percent (50%) of public entrances of covered entities to be accessible. These commenters also raised concerns about the impact upon existing facilities of the new sixty percent (60%) requirement.

The Department believes that these commenters misunderstand the 1991 Standards. As explained above, the requirements of the 1991 Standards generally require more than fifty percent (50%) of entrances in small facilities to be accessible. Model codes require that most buildings have more than one means of egress. Most buildings have more than one entrance, and the requirements of the 1991 Standards typically resulted in these buildings having more than one accessible entrance. Requiring at least sixty percent (60%) of public entrances to be accessible is not expected to result in a substantial increase in the number of accessible entrances compared to the requirements of the 1991 Standards. In some very large facilities this change may result in fewer accessible entrances being required by the 2010 Standards. However, the Department believes that the realities of good commercial design will result in more accessible entrances being provided for the convenience of all users.

The 1991 Standards and the 2010 Standards also contain exceptions that limit the number of accessible entrances required in alterations to existing facilities. When entrances to an existing facility are altered and the facility has an accessible entrance, the entrance being altered is not required to be accessible, unless a primary function area also is altered and then an accessible path of travel must be provided to the primary function area to the extent that the cost to do so is not disproportionate to the overall cost of the alteration.

Alterations to Existing Elevators. When a single space or element is altered, the 1991 Standards, at sections 4.1.6(1)(a) and (b), require the space or element to be made accessible. When an element in one elevator is altered, the 2010 Standards, at section 206.6.1, require the same element to be altered in all elevators that are programmed to respond to the same call button as the altered elevator.

The 2010 Standards, at sections 407.2.1 - 407.4.7.1.2, also contain exceptions to the technical requirements for elevators when existing elevators are altered that minimize the impact of this change.

Commenters expressed concerns about the requirement that when an element in one elevator is altered, the 2010 Standards, at section 206.6.1, will require the same element to be altered in all elevators that are programmed to respond to the same call button as the altered elevator. Commenters noted that such a requirement is burdensome and will result in costly efforts without significant benefit to individuals with disabilities.

The Department believes that this requirement is necessary to ensure that when an individual with a disability presses a call button, an accessible elevator will arrive. Without this requirement, individuals with disabilities would have to wait unnecessarily for an accessible elevator to make its way to them arbitrarily. The Department also believes that the effort required to meet this provision is minimal in the majority of situations because it is typical to upgrade all of the elevators in a bank at the same time.

Accessible Routes in Dwelling Units with Mobility Features. Sections 4.34.1 and 4.34.2 of the UFAS require the living area, kitchen and dining area, bedroom, bathroom, and laundry area, where provided, in covered dwelling units with mobility features to be on an accessible route. Where covered dwelling units have two or more bedrooms, at least two bedrooms are required to be on an accessible route.

The 2010 Standards at sections 233.3.1.1, 809.1, 809.2, 809.2.1, and 809.4 will require all spaces and elements within dwelling units with mobility features to be on an accessible route. These changes exempt unfinished attics and unfinished basements from the accessible route requirement. Section 233.3.5 of the 2010 Standards also includes an exception to the dispersion requirement that permits accessible single-story dwelling units to be constructed, where multi-story dwelling units are one of the types of units provided.

Location of Accessible Routes. Section 4.3.2(1) of the 1991 Standards requires accessible routes connecting site arrival points and accessible building entrances to coincide with general circulation paths, to the maximum extent feasible. The 2010 Standards require all accessible routes to coincide with or be located in the same general area as general circulation paths. Additionally, a new provision specifies that where a circulation path is interior, the required accessible route must also be located in the interior of the facility. The change affects a limited number of buildings. Section 206.3 of the 2010 Standards requires all accessible routes to coincide with or be located in the same general area as general circulation paths. Designing newly constructed interior accessible routes to coincide with or to be located in the same area as general circulation paths will not typically present a difficult design challenge and is expected to impose limited design constraints. The change will have no impact on exterior accessible routes. The 1991 Standards and the 2010 Standards also require accessible routes to be located in the interior of the facility where general circulation paths are located in the interior of the facility. The revision affects a limited number of buildings.

Location of Accessible Routes to Stages. The 1991 Standards at section 4.33.5 require an accessible route to connect the accessible seating and the performing area.

Section 206.2.6 of the 2010 Standards requires the accessible route to directly connect the seating area and the accessible seating, stage, and all areas of the stage, where a circulation path directly connects the seating area and the stage. Both the 1991 Standards and the 2010 Standards also require an accessible route to connect the stage and ancillary areas, such as dressing rooms, used by performers. The 2010 Standards do not require an additional accessible route to be provided to the stage. Rather, the changes specify where the accessible route to the stage, which is required by the 1991 Standards, must be located.

207 Accessible Means of Egress

207.1 General. Means of egress shall comply with section 1003.2.13 of the International Building Code (2000 edition and 2001 Supplement) or section 1007 of the International Building Code (2003 edition) (incorporated by reference, see "Referenced Standards" in Chapter 1).

EXCEPTIONS:

1. Where means of egress are permitted by local building or life safety codes to share a common path of egress travel, accessible means of egress shall be permitted to share a common path of egress travel.

2. Areas of refuge shall not be required in detention and correctional facilities.

207.2 Platform Lifts. Standby power shall be provided for platform lifts permitted by section 1003.2.13.4 of the International Building Code (2000 edition and 2001 Supplement) or section 1007.5 of the International Building Code (2003 edition) (incorporated by reference, see "Referenced Standards" in Chapter 1) to serve as a part of an accessible means of egress.

Guidance

General. The 1991 Standards at sections 4.1.3(9); 4.1.6(1)(g); and 4.3.10 establish scoping and technical requirements for accessible means of egress. Section 207.1 of the 2010 Standards reference the International Building Code (IBC) for scoping and technical requirements for accessible means of egress.

The 1991 Standards require the same number of accessible means of egress to be provided as the number of exits required by applicable building and fire codes. The IBC requires at least one accessible means of egress and at least two accessible means of egress where more than one means of egress is required by other sections of the building code. The changes in the 2010 Standards are expected to have minimal impact since the model fire and life safety codes, which are adopted by all of the states, contain equivalent requirements with respect to the number of accessible means of egress.

The 1991 Standards require areas of rescue assistance or horizontal exits in facilities with levels above or below the level of exit discharge. Areas of rescue assistance are spaces that have direct access to an exit, stair, or enclosure where individuals who are unable to use stairs can go to call for assistance and wait for evacuation. The 2010 Standards incorporate the requirements established by the IBC. The IBC requires an evacuation elevator designed with standby power and other safety features that can be used for emergency evacuation of individuals with disabilities in facilities with four or more stories above or below the exit discharge level, and allows exit stairways and evacuation elevators to be used as an accessible means of egress in conjunction with areas of refuge or horizontal exits. The change is expected to have minimal impact since the model fire and life safety codes, adopted by most states, already contain parallel requirements with respect to evacuation elevators.

The 1991 Standards exempt facilities equipped with a supervised automatic sprinkler system from providing areas of rescue assistance, and also exempt alterations to existing facilities from providing an accessible means of egress. The IBC exempts buildings equipped with a supervised automatic sprinkler system from certain technical requirements for areas of refuge, and also exempts alterations to existing facilities from providing an accessible means of egress.

The 1991 and 2010 Standards require signs that provide direction to or information about functional spaces to meet certain technical requirements. The 2010 Standards, at section 216.4, address exit signs. This section is consistent with the requirements of the IBC. Signs used for means of egress are covered by this scoping requirement. The requirements in the 2010 Standards require tactile signs complying with sections 703.1, 703.2 and 703.5 at doors at exit passageways, exit discharge, and at exit stairways. Directional exit signs and signs at areas of refuge required by section 216.4.3 must have visual characters and features complying with section 703.5.

Standby Power for Platform Lifts. The 2010 Standards at section 207.2 require standby power to be provided for platform lifts that are permitted to serve as part of an accessible means of egress by the IBC. The IBC permits platform lifts to serve as part of an accessible means of egress in a limited number of places where platform lifts are allowed in new construction. The 1991 Standards, at 4.1.3 (5) Exception 4 (a) through (d), and the 2010 Standards, at sections 206.7.1 through 206.7.10, similarly limit the places where platform lifts are allowed in new construction.

Commenters urged the Department to reconsider provisions that would require standby power to be provided for platform lifts. Concerns were raised that ensuring standby power would be too burdensome. The Department views this issue as a fundamental life safety issue. Lift users face the prospect of being trapped on the lift in the event of a power failure if standby power is not provided. The lack of standby power could be life-threatening in situations where the power failure is associated with a fire or other emergency. The use of a platform lift is generally only one of the options available to covered entities. Covered entities that are concerned about the costs associated with maintaining standby power for a lift may wish to explore design options that would incorporate the use of a ramp.

208 Parking Spaces

208.1 General. Where parking spaces are provided, parking spaces shall be provided in accordance with 208.

EXCEPTION: Parking spaces used exclusively for buses, trucks, other delivery vehicles, law enforcement vehicles, or vehicular impound shall not be required to comply with 208 provided that lots accessed by the public are provided with a passenger loading zone complying with 503.

208.2 Minimum Number. Parking spaces complying with 502 shall be provided in accordance with Table 208.2 except as required by 208.2.1, 208.2.2, and 208.2.3. Where more than one parking facility is provided on a site, the number of accessible spaces provided on the site shall be calculated according to the number of spaces required for each parking facility.

Table 208.2 Parking Spaces

Total Number of Parking Spaces Provided in Parking Facility	Minimum Number of Required Accessible Parking Spaces
1 to 25	1
26 to 50	2
51 to 75	3
76 to 100	4
101 to 150	5
151 to 200	6
201 to 300	7
301 to 400	8
401 to 500	9
501 to 1000	2 percent of total
1001 and over	20, plus 1 for each 100, or fraction thereof, over 1000

Advisory

208.2 Minimum Number. The term "parking facility" is used Section 208.2 instead of the term "parking lot" so that it is clear that both parking lots and parking structures are required to comply with this section. The number of parking spaces required to be accessible is to be calculated separately for each parking facility; the required number is not to be based on the total number of parking spaces provided in all of the parking facilities provided on the site.

208.2.1 Hospital Outpatient Facilities. Ten percent of patient and visitor parking spaces provided to serve hospital outpatient facilities shall comply with 502.

Advisory

208.2.1 Hospital Outpatient Facilities. The term "outpatient facility" is not defined in this document but is intended to cover facilities or units that are located in hospitals and that provide regular and continuing medical treatment without an overnight stay. Doctors' offices, independent clinics, or other facilities not located in hospitals are not considered hospital outpatient facilities for purposes of this document.

208.2.2 Rehabilitation Facilities and Outpatient Physical Therapy Facilities. Twenty percent of patient and visitor parking spaces provided to serve rehabilitation facilities specializing in treating conditions that affect mobility and outpatient physical therapy facilities shall comply with 502.

Advisory

208.2.2 Rehabilitation Facilities and Outpatient Physical Therapy Facilities. Conditions that affect mobility include conditions requiring the use or assistance of a brace, cane, crutch, prosthetic device, wheelchair, or powered mobility aid; arthritic, neurological, or orthopedic conditions that severely limit one's ability to walk; respiratory diseases and other conditions which may require the use of portable oxygen; and cardiac conditions that impose significant functional limitations.

208.2.3 Residential Facilities. Parking spaces provided to serve residential facilities shall comply with 208.2.3.

208.2.3.1 Parking for Residents. Where at least one parking space is provided for each residential dwelling unit, at least one parking space complying with 502 shall be provided for each residential dwelling unit required to provide mobility features complying with 809.2 through 809.4.

208.2.3.2 Additional Parking Spaces for Residents. Where the total number of parking spaces provided for each residential dwelling unit exceeds one parking space per residential dwelling unit, 2 percent, but no fewer than one space, of all the parking spaces not covered by 208.2.3.1 shall comply with 502.

208.2.3.3 Parking for Guests, Employees, and Other Non-Residents. Where parking spaces are provided for persons other than residents, parking shall be provided in accordance with Table 208.2.

208.2.4 Van Parking Spaces. For every six or fraction of six parking spaces required by 208.2 to comply with 502, at least one shall be a van parking space complying with 502.

208.3 Location. Parking facilities shall comply with 208.3

208.3.1 General. Parking spaces complying with 502 that serve a particular building or facility shall be located on the shortest accessible route from parking to an entrance complying with 206.4. Where parking serves more than one accessible entrance, parking spaces complying with 502 shall be dispersed and located on the shortest accessible route to the accessible entrances. In parking facilities that do not serve a particular building or facility, parking spaces complying with 502 shall be located on the shortest accessible route to an accessible pedestrian entrance of the parking facility.

> **EXCEPTIONS:**
>
> **1.** All van parking spaces shall be permitted to be grouped on one level within a multi-story parking facility.
>
> **2.** Parking spaces shall be permitted to be located in different parking facilities if substantially equivalent or greater accessibility is provided in terms of distance from an accessible entrance or entrances, parking fee, and user convenience.

> *Advisory*
> *208.3.1 General Exception 2.* Factors that could affect "user convenience" include, but are not limited to, protection from the weather, security, lighting, and comparative maintenance of the alternative parking site.

208.3.2 Residential Facilities. In residential facilities containing residential dwelling units required to provide mobility features complying with 809.2 through 809.4, parking spaces provided in accordance with 208.2.3.1 shall be located on the shortest accessible route to the residential dwelling unit entrance they serve. Spaces provided in accordance with 208.2.3.2 shall be dispersed throughout all types of parking provided for the residential dwelling units.

> **EXCEPTION:** Parking spaces provided in accordance with 208.2.3.2 shall not be required to be dispersed throughout all types of parking if substantially equivalent or greater accessibility is provided in terms of distance from an accessible entrance, parking fee, and user convenience.

> *Advisory*
> *208.3.2 Residential Facilities Exception.* Factors that could affect "user convenience" include, but are not limited to, protection from the weather, security, lighting, and comparative maintenance of the alternative parking site.

Guidance

General. Where parking spaces are provided, the 1991 Standards, at sections 4.1.2 (5)(a) and (7) and 7(a), and the 2010 Standards, at section 208.1, require a specified number of the parking spaces to be accessible. The 2010 Standards, at section 208, include an exception that exempts parking spaces used exclusively for buses, trucks, delivery vehicles, law enforcement vehicles, or for purposes of vehicular impound, from the scoping requirement for parking spaces, provided that when these lots are accessed by the public the lot has an accessible passenger loading zone.

The 2010 Standards require accessible parking spaces to be identified by signs that display the International Symbol of Accessibility. Section 216.5, Exceptions 1 and 2, of the 2010 Standards exempt certain accessible parking spaces from this signage requirement. The first exception exempts sites that have four or fewer parking spaces from the signage requirement. Residential facilities where parking spaces are assigned to specific dwelling units are also exempted from the signage requirement.

Commenters stated that the first exception, by allowing a small parking lot with four or fewer spaces not to post a sign at its one accessible space, is problematic because it could allow all drivers to park in accessible parking spaces. The Department believes that this exception provides necessary relief for small business entities that may otherwise face the prospect of having between twenty-five percent (25%) and one hundred percent (100%) of their limited parking area unavailable to their customers because they are reserved for the exclusive use of persons whose vehicles display accessible tags or parking placards. The 2010 Standards still require these businesses to ensure that at least one of their available parking spaces is designed to be accessible.

A commenter stated that accessible parking spaces must be clearly marked. The Department notes that section 502.6 of the 2010 Standards provides that accessible parking spaces must be identified by signs that include the International Symbol of Accessibility. Also, section 502.3.3 of the 2010 Standards requires that access aisles be marked so as to discourage parking in them.

Access Aisle. Section 502.3 of the 2010 Standards requires that an accessible route adjoin each access aisle serving accessible parking spaces. The accessible route connects each access aisle to accessible entrances.

Commenters questioned why the 2010 Standards would permit an accessible route used by individuals with disabilities to coincide with the path of moving vehicles. The Department believes that the 2010 Standards appropriately recognize that not all parking facilities provide separate pedestrian routes. Section 502.3 of the 2010 Standards provides the flexibility necessary to permit designers and others to determine the most appropriate location of the accessible route to the accessible entrances. If all pedestrians using the parking facility are expected to share the vehicular lanes, then the ADA permits covered entities to use the vehicular lanes as part of the accessible route. The advisory note in section 502.3 of the 2010 Standards, however, calls attention to the fact that this practice, while permitted, is not ideal. Accessible parking spaces must be located on the shortest accessible route of travel to an accessible entrance. Accessible parking spaces and the required accessible route should be located where individuals with disabilities do not have to cross vehicular lanes or pass behind parked vehicles to have access to an accessible entrance. If it is necessary to cross a vehicular lane because, for example, local fire engine access requirements prohibit parking immediately adjacent to a building, then a marked crossing running perpendicular to the vehicular route should be included as part of the accessible route to an accessible entrance.

Van Accessible Parking Spaces. The 1991 Standards, at sections 4.1.2 (5)(b), 4.6.3, 4.6.4, and 4.6.5, require one in every eight accessible parking spaces to be van accessible. Section 208.2.4 of the 2010 Standards requires one in every six accessible parking spaces to be van accessible.

A commenter asked whether automobiles other than vans may park in van accessible parking spaces. The 2010 Standards do not prohibit automobiles other than vans from using van accessible parking spaces. The Department does not distinguish between vehicles that are actual "vans" versus other vehicles such as trucks, station wagons, sport utility vehicles, etc. since many vehicles other than vans may be used by individuals with disabilities to transport mobility devices.

Commenters´ opinions were divided on this point. Facility operators and others asked for a reduction in the number of required accessible parking spaces, especially the number of van accessible parking spaces, because they claimed these spaces often are not used. Individuals with disabilities, however, requested an increase in the scoping requirements for these parking spaces.

The Department is aware that a strong difference of opinion exists between those who use such spaces and those who must provide or maintain them. Therefore, the Department did not increase the total number of accessible spaces required. The only change was to increase the proportion of spaces that must be accessible to vans and other vehicles equipped to transport mobility devices.

Direct Access Entrances from Parking Structures. Where levels in a parking garage have direct connections for pedestrians to another facility, the 1991 Standards, at section 4.1.3(8)(b)(i), require at least one of the direct connections to be accessible. The 2010 Standards, at section 206.4.2, require all of these direct connections to be accessible.

209 Passenger Loading Zones and Bus Stops

209.1 General. Passenger loading zones shall be provided in accordance with 209.

209.2 Type. Where provided, passenger loading zones shall comply with 209.2.

209.2.1 Passenger Loading Zones. Passenger loading zones, except those required to comply with 209.2.2 and 209.2.3, shall provide at least one passenger loading zone complying with 503 in every continuous 100 linear feet (30 m) of loading zone space, or fraction thereof.

209.2.2 Bus Loading Zones. In bus loading zones restricted to use by designated or specified public transportation vehicles, each bus bay, bus stop, or other area designated for lift or ramp deployment shall comply with 810.2.

Advisory

209.2.2 Bus Loading Zones. The terms "designated public transportation" and "specified public transportation" are defined by the Department of Transportation at 49 CFR 37.3 in regulations implementing the Americans with Disabilities Act. These terms refer to public transportation services provided by public or private entities, respectively. For example, designated public transportation vehicles include buses and vans operated by public transit agencies, while specified public transportation vehicles include tour and charter buses, taxis and limousines, and hotel shuttles operated by private entities.

209.2.3 On-Street Bus Stops. On-street bus stops shall comply with 810.2 to the maximum extent practicable.

209.3 Medical Care and Long-Term Care Facilities. At least one passenger loading zone complying with 503 shall be provided at an accessible entrance to licensed medical care and licensed long-term care facilities where the period of stay exceeds twenty-four hours.

209.4 Valet Parking. Parking facilities that provide valet parking services shall provide at least one passenger loading zone complying with 503.

209.5 Mechanical Access Parking Garages. Mechanical access parking garages shall provide at least one passenger loading zone complying with 503 at vehicle drop-off and vehicle pick-up areas.

Guidance

Passenger Loading Zones at Medical Care and Long-Term Care Facilities. Sections 6.1 and 6.2 of the 1991 Standards and section 209.3 of the 2010 Standards require medical care and long-term care facilities, where the period of stay exceeds 24 hours, to provide at least one accessible passenger loading zone at an accessible entrance. The 1991 Standards also require a canopy or roof overhang at this passenger loading zone. The 2010 Standards do not require a canopy or roof overhang.

Commenters urged the Department to reinstate the requirement for a canopy or roof overhang at accessible passenger loading zones at medical care and long-term care facilities. While the Department recognizes that a canopy or roof overhang may afford useful protection from inclement weather conditions to everyone using a facility, it is not clear that the absence of such protection would impede access by individuals with disabilities. Therefore, the Department declined to reinstate that requirement.

Passenger Loading Zones. Where passenger loading zones are provided, the 1991 Standards, at sections 4.1.2(5) and 4.6.6, require at least one passenger loading zone to be accessible. Sections 209.2.1 and 503 of the 2010 Standards, require facilities such as airport passenger terminals that have long, continuous passenger loading zones to provide one accessible passenger loading zone in every continuous 100 linear feet of loading zone space. The 1991 Standards and the 2010 Standards both include technical requirements for the vehicle pull-up space (96 inches wide minimum and 20 feet long minimum). Accessible passenger loading zones must have an access aisle that is 60 inches wide minimum and extends the full length of the vehicle pull-up space. The 1991 Standards permit the access aisle to be on the same level as the vehicle pull-up space, or on the sidewalk. The 2010 Standards require the access aisle to be on the same level as the vehicle pull-up space and to be marked so as to discourage parking in the access aisle.

Commenters expressed concern that certain covered entities, particularly airports, cannot accommodate the requirements of the 2010 Standards to provide passenger loading zones, and urged a revision that would require one accessible passenger loading zone located in reasonable proximity to each building entrance served by the curb.

Commenters raised a variety of issues about the requirements at section 503 of the 2010 Standards stating that the requirements for an access aisle, width, length, and marking of passenger loading zones are not clear, do not fully meet the needs of individuals with disabilities, may run afoul of state or local requirements, or may not be needed because many passenger loading zones are typically staffed by doormen or valet parkers. The wide range of opinions expressed in these comments indicates that this provision is controversial. However, none of these comments provided sufficient data to enable the Department to determine that the requirement is not appropriate.

Valet Parking and Mechanical Access Parking Garages. The 1991 Standards, at sections 4.1.2(5)(a) and (e), and sections 208.2, 209.4, and 209.5 of the 2010 Standards require parking facilities that provide valet parking services to have an accessible passenger loading zone. The 2010 Standards extend this requirement to mechanical access parking garages. The 1991 Standards contained an exception that exempted valet parking facilities from providing accessible parking spaces. The 2010 Standards eliminate this exception. The reason for not retaining the provision is that valet parking is a service, not a facility type.

Commenters questioned why the exception for valet parking facilities from providing accessible parking spaces was eliminated. The provision was eliminated because valet parkers may not have the skills necessary to drive a vehicle that is equipped to be accessible, including use of hand controls, or when a seat is not present to accommodate a driver using a wheelchair. In that case, permitting the individual with a disability to self-park may be a required reasonable modification of policy by a covered entity.

210 Stairways

210.1 General. Interior and exterior stairs that are part of a means of egress shall comply with 504.

EXCEPTIONS:

1. In detention and correctional facilities, stairs that are not located in public use areas shall not be required to comply with 504.

2. In alterations, stairs between levels that are connected by an accessible route shall not be required to comply with 504, except that handrails complying with 505 shall be provided when the stairs are altered.

3. In assembly areas, aisle stairs shall not be required to comply with 504.

4. Stairs that connect play components shall not be required to comply with 504.

Advisory

210.1 General. Although these requirements do not mandate handrails on stairs that are not part of a means of egress, State or local building codes may require handrails or guards.

Guidance

The 1991 Standards require stairs to be accessible only when they provide access to floor levels not otherwise connected by an accessible route (e.g., where the accessible route is provided by an elevator, lift, or ramp). The 2010 Standards, at sections 210.1 and 504, require all *newly constructed stairs* that are part of a *means of egress* to comply with the requirements for accessible stairs, which include requirements for accessible treads, risers, and handrails. In existing facilities, where floor levels are connected by an accessible route, only the handrail requirement will apply when the stairs are altered. Exception 2 to section 210.1 of the 2010 Standards permits altered stairs to not comply with the requirements for accessible treads and risers where there is an accessible route between floors served by the stairs.

Most commenters were in favor of this requirement for handrails in alterations and stated that adding handrails to stairs during alterations would be feasible and not costly while providing important safety benefits. The Department believes that it strikes an appropriate balance by focusing the expanded requirements on new construction. The 2010 Standards apply to stairs which are part of a required means of egress. Few stairways are not part of a means of egress. The 2010 Standards are consistent with most building codes which do not exempt stairways when the route is also served by a ramp or elevator.

211 Drinking Fountains

211.1 General. Where drinking fountains are provided on an exterior site, on a floor, or within a secured area they shall be provided in accordance with 211.

> **EXCEPTION:** In detention or correctional facilities, drinking fountains only serving holding or housing cells not required to comply with 232 shall not be required to comply with 211.

211.2 Minimum Number. No fewer than two drinking fountains shall be provided. One drinking fountain shall comply with 602.1 through 602.6 and one drinking fountain shall comply with 602.7.

> **EXCEPTION:** Where a single drinking fountain complies with 602.1 through 602.6 and 602.7, it shall be permitted to be substituted for two separate drinking fountains.

211.3 More Than Minimum Number. Where more than the minimum number of drinking fountains specified in 211.2 are provided, 50 percent of the total number of drinking fountains provided shall comply with 602.1 through 602.6, and 50 percent of the total number of drinking fountains provided shall comply with 602.7.

> **EXCEPTION:** Where 50 percent of the drinking fountains yields a fraction, 50 percent shall be permitted to be rounded up or down provided that the total number of drinking fountains complying with 211 equals 100 percent of drinking fountains.

Guidance

Sections 4.1.3(10) and 4.15 of the 1991 Standards and sections 211 and 602 of the 2010 Standards require drinking fountains to be provided for persons who use wheelchairs and for others who stand. The 1991 Standards require wall and post-mounted cantilevered drinking fountains mounted at a height for wheelchair users to provide clear floor space for a forward approach with knee and toe clearance and free standing or built-in drinking fountains to provide clear floor space for a parallel approach. The 2010 Standards require drinking fountains mounted at a height for wheelchair users to provide clear floor space for a forward approach with knee and toe clearance, and include an exception for a parallel approach for drinking fountains installed at a height to accommodate very small children. The 2010 Standards also include a technical requirement for drinking fountains for standing persons.

---

212 Kitchens, Kitchenettes, and Sinks

212.1 General. Where provided, kitchens, kitchenettes, and sinks shall comply with 212.

212.2 Kitchens and Kitchenettes. Kitchens and kitchenettes shall comply with 804.

212.3 Sinks. Where sinks are provided, at least 5 percent, but no fewer than one, of each type provided in each accessible room or space shall comply with 606.

> **EXCEPTION:** Mop or service sinks shall not be required to comply with 212.3.

Guidance

The 1991 Standards, at sections 4.24, and 9.2.2(7), contain technical requirements for sinks and only have specific scoping requirements for sinks in transient lodging. Section 212.3 of the 2010 Standards requires at least five percent (5%) of sinks in each accessible space to comply with the technical requirements for sinks. The technical requirements address clear floor space, height, faucets, and exposed pipes and surfaces. The 1991 Standards, at section 4.24, and the 2010 Standards, at section 606, both require the clear floor space at sinks to be positioned for a forward approach and knee and toe clearance to be provided under the sink. The 1991 Standards, at section 9.2.2(7), allow the clear floor space at kitchen sinks and wet bars in transient lodging guest rooms with mobility features to be positioned for either a forward approach with knee and toe clearance or for a parallel approach.

The 2010 Standards include an exception that permits the clear floor space to be positioned for a parallel approach at kitchen sinks in any space where a cook top or conventional range is not provided, and at a wet bar.

A commenter stated that it is unclear what the difference is between a sink and a lavatory, and that this is complicated by requirements that apply to sinks (five percent (5%) accessible) and lavatories (at least one accessible). The term "lavatory" generally refers to the specific type of plumbing fixture required for hand washing in toilet and bathing facilities. The more generic term "sink" applies to all other types of sinks located in covered facilities.

A commenter recommended that the mounting height of sinks and lavatories should take into consideration the increased use of three-wheeled scooters and some larger wheelchairs. The Department is aware that the use of three-wheeled scooters and larger wheelchairs may be increasing and that some of these devices may require changes in space requirements in the future. The Access Board is funding research to obtain data that may be used to develop design guidelines that provide access to individuals using these mobility devices.

213 Toilet Facilities and Bathing Facilities

213.1 General. Where toilet facilities and bathing facilities are provided, they shall comply with 213. Where toilet facilities and bathing facilities are provided in facilities permitted by 206.2.3 Exceptions 1 and 2 not to connect stories by an accessible route, toilet facilities and bathing facilities shall be provided on a story connected by an accessible route to an accessible entrance.

213.2 Toilet Rooms and Bathing Rooms. Where toilet rooms are provided, each toilet room shall comply with 603. Where bathing rooms are provided, each bathing room shall comply with 603.

EXCEPTIONS:

1. In alterations where it is technically infeasible to comply with 603, altering existing toilet or bathing rooms shall not be required where a single unisex toilet room or bathing room complying with 213.2.1 is provided and located in the same area and on the same floor as existing inaccessible toilet or bathing rooms.

2. Where exceptions for alterations to qualified historic buildings or facilities are permitted by 202.5, no fewer than one toilet room for each sex complying with 603 or one unisex toilet room complying with 213.2.1 shall be provided.

3. Where multiple single user portable toilet or bathing units are clustered at a single location, no more than 5 percent of the toilet units and bathing units at each cluster shall be required to comply with 603. Portable toilet units and bathing units complying with 603 shall be identified by the International Symbol of Accessibility complying with 703.7.2.1.

4. Where multiple single user toilet rooms are clustered at a single location, no more than 50 percent of the single user toilet rooms for each use at each cluster shall be required to comply with 603.

Advisory

213.2 Toilet Rooms and Bathing Rooms. These requirements allow the use of unisex (or single-user) toilet rooms in alterations when technical infeasibility can be demonstrated. Unisex toilet rooms benefit people who use opposite sex personal care assistants. For this reason, it is advantageous to install unisex toilet rooms in addition to accessible single-sex toilet rooms in new facilities.

213.2 Toilet Rooms and Bathing Rooms Exceptions 3 and 4. A "cluster" is a group of toilet rooms proximate to one another. Generally, toilet rooms in a cluster are within sight of, or adjacent to, one another.

213.2.1 Unisex (Single-Use or Family) Toilet and Unisex Bathing Rooms. Unisex toilet rooms shall contain not more than one lavatory, and two water closets without urinals or one water closet and one urinal. Unisex bathing rooms shall contain one shower or one shower and one bathtub, one lavatory, and one water closet. Doors to unisex toilet rooms and unisex bathing rooms shall have privacy latches.

213.3 Plumbing Fixtures and Accessories. Plumbing fixtures and accessories provided in a toilet room or bathing room required to comply with 213.2 shall comply with 213.3.

213.3.1 Toilet Compartments. Where toilet compartments are provided, at least one toilet compartment shall comply with 604.8.1. In addition to the compartment required to comply with 604.8.1, at least one compartment shall comply with 604.8.2 where six or more toilet compartments are provided, or where the combination of urinals and water closets totals six or more fixtures.

Advisory

213.3.1 Toilet Compartments. A toilet compartment is a partitioned space that is located within a toilet room, and that normally contains no more than one water closet. A toilet compartment may also contain a lavatory. A lavatory is a sink provided for hand washing. Full-height partitions and door assemblies can comprise toilet compartments where the minimum required spaces are provided within the compartment.

213.3.2 Water Closets. Where water closets are provided, at least one shall comply with 604.

213.3.3 Urinals. Where more than one urinal is provided, at least one shall comply with 605.

213.3.4 Lavatories. Where lavatories are provided, at least one shall comply with 606 and shall not be located in a toilet compartment.

213.3.5 Mirrors. Where mirrors are provided, at least one shall comply with 603.3.

213.3.6 Bathing Facilities. Where bathtubs or showers are provided, at least one bathtub complying with 607 or at least one shower complying with 608 shall be provided.

213.3.7 Coat Hooks and Shelves. Where coat hooks or shelves are provided in toilet rooms without toilet compartments, at least one of each type shall comply with 603.4. Where coat hooks or shelves are provided in toilet compartments, at least one of each type complying with 604.8.3 shall be provided in toilet compartments required to comply with 213.3.1. Where coat hooks or shelves are provided in bathing facilities, at least one of each type complying with 603.4 shall serve fixtures required to comply with 213.3.6.

Guidance

General. Where toilet facilities and bathing facilities are provided, they must comply with section 213 of the 2010 Standards.

A commenter recommended that all accessible toilet facilities, toilet rooms, and compartments should be required to have signage indicating that such spaces are restricted solely for the use of individuals with disabilities. The Department believes that it is neither necessary nor appropriate to restrict the use of accessible toilet facilities. Like many other facilities designed to be accessible, accessible toilet facilities can and do serve a wide range of individuals with and without disabilities.

A commenter recommended that more than one wheelchair accessible compartment be provided in toilet rooms serving airports and train stations because these compartments are likely to be occupied by individuals with luggage and persons with disabilities often take longer to use them. The Access Board is examining airport terminal accessibility as part of an ongoing effort to facilitate accessibility and promote effective design. As part of these efforts, the Access Board will examine requirements for accessible toilet compartments in larger airport restrooms. The Department declines to change the scoping for accessible toilet compartments at this time.

Ambulatory Accessible Toilet Compartments. Section 213.3.1 of the 2010 Standards requires multi-user men's toilet rooms, where the total of toilet compartments and urinals is six or more, to contain at least one ambulatory accessible compartment. The 1991 Standards count only toilet stalls (compartments) for this purpose. The 2010 Standards establish parity between multi-user women's toilet rooms and multi-user men's toilet rooms with respect to ambulatory accessible toilet compartments.

Urinals. Men's toilet rooms with only one urinal will no longer be required to provide an accessible urinal under the 2010 Standards. Such toilet rooms will still be required to provide an accessible toilet compartment. Commenters urged that the exception be eliminated. The Department believes that this change will provide flexibility to many small businesses and it does not alter the requirement that all common use restrooms must be accessible.

Multiple Single-User Toilet Rooms. Where multiple single-user toilet rooms are clustered in a single location, fifty percent (50%), rather than the one hundred percent (100%) required by the 1991 Standards, are required to be accessible by section 213.2, Exception 4 of the 2010 Standards. Section 216.8 of the 2010 Standards requires that accessible single-user toilet rooms must be identified by the International Symbol of Accessibility where all single-user toilet rooms are not accessible.

Hospital Patient Toilet Rooms. An exception was added in section 223.1 of the 2010 Standards to allow toilet rooms that are part of critical or intensive care patient sleeping rooms to no longer be required to provide mobility features.

Water Closet Location and Rear Grab Bar. Section 604.2 of the 2010 Standards allows greater flexibility for the placement of the centerline of wheelchair accessible and ambulatory accessible water closets. Section 604.5.2, Exception 1 permits a shorter grab bar on the rear wall where there is not enough wall space due to special circumstances (e.g., when a lavatory or other recessed fixture is located next to the water closet and the wall behind the lavatory is recessed so that the lavatory does not overlap the required clear floor space at the water closet). The 1991 Standards contain no exception for grab bar length, and require the water closet centerline to be exactly 18 inches from the side wall, while the 2010 Standards requirement allows the centerline to be between 16 and 18 inches from the side wall in wheelchair accessible toilet compartments and 17 to 19 inches in ambulatory accessible toilet compartments.

Water Closet Clearance. Section 604.3 of the 2010 Standards represents a change in the accessibility requirements where a lavatory is installed adjacent to the water closet. The 1991 Standards allow the nearest side of a lavatory to be placed 18 inches minimum from the water closet centerline and 36 inches minimum from the side wall adjacent to the water closet. However, locating the lavatory so close to the water closet prohibits many individuals with disabilities from using a side transfer. To allow greater transfer options, including side transfers, the 2010 Standards prohibit lavatories from overlapping the clear floor space at water closets, except in covered residential dwelling units.

A majority of commenters, including persons who use wheelchairs, strongly agreed with the requirement to provide enough space for a side transfer. These commenters believed that the requirement will increase the usability of accessible single-user toilet rooms by making side transfers possible for many individuals who use wheelchairs and would have been unable to transfer to a water closet using a side transfer even if the water closet complied with the 1991 Standards. In addition, many commenters noted that the additional clear floor space at the side of the water closet is also critical for those providing assistance with transfers and personal care for persons with disabilities. Numerous comments noted that this requirement is already included in other model accessibility standards and many state and local building codes and its adoption in the 2010 Standards is a important part of harmonization efforts. The Department agrees that the provision of enough clear floor space to permit side transfers at water closets is an important feature that must be provided to ensure access for persons with disabilities in toilet and bathing facilities. Furthermore, the adoption of this requirement closely harmonizes with the model codes and many state and local building codes.

Other commenters urged the Department not to adopt section 604.3 of the 2010 Standards claiming that it will require single-user toilet rooms to be two feet wider than the 1991 Standards require, and this additional requirement will be difficult to meet. Multiple commentators also expressed concern that the size of single-user toilet rooms would be increased but they did not specify how much larger such toilet rooms would have to be in their estimation. In response to these concerns, the Department developed a series of single-user toilet room floor plans demonstrating that the total square footage between representative layouts complying with the 1991 Standards and the 2010 Standards are comparable. The Department believes the floor plan comparisons clearly show that size differences between the two Standards are not substantial and several of the 2010 Standards-compliant plans do not require additional square footage compared to the 1991 Standards plans. These single-user toilet room floor plans are shown below.

Several commenters concluded that alterations of single-user toilet rooms should be exempt from the requirements of section 604.3 of the 2010 Standards because of the significant reconfiguration and reconstruction that would be required, such as moving plumbing fixtures, walls, and/or doors at significant additional expense. The Department disagrees with this conclusion since it fails to take into account several key points. The 2010 Standards contain provisions for in-swinging doors, 603.2.3, Exception 2, and recessed fixtures adjacent to water closets, 604.5.2, Exception 1. These provisions give flexibility to create more compact room designs and maintain required clearances around fixtures. As with the 1991 Standards, any alterations must comply to the extent that it is technically feasible to do so.

The requirements at section 604.3.2 of the 2010 Standards specify how required clearance around the water closet can overlap with specific elements and spaces. An exception that applies only to covered residential dwelling units permits a lavatory to be located no closer than 18 inches from the centerline of the water closet. The requirements at section 604.3.2 of the 2010 Standards increase accessibility for individuals with disabilities. One commenter expressed concern about other items that might overlap the clear floor space, such as dispensers, shelves, and coat hooks on the side of the water closet where a wheelchair would be positioned for a transfer. Section 604.3.2 of the 2010 Standards allows items such as associated grab bars, dispensers, sanitary napkin disposal units, coat hooks, and shelves to overlap the clear floor space. These are items that typically do not affect the usability of the clear floor space.

Toilet Room Doors. Sections 4.22.2 and 4.22.3 of the 1991 Standards and Section 603.2.3 of the 2010 Standards permit the doors of all toilet or bathing rooms with in-swinging doors to swing into the required turning space, but not into the clear floor space required at any fixture. In single-user toilet rooms or bathing rooms, Section 603.2.3 Exception 2 of the 2010 Standards permits the door to swing into the clear floor space of an accessible fixture if a clear floor space that measures at least 30 inches by 48 inches is provided outside of the door swing.

Several commenters expressed reservations about Exception 2 of Section 603.2.3. Concerns were raised that permitting doors of single-user toilet or bathing rooms with in-swinging doors to swing into the clearance around any fixture will result in inaccessibility to individuals using larger wheelchairs and scooters. Additionally, a commenter stated that the exception would require an unacceptable amount of precision maneuvering by individuals who use standard size wheelchairs. The Department believes that this provision achieves necessary flexibility while providing a minimum standard for maneuvering space. The standard does permit additional maneuvering space to be provided, if needed.

In the NPRM, the Department provided a series of plan drawings illustrating comparisons of the minimum size single-user toilet rooms. These floor plans showed typical examples that met the minimum requirements of the proposed ADA Standards. A commenter was of the opinion that the single-user toilet plans shown in the NPRM demonstrated that the new requirements will not result in a substantial increase in room size. Several other commenters representing industry offered criticisms of the single-user toilet floor plans to support their assertion that a 2010 Standards-compliant single-user toilet room will never be smaller and will likely be larger than such a toilet room required under the 1991 Standards. Commenters also asserted that the floor plans prepared by the Department were of a very basic design which could be accommodated in a minimal sized space whereas the types of facilities their customers demand would require additional space to be added to the rooms shown in the floor plans. The Department recognizes that there are many design choices that can affect the size of a room or space. Choices to install additional features may result in more space being needed to provide sufficient clear floor space for that additional feature to comply. However, many facilities that have these extra features also tend to have ample space to meet accessibility requirements. Other commenters asserted that public single-user toilet rooms always include a closer and a latch on the entry door, requiring a larger clear floor space than shown on the push side of the door shown in Plan 1B. The Department acknowledges that in instances where a latch is provided and a closer is required by other regulations or codes, the minimum size of a room with an out-swinging door may be slightly larger than as shown in Plan 1C.

Additional floor plans of single-user toilet rooms are now included in further response to the commentary received.

Comparison of Single-User Toilet Room Layouts

1991 Standards

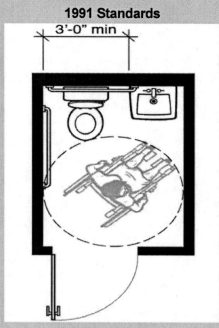

2010 Standards

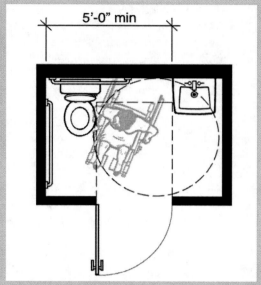

Plan-1A: 1991 Standards Minimum with Out-Swinging Door

Plan-1B: 2010 Standards Minimum with Out-Swinging Door

5'-0" x 7'-3" • 36.25 Square Feet

This plan shows a typical example of a single-user toilet room that meets the minimum requirements of the 1991 Standards. The size of this space is determined by the minimum width required for the water closet and lavatory between the side walls, the minimum wheelchair turning space, and the space required for the out-swinging door. A lavatory with knee space can overlap the clear floor space required for the water closet provided that at least 36 inches of clearance is maintained between the side wall next to the water closet and the lavatory (see section 4.16.2 and Fig. 28 of the 1991 Standards). A wheelchair turning space meeting section 4.2.3 of the 1991 Standards must be provided. The size of this room requires that the entry door swing out. The room would be larger if the door were in-swinging.

7'-0" x 5'-0" • 35.00 Square Feet

This plan shows a typical example of a single-user toilet room that meets the minimum requirements of the 2010 Standards. Features include: five-foot minimum width between the side wall of the water closet and the lavatory; 60-inch minimum circular wheelchair turning space; and 36-inch by 48-inch clear maneuvering space for the out-swinging entry door. Section 604.3.1 of the 2010 Standards requires a floor clearance at a water closet that is a minimum of 60 inches wide by 56 inches deep regardless of approach. Section 604.3.2 prohibits any other plumbing fixtures from being located in this clear space, except in residential dwelling units. The 2010 Standards, at section 304.3, allows the turning space to extend into toe and knee space provided beneath fixtures and other elements. Required maneuvering space for the entry door (inside the room) must be clear of all fixtures. If the door had both a closer and latch, section 404.2.4.1 and Figure 404.2.4.1(c) require additional space on the latch side.

This layout is three point five percent (3.5%) smaller than the accompanying Plan-1A: 1991 Standards Minimum with Out-Swinging Door example.

Comparison of Single-User Toilet Room Layouts

1991 Standards N/A   **2010 Standards**

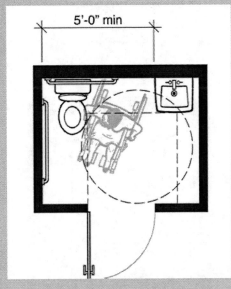

5'-0" min

Plan-1C: 2010 Standards Minimum with Out-Swinging Door

(entry door has both closer and latch)

7'-0" x 5'-6" 38.50 Square Feet

This plan shows the same typical features of a single-user toilet room that meets the minimum requirements of the 2010 Standards as Plan-1B does except the entry door has both a closer and latch. Because the door has both a closer and latch, a minimum additional foot of maneuvering space is required on the latch side (see section 404.2.4.1 and Figure 404.2.4.1(c) of the 2010 Standards).

This layout is six point two percent (6.2%) larger than the accompanying Plan-1A: 1991 Standards Minimum with Out-Swinging Door example.

Comparison of Single-User Toilet Room Layouts

1991 Standards

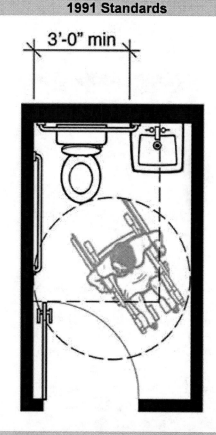

2010 Standards

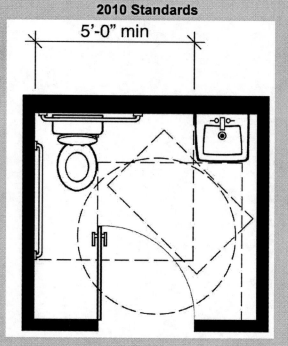

Plan-2B: 2010 Standards Minimum with In-Swinging Door

7'-0" x 6'-6" 45.50 Square Feet

This plan shows a typical example of a single-user toilet room that meets the minimum requirements of the 2010 Standards when the entry door swings into the room. In the 2010 Standards an exception allows the entry door to swing over the clear floor spaces and clearances required at the fixtures if a clear floor space complying with section 305.3 (minimum 30 inches by 48 inches) is provided outside the arc of the door swing, section 603.3.3 exception 2. The required maneuvering space for the door, section 404.2.4.1 and Figure 404.2.4.1(a), also is a factor in room size. This clear space cannot be obstructed by the plumbing fixtures. Note that this layout provides more space for turning when the door is closed than Plan-1B.

This layout is seven percent (7%) larger than the accompanying Plan-2A: 1991 Standards Minimum with In-Swinging Door example.

Plan-2A: 1991 Standards Minimum with In-Swinging Door

5'-0" x 8'-6" 42.50 Square Feet

This plan shows a typical example of a single-user toilet room that meets the minimum requirements of the 1991 Standards. Depending on the width of the hallway and other circulation issues, it can be preferable to swing the entry door into the toilet room. Businesses and public entities typically prefer to have an in-swinging door. The in-swinging door increases overall room size because it cannot swing over the required clear floor space at any accessible fixture, (see section 4.22.2 of the 1991 Standards). This increases the room depth from Plan-1A. The door is permitted to swing over the required turning space shown as a 60-inch circle.

Comparison of Single-User Toilet Room Layouts

1991 Standards N/A   **2010 Standards**

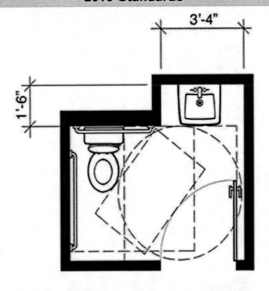

Plan-2C: 2010 Standards Minimum
with In-Swinging Door

7'-0" x 6'-6" 40.00 Square Feet
(plumbing chase not included)

This plan shows the same typical features of a single-user toilet room that meets the minimum requirements of the 2010 Standards as Plan-2B when the entry door swings into the room. Note that this layout also provides more space for turning when the door is closed than Plan-1B.

This layout is six point two five percent (6.25%) smaller than the accompanying Plan-2A: 1991 Standards Minimum with In-Swinging Door example.

Comparison of Single-User Toilet Room Layouts

1991 Standards N/A | **1991 Standards and 2010 Standards**

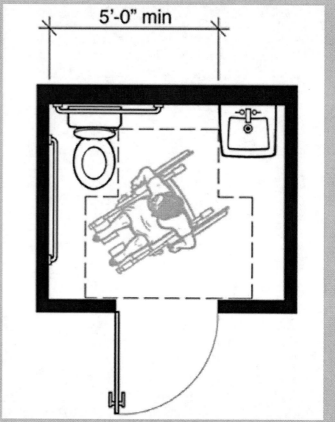

Plan-3: Meets Both 1991 Standards and 2010 Standards

7'-0" x 5'-9" 40.25 Square Feet

This plan shows an example of a single-user toilet room that meets the minimum requirements of both the 1991 Standards and 2010 Standards. A T-shaped turning space has been used (see Fig. 3(a) of the 1991 Standards and Figure 304.3.2 of the 2010 Standards) to maintain a compact room size. An out-swinging door also minimizes the overall layout depth and cannot swing over the required clear floor space or clearance at any accessible plumbing fixture.

This layout is eleven percent (11%) larger than the Plan-1A: 1991 Standards Minimum with Out-Swinging Door example shown at the beginning of these plan comparisons.

Comparison of Single-User Toilet Room "Pairs" With Fixtures Side-by-Side
1991 Standards   **2010 Standards**

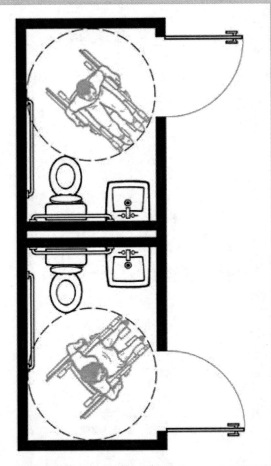

**Plan-1B Pair: 2010 Standards with
Out-Swinging Doors**

**Two 7'-0" x 5'-0" Rooms-
70.00 Square Feet Total**

**Plan-1A Pair: 1991 Standards with
Out-Swinging Doors**

**Two 5'-0" x 7'-3" Rooms–
72.50 Square Feet Total**

These plans show men's/women's room configurations using Plans 1A and 1B.

Comparison of Single-User Toilet Room "Pairs" With Fixtures Side-by-Side

1991 Standards N/A	2010 Standards

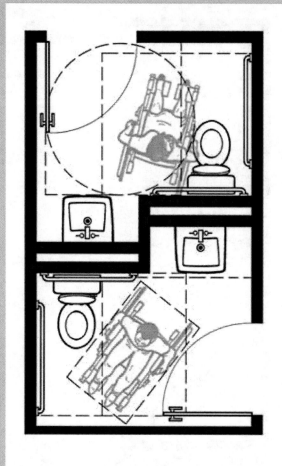

**Plan-2C Pair: 2010 Standards with
In-Swinging Doors**

**Two 7'-2" x 6'-6" Rooms -
82.00 Square Feet Total**

This plan shows a men's/women's room
configuration using Plan 2C.

Toilet Paper Dispensers. The provisions for toilet paper dispensers at section 604.7 of the 2010 Standards require the dispenser to be located seven inches minimum and nine inches maximum in front of the water closet measured to the centerline of the dispenser. The paper outlet of the dispenser must be located 15 inches minimum and 48 inches maximum above the finish floor. In the 1991 Standards the location of the toilet paper dispenser is determined by the centerline and forward edge of the dispenser. In the 2010 Standards the mounting location of the toilet paper dispenser is determined by the centerline of the dispenser and the location of the outlet for the toilet paper.

One commenter discussed the difficulty of using large roll toilet paper dispensers and dispensers with two standard size rolls stacked on top of each other. The size of the large dispensers can block access to the grab bar and the outlet for the toilet paper can be too low or too high to be usable. Some dispensers also control the delivery of the toilet paper which can make it impossible to get the toilet paper. Toilet paper dispensers that control delivery or do not allow continuous paper flow are not permitted by the 1991 Standards or the 2010 Standards. Also, many of the large roll toilet paper dispensers do not comply with the 2010 Standards since their large size does not allow them to be mounted 12 inches above or 1 1/2 inches below the side grab bar as required by section 609.3.

Shower Spray Controls. In accessible bathtubs and shower compartments, sections 607.6 and 608.6 of the 2010 Standards require shower spray controls to have an on/off control and to deliver water that is 120¡F (49¡C) maximum. Neither feature was required by the 1991 Standards, but may be required by plumbing codes. Delivering water that is no hotter than 120¡F (49¡C) will require controlling the maximum temperature at each accessible shower spray unit.

Shower Compartments. The 1991 Standards at sections 4.21 and 9.1.2 and the 2010 Standards at section 608 contain technical requirements for transfer-type and roll-in shower compartments. The 2010 Standards provide more flexibility than the 1991 Standards as follows:

• Transfer-type showers are exactly 36 inches wide by 36 inches long.

• The 1991 Standards and the 2010 Standards permit a 1/2-inch maximum curb in transfer-type showers. The 2010 Standards add a new exception that permits a 2-inch maximum curb in transfer-type showers in alterations to existing facilities, where recessing the compartment to achieve a 1/2-inch curb will disturb the structural reinforcement of the floor slab.

• Roll-in showers are 30 inches wide minimum by 60 inches long minimum. Alternate roll-in showers are 36 inches wide by 60 inches long minimum, and have a 36-inch minimum wide opening on the long side of the compartment. The 1991 Standards require alternate roll-in showers in a portion of accessible transient lodging guest rooms, but provision of this shower type in other facilities is generally permitted as an equivalent facilitation. The 1991 Standards require a seat to be provided adjacent to the opening; and require the controls to be located on the side adjacent to the seat. The 2010 Standards permit alternate roll-in showers to be used in any facility, only require a seat in transient lodging guest rooms, and allow location of controls on the back wall opposite the seat as an alternative.

Commenters raised concerns that adding a new exception that permits a 2-inch maximum curb in transfer-type showers in alterations to existing facilities, where recessing the compartment to achieve a 1/2-inch curb will disturb the structural reinforcement of the floor slab, will impair the ability of individuals with disabilities to use transfer-type showers.

The exception in section 608.7 of the 2010 Standards permitting a 2-inch maximum curb in transfer-type showers is allowed only in existing facilities where provision of a 1/2-inch high threshold would disturb the structural reinforcement of the floor slab. Whenever this exception is used the least high threshold that can be used should be provided, up to a maximum height of 2 inches. This exception is intended to provide some flexibility where the existing structure precludes full compliance.

Toilet and Bathing Rooms. Section 213 of the 2010 Standards sets out the scoping requirements for toilet and bathing rooms.

Commenters recommended that section 213, Toilet Facilities and Bathing Facilities, of the 2010

Standards include requirements that unisex toilet and bathing rooms be provided in certain facilities. These commenters suggested that unisex toilet and bathing rooms are most useful as companion care facilities.

Model plumbing and building codes require single-user (unisex or family) toilet facilities in certain occupancies, primarily assembly facilities, covered malls, and transportation facilities. These types of toilet rooms provide flexibility for persons needing privacy so that they can obtain assistance from family members or persons of the opposite sex. When these facilities are provided, both the 1991 Standards and 2010 Standards require that they be accessible. The 2010 Standards do not scope unisex toilet facilities because plumbing codes generally determine the number and type of plumbing fixtures to be provided in a particular occupancy and often determine whether an occupancy must provide separate sex facilities in addition to single-user facilities. However, the scoping at section 213.2.1 of the 2010 Standards coordinates with model plumbing and building code requirements which will permit a small toilet room with two water closets or one water closet and one urinal to be considered a single-user toilet room provided that the room has a privacy latch. In this way, a person needing assistance from a person of the opposite sex can lock the door to use the facility while temporarily inconveniencing only one other potential user. These provisions strike a reasonable balance and impose less impact on covered entities.

A commenter recommended that in shower compartments rectangular seats as provided in section 610.3.1 of the 2010 Standards should not be permitted as a substitute for L-shaped seats as provided in 610.3.2.

The 2010 Standards do not indicate a preference for either rectangular or L-shaped seats in shower compartments. L-shaped seats in transfer and certain roll-in showers have been used for many years to provide users with poor balance additional support because they can position themselves in the corner while showering.

214 Washing Machines and Clothes Dryers

214.1 General. Where provided, washing machines and clothes dryers shall comply with 214.

214.2 Washing Machines. Where three or fewer washing machines are provided, at least one shall comply with 611. Where more than three washing machines are provided, at least two shall comply with 611.

214.3 Clothes Dryers. Where three or fewer clothes dryers are provided, at least one shall comply with 611. Where more than three clothes dryers are provided, at least two shall comply with 611.

Guidance

Sections 214.2 (washing machines) and 214.3 (clothes dryers) of the 2010 Standards specify the number of each type of these machines required to be accessible (one to two depending upon the total number of machines provided) and section 611 specifies the technical requirements. An exception will permit the maximum height for the tops of these machines to be 2 inches higher than the general requirement for maximum high reach over an obstruction.

A commenter objected to the scoping provision for accessible washing machines and clothes dryers stating that the probability is low that more than one accessible machine would be needed at the same time in the laundry facility of a place of transient lodging.

The scoping in this provision is based on the relative size of the facility. The Department assumes that the size of the facility (and, therefore, the number of accessible machines provided) will be determined by the covered entity's assessment of the demand for laundry facilities. The Department declines to assume that persons with disabilities will have less use for accessible facilities in transient lodging than in other public accommodations.

215 Fire Alarm Systems

215.1 General. Where fire alarm systems provide audible alarm coverage, alarms shall comply with 215.

EXCEPTION: In existing facilities, visible alarms shall not be required except where an existing fire alarm system is upgraded or replaced, or a new fire alarm system is installed.

Advisory

215.1 General. Unlike audible alarms, visible alarms must be located within the space they serve so that the signal is visible. Facility alarm systems (other than fire alarm systems) such as those used for tornado warnings and other emergencies are not required to comply with the technical criteria for alarms in Section 702. Every effort should be made to ensure that such alarms can be differentiated in their signal from fire alarms systems and that people who need to be notified of emergencies are adequately safeguarded. Consult local fire departments and prepare evacuation plans taking into consideration the needs of every building occupant, including people with disabilities.

215.2 Public and Common Use Areas. Alarms in public use areas and common use areas shall comply with 702.

215.3 Employee Work Areas. Where employee work areas have audible alarm coverage, the wiring system shall be designed so that visible alarms complying with 702 can be integrated into the alarm system.

215.4 Transient Lodging. Guest rooms required to comply with 224.4 shall provide alarms complying with 702.

215.5 Residential Facilities. Where provided in residential dwelling units required to comply with 809.5, alarms shall comply with 702.

216 Signs

216.1 General. Signs shall be provided in accordance with 216 and shall comply with 703.

EXCEPTIONS:

1. Building directories, menus, seat and row designations in assembly areas, occupant names, building addresses, and company names and logos shall not be required to comply with 216.

2. In parking facilities, signs shall not be required to comply with 216.2, 216.3, and 216.6 through 216.12.

3. Temporary, 7 days or less, signs shall not be required to comply with 216.

4. In detention and correctional facilities, signs not located in public use areas shall not be required to comply with 216.

216.2 Designations. Interior and exterior signs identifying permanent rooms and spaces shall comply with 703.1, 703.2, and 703.5. Where pictograms are provided as designations of permanent interior rooms and spaces, the pictograms shall comply with 703.6 and shall have text descriptors complying with 703.2 and 703.5.

EXCEPTION: Exterior signs that are not located at the door to the space they serve shall not be required to comply with 703.2.

Advisory

216.2 Designations. Section 216.2 applies to signs that provide designations, labels, or names for interior rooms or spaces where the sign is not likely to change over time. Examples include interior signs labeling restrooms, room and floor numbers or letters, and room names. Tactile text descriptors are required for pictograms that are provided to label or identify a permanent room or space. Pictograms that provide information about a room or space, such as "no smoking," occupant logos, and the International Symbol of Accessibility, are not required to have text descriptors.

216.3 Directional and Informational Signs. Signs that provide direction to or information about interior spaces and facilities of the site shall comply with 703.5.

Advisory

216.3 Directional and Informational Signs. Information about interior spaces and facilities includes rules of conduct, occupant load, and similar signs. Signs providing direction to rooms or spaces include those that identify egress routes.

216.4 Means of Egress. Signs for means of egress shall comply with 216.4.

216.4.1 Exit Doors. Doors at exit passageways, exit discharge, and exit stairways shall be identified by tactile signs complying with 703.1, 703.2, and 703.5.

Advisory

216.4.1 Exit Doors. An exit passageway is a horizontal exit component that is separated from the interior spaces of the building by fire-resistance-rated construction and that leads to the exit discharge or public way. The exit discharge is that portion of an egress system between the termination of an exit and a public way.

216.4.2 Areas of Refuge. Signs required by section 1003.2.13.5.4 of the International Building Code (2000 edition) or section 1007.6.4 of the International Building Code (2003 edition) (incorporated by reference, see "Referenced Standards" in Chapter 1) to provide instructions in areas of refuge shall comply with 703.5.

216.4.3 Directional Signs. Signs required by section 1003.2.13.6 of the International Building Code (2000 edition) or section 1007.7 of the International Building Code (2003 edition) (incorporated by reference, see "Referenced Standards" in Chapter 1) to provide directions to accessible means of egress shall comply with 703.5.

216.5 Parking. Parking spaces complying with 502 shall be identified by signs complying with 502.6.

EXCEPTIONS:

1. Where a total of four or fewer parking spaces, including accessible parking spaces, are provided on a site, identification of accessible parking spaces shall not be required.

2. In residential facilities, where parking spaces are assigned to specific residential dwelling units, identification of accessible parking spaces shall not be required.

216.6 Entrances. Where not all entrances comply with 404, entrances complying with 404 shall be identified by the International Symbol of Accessibility complying with 703.7.2.1. Directional signs complying with 703.5 that indicate the location of the nearest entrance complying with 404 shall be provided at entrances that do not comply with 404.

Advisory

216.6 Entrances. Where a directional sign is required, it should be located to minimize backtracking. In some cases, this could mean locating a sign at the beginning of a route, not just at the inaccessible entrances to a building.

216.7 Elevators. Where existing elevators do not comply with 407, elevators complying with 407 shall be clearly identified with the International Symbol of Accessibility complying with 703.7.2.1.

216.8 Toilet Rooms and Bathing Rooms. Where existing toilet rooms or bathing rooms do not comply with 603, directional signs indicating the location of the nearest toilet room or bathing room complying with 603 within the facility shall be provided. Signs shall comply with 703.5 and shall include the International Symbol of Accessibility complying with 703.7.2.1. Where existing toilet rooms or bathing rooms do not comply with 603, the toilet rooms or bathing rooms complying with 603 shall be identified by the International Symbol of Accessibility complying with 703.7.2.1. Where clustered single user toilet rooms or bathing facilities are permitted to use exceptions to 213.2, toilet rooms or bathing facilities complying with 603 shall be identified by the International Symbol of Accessibility complying with 703.7.2.1 unless all toilet rooms and bathing facilities comply with 603.

216.9 TTYs. Identification and directional signs for public TTYs shall be provided in accordance with 216.9.

216.9.1 Identification Signs. Public TTYs shall be identified by the International Symbol of TTY complying with 703.7.2.2.

216.9.2 Directional Signs. Directional signs indicating the location of the nearest public TTY shall be provided at all banks of public pay telephones not containing a public TTY. In addition, where signs provide direction to public pay telephones, they shall also provide direction to public TTYs. Directional signs shall comply with 703.5 and shall include the International Symbol of TTY complying with 703.7.2.2.

216.10 Assistive Listening Systems. Each assembly area required by 219 to provide assistive listening systems shall provide signs informing patrons of the availability of the assistive listening system. Assistive listening signs shall comply with 703.5 and shall include the International Symbol of Access for Hearing Loss complying with 703.7.2.4.

> **EXCEPTION:** Where ticket offices or windows are provided, signs shall not be required at each assembly area provided that signs are displayed at each ticket office or window informing patrons of the availability of assistive listening systems.

216.11 Check-Out Aisles. Where more than one check-out aisle is provided, check-out aisles complying with 904.3 shall be identified by the International Symbol of Accessibility complying with 703.7.2.1. Where check-out aisles are identified by numbers, letters, or functions, signs identifying check-out aisles complying with 904.3 shall be located in the same location as the check-out aisle identification.

> **EXCEPTION:** Where all check-out aisles serving a single function comply with 904.3, signs complying with 703.7.2.1 shall not be required.

216.12 Amusement Rides. Signs identifying the type of access provided on amusement rides shall be provided at entries to queues and waiting lines. In addition, where accessible unload areas also serve as accessible load areas, signs indicating the location of the accessible load and unload areas shall be provided at entries to queues and waiting lines.

Advisory

216.12 Amusement Rides. Amusement rides designed primarily for children, amusement rides that are controlled or operated by the rider, and amusement rides without seats, are not required to provide wheelchair spaces, transfer seats, or transfer systems, and need not meet the sign requirements in 216.12. The load and unload areas of these rides must, however, be on an accessible route and must provide turning space.

Guidance

The preceding types of signs, though they are not specifically subject to the 1991 Standards requirement for signs, will now be explicitly exempted by sections 216 and 703 of the 2010 Standards. These types of signs include: seat and row designations in assembly areas; occupant names, building addresses; company names and logos; signs in parking facilities (except those identifying accessible parking spaces and means of egress); and exterior signs identifying permanent rooms and spaces that are not located at the door to the space they serve. This requirement also clarifies that the exception for temporary signs applies to signs used for seven days or less.

The 2010 Standards retain the option to provide one sign where both visual and tactile characters are provided or two signs, one with visual, and one with tactile characters.

---

217 Telephones

217.1 General. Where coin-operated public pay telephones, coinless public pay telephones, public closed-circuit telephones, public courtesy phones, or other types of public telephones are provided, public telephones shall be provided in accordance with 217 for each type of public telephone provided. For purposes of this section, a bank of telephones shall be considered to be two or more adjacent telephones.

Advisory

217.1 General. These requirements apply to all types of public telephones including courtesy phones at airports and rail stations that provide a free direct connection to hotels, transportation services, and tourist attractions.

217.2 Wheelchair Accessible Telephones. Where public telephones are provided, wheelchair accessible telephones complying with 704.2 shall be provided in accordance with Table 217.2.

> **EXCEPTION:** Drive-up only public telephones shall not be required to comply with 217.2.

Table 217.2 Wheelchair Accessible Telephones	
Number of Telephones Provided on a Floor, Level, or Exterior Site	Minimum Number of Required Wheelchair Accessible Telephones
1 or more single units	1 per floor, level, and exterior site
1 bank	1 per floor, level, and exterior site
2 or more banks	1 per bank

217.3 Volume Controls. All public telephones shall have volume controls complying with 704.3.

217.4 TTYs. TTYs complying with 704.4 shall be provided in accordance with 217.4.

Advisory

217.4 TTYs. Separate requirements are provided based on the number of public pay telephones provided at a bank of telephones, within a floor, a building, or on a site. In some instances one TTY can be used to satisfy more than one of these requirements. For example, a TTY required for a bank can satisfy the requirements for a building. However, the requirement for at least one TTY on an exterior site cannot be met by installing a TTY in a bank inside a building. Consideration should be given to phone systems that can accommodate both digital and analog transmissions for compatibility with digital and analog TTYs.

217.4.1 Bank Requirement. Where four or more public pay telephones are provided at a bank of telephones, at least one public TTY complying with 704.4 shall be provided at that bank.

    EXCEPTION: TTYs shall not be required at banks of telephones located within 200 feet (61 m) of, and on the same floor as, a bank containing a public TTY.

217.4.2 Floor Requirement. TTYs in public buildings shall be provided in accordance with 217.4.2.1. TTYs in private buildings shall be provided in accordance with 217.4.2.2.

217.4.2.1 Public Buildings. Where at least one public pay telephone is provided on a floor of a public building, at least one public TTY shall be provided on that floor.

217.4.2.2 Private Buildings. Where four or more public pay telephones are provided on a floor of a private building, at least one public TTY shall be provided on that floor.

217.4.3 Building Requirement. TTYs in public buildings shall be provided in accordance with 217.4.3.1. TTYs in private buildings shall be provided in accordance with 217.4.3.2.

217.4.3.1 Public Buildings. Where at least one public pay telephone is provided in a public building, at least one public TTY shall be provided in the building. Where at least one public pay telephone is provided in a public use area of a public building, at least one public TTY shall be provided in the public building in a public use area.

217.4.3.2 Private Buildings. Where four or more public pay telephones are provided in a private building, at least one public TTY shall be provided in the building.

217.4.4 Exterior Site Requirement. Where four or more public pay telephones are provided on an exterior site, at least one public TTY shall be provided on the site.

217.4.5 Rest Stops, Emergency Roadside Stops, and Service Plazas. Where at least one public pay telephone is provided at a public rest stop, emergency roadside stop, or service plaza, at least one public TTY shall be provided.

217.4.6 Hospitals. Where at least one public pay telephone is provided serving a hospital emergency room, hospital recovery room, or hospital waiting room, at least one public TTY shall be provided at each location.

217.4.7 Transportation Facilities. In transportation facilities, in addition to the requirements of 217.4.1 through 217.4.4, where at least one public pay telephone serves a particular entrance to a bus or rail facility, at least one public TTY shall be provided to serve that entrance. In airports, in addition to the requirements of 217.4.1 through 217.4.4, where four or more public pay telephones are located in a terminal outside the security areas, a concourse within the security areas, or a baggage claim area in a terminal, at least one public TTY shall be provided in each location.

217.4.8 Detention and Correctional Facilities. In detention and correctional facilities, where at least one pay telephone is provided in a secured area used only by detainees or inmates and security personnel, at least one TTY shall be provided in at least one secured area.

217.5 Shelves for Portable TTYs. Where a bank of telephones in the interior of a building consists of three or more public pay telephones, at least one public pay telephone at the bank shall be provided with a shelf and an electrical outlet in accordance with 704.5.

EXCEPTIONS:

1. Secured areas of detention and correctional facilities where shelves and outlets are prohibited for purposes of security or safety shall not be required to comply with 217.5.

2. The shelf and electrical outlet shall not be required at a bank of telephones with a TTY.

Guidance

Drive-up Public Telephones. Where public telephones are provided, the 1991 Standards, at section 4.1.3(17)(a), and section 217.2 of the 2010 Standards, require a certain number of telephones to be wheelchair accessible. The 2010 Standards add a new exception that exempts drive-up public telephones.

Text Telephones (TTY). Section 4.1.3(17) of the 1991 Standards requires a public TTY to be provided if there are four or more public pay telephones at a site and at least one is in an interior location. Section 217.4.2 of the 2010 Standards requires that a building or facility provide a public TTY on each floor that has four or more public telephones, and in each telephone bank that has four or more telephones. Additionally, section 217.4.4 of the 2010 Standards requires that at least one public TTY be installed where four or more public pay telephones are provided on an exterior site. Section 217.4.5 of the 2010 Standards also requires that a public TTY be provided where at least one public pay telephone is provided at a public rest stop, emergency roadside stop, or service plaza. Section 217.4.6 of the 2010 Standards also requires that a public TTY be provided at each location where at least one public pay telephone is provided serving a hospital emergency room, a hospital recovery room, or a hospital waiting room. Section 217.4.7 of the 2010 Standards also requires that, in addition to the requirements for a public TTY to be provided at each location where at least four or more public pay telephones are provided at a bank of pay telephones and where at least one public pay telephone is provided on a floor or in a public building, where at least one public pay telephone serves a particular entrance to a bus or rail facility at least one public TTY must serve that entrance. In airports, in addition to the requirements for the provision of a public TTY at phone banks, on floors, and in public buildings with pay phones, where four or more public pay phones are located in a terminal outside the security areas, in a concourse within the security areas, or a baggage claim area in a terminal at least one public TTY must be provided. Section 217.4.8 of the 2010 Standards also requires that a TTY be provided in at least one secured area where at least one pay telephone is provided in a secured area used only by detainees or inmates and security personnel in detention and correctional facilities.

Wheelchair Accessible Telephones

Section 217.2 of the 2010 Standards requires that where public telephones are provided wheelchair accessible telephones complying with section 704.2 must be provided in accordance with Table 217.2.

A commenter stated that requiring installation of telephones within the proposed reach range requirements would adversely impact public and telephone owners and operators. According to the commenter, individuals without disabilities will not use telephones that are installed within the reach range requirements because they may be inconvenienced by having to stoop to operate these telephones, and, therefore, owners and operators will lose revenue due to less use of public telephones.

This comment misunderstands the scoping requirements for wheelchair accessible telephones. Section 217.2 of the 2010 Standards provides that where one or more single units are provided, only one unit per floor, level, or exterior site is required to be wheelchair accessible. However, where banks of telephones are provided, only one telephone in each bank is required to be wheelchair accessible. The Department believes these scoping requirements for wheelchair accessible telephones are reasonable and will not result in burdensome obligations or lost revenue for owners and operators.

---

218 Transportation Facilities

218.1 General. Transportation facilities shall comply with 218.

218.2 New and Altered Fixed Guideway Stations. New and altered stations in rapid rail, light rail, commuter rail, intercity rail, high speed rail, and other fixed guideway systems shall comply with 810.5 through 810.10.

218.3 Key Stations and Existing Intercity Rail Stations. Key stations and existing intercity rail stations shall comply with 810.5 through 810.10.

218.4 Bus Shelters. Where provided, bus shelters shall comply with 810.3.

218.5 Other Transportation Facilities. In other transportation facilities, public address systems shall comply with 810.7 and clocks shall comply with 810.8.

Guidance

Detectable Warnings. Detectable warnings provide a distinctively textured surface of truncated domes. The 1991 Standards at sections 4.1.3(15), 4.7.7, 4.29.2, 4.29.5, 4.29.6, and 10.3.1(8) require detectable warnings at curb ramps, hazardous vehicular areas, reflecting pools, and transit platform edges. The 2010 Standards at sections 218, 810.5, 705.1, and 705.2 only require detectable warnings at transit platform edges. The technical specifications for the diameter and spacing of the truncated domes have also been changed. The 2010 Standards also delete the requirement for the material used to contrast in resiliency or sound-on-cane contact from adjoining walking surfaces at interior locations.

The 2010 Standards apply to detectable warnings on developed sites. They do not apply to the public right-of-way. Scoping for detectable warnings at all locations other than transit platform edges has been eliminated from the 2010 Standards. However, because detectable warnings have been shown to significantly benefit individuals with disabilities at transit platform edges, the 2010 Standards provide scoping and technical requirements for detectable warnings at transit platform edges.

---

219 Assistive Listening Systems

219.1 General. Assistive listening systems shall be provided in accordance with 219 and shall comply with 706.

219.2 Required Systems. In each assembly area where audible communication is integral to the use of the space, an assistive listening system shall be provided.

> **EXCEPTION:** Other than in courtrooms, assistive listening systems shall not be required where audio amplification is not provided.

219.3 Receivers. Receivers complying with 706.2 shall be provided for assistive listening systems in each assembly area in accordance with Table 219.3. Twenty-five percent minimum of receivers provided, but no fewer than two, shall be hearing-aid compatible in accordance with 706.3.

> **EXCEPTIONS:**
>
> 1. Where a building contains more than one assembly area and the assembly areas required to provide assistive listening systems are under one management, the total number of required receivers shall be permitted to be calculated according to the total number of seats in the assembly areas in the building provided that all receivers are usable with all systems.
>
> 2. Where all seats in an assembly area are served by an induction loop assistive listening system, the minimum number of receivers required by Table 219.3 to be hearing-aid compatible shall not be required to be provided.

Table 219.3 Receivers for Assistive Listening Systems (text version)		
Capacity of Seating in Assembly Area	Minimum Number of Required Receivers	Minimum Number of Required Receivers Required to be Hearing-aid Compatible
50 or less	2	2
51 to 200	2, plus 1 per 25 seats over 50 seats[1]	2
201 to 500	2, plus 1 per 25 seats over 50 seats[1]	1 per 4 receivers1
501 to 1000	20, plus 1 per 33 seats over 500 seats[1]	1 per 4 receivers1
1001 to 2000	35, plus 1 per 50 seats over 1000 seats[1]	1 per 4 receivers1
2001 and over	55 plus 1 per 100 seats over 2000 seats[1]	1 per 4 receivers1

[1] Or fraction thereof.

Guidance

Signs. Section 216.10 of the 2010 Standards requires each covered assembly area to provide signs at each auditorium to inform patrons that assistive listening systems are available. However, an exception to this requirement permits assembly areas that have ticket offices or ticket windows to display the required signs at the ticket window.

A commenter recommended eliminating the exception at 216.10 because, for example, people who buy tickets through the mail, by subscription, or on-line may not need to stop at a ticket office or window upon arrival at the assembly area. The Department believes that an individual's decision to purchase tickets before arriving at a performance does not limit the discretion of the assembly operator to use the ticket window to provide other services to its patrons. The Department retained the exception at 216.10 to permit the venue operator some flexibility in determining how to meet the needs of its patrons.

Audible Communication. The 1991 Standards, at section 4.1.3(19)(b), require assembly areas, where audible communication is integral to the use of the space, to provide an assistive listening system if they have an audio amplification system or an occupant load of 50 or more people and have fixed seating. The 2010 Standards at section 219 require assistive listening systems in spaces where communication is integral to the space and audio amplification is provided and in courtrooms.

The 1991 Standards require receivers to be provided for at least four percent (4%) of the total number of fixed seats. The 2010 Standards, at section 219.3, revise the percentage of receivers required according to a table that correlates the required number of receivers to the seating capacity of the facility. Small facilities will continue to provide receivers for four percent (4%) of the seats. The required percentage declines as the size of the facility increases. The changes also require at least twenty-five percent (25%), but no fewer than two, of the receivers to be hearing-aid compatible. Assembly areas served by an induction loop assistive listening system will not have to provide hearing-aid compatible receivers.

Commenters were divided in their opinion of this change. The Department believes that the reduction in the required number of assistive listening systems for larger assembly areas will meet the needs of individuals with disabilities. The new requirement to provide hearing-aid compatible receivers should make assistive listening systems more usable for people who have been underserved until now.

Concerns were raised that the requirement to provide assistive listening systems may have an adverse impact on restaurants. This comment misunderstands the scope of coverage. The 2010 Standards define the term "assembly area" to include facilities used for entertainment, educational, or civic gatherings. A restaurant would fall within this category only if it is presenting programs to educate or entertain diners, and it provides an audio amplification system.

Same Management or Building. The 2010 Standards add a new exception that allows multiple assembly areas that are in the same building and under the same management, such as theaters in a multiplex cinema and lecture halls in a college building, to calculate the number of receivers required based on the total number of seats in all the assembly areas, instead of each assembly area separately, where the receivers are compatible with the assistive listening systems used in each of the assembly areas.

Mono Jacks, Sound Pressure, Etc. Section 4.33.7 of the 1991 Standards does not contain specific technical requirements for assistive listening systems. The 2010 Standards at section 706 require assistive listening systems to have standard mono jacks and will require hearing-aid compatible receivers to have neck loops to interface with telecoils in hearing aids. The 2010 Standards also specify sound pressure level, signal-to-noise ratio, and peak clipping level. Currently available assistive listening systems typically meet these technical requirements.

220 Automatic Teller Machines and Fare Machines

220.1 General. Where automatic teller machines or self-service fare vending, collection, or adjustment machines are provided, at least one of each type provided at each location shall comply with 707. Where bins are provided for envelopes, waste paper, or other purposes, at least one of each type shall comply with 811.

Advisory

220.1 General. If a bank provides both interior and exterior ATMs, each such installation is considered a separate location. Accessible ATMs, including those with speech and those that are within reach of people who use wheelchairs, must provide all the functions provided to customers at that location at all times. For example, it is unacceptable for the accessible ATM only to provide cash withdrawals while inaccessible ATMs also sell theater tickets.

Guidance

Section 707 of the 2010 Standards adds specific technical requirements for speech output, privacy, tactilely-discernible input controls, display screens, and Braille instructions to the general accessibility requirements set out in the 1991 Standards. Machines shall be speech enabled and exceptions are provided that cover when audible tones are permitted, when advertisements or similar information are provided, and where speech synthesis cannot be supported. The 1991 Standards require these machines to be accessible to and independently usable by persons with visual impairments, but do not contain any technical specifications.

221 Assembly Areas

221.1 General. Assembly areas shall provide wheelchair spaces, companion seats, and designated aisle seats complying with 221 and 802. In addition, lawn seating shall comply with 221.5.

[See additional requirements at 28 CFR 35.151(g) and 28 CFR 36.406(f).]

221.2 Wheelchair Spaces. Wheelchair spaces complying with 221.2 shall be provided in assembly areas with fixed seating.

221.2.1 Number and Location. Wheelchair spaces shall be provided complying with 221.2.1.

221.2.1.1 General Seating. Wheelchair spaces complying with 802.1 shall be provided in accordance with Table 221.2.1.1.

Table 221.2.1. Number of Wheelchair Spaces in Assembly Areas	
Number of Seats	Minimum Number of Required Wheelchair Spaces
4 to 25	1
26 to 50	2
51 to 150	4
151 to 300	5
301 to 500	6
501 to 5000	6, plus 1 for each 150, or fraction thereof, between 501 through 5000
5001 and over	36, plus 1 for each 200, or fraction thereof, over 5000

221.2.1.2 Luxury Boxes, Club Boxes, and Suites in Arenas, Stadiums, and Grandstands. In each luxury box, club box, and suite within arenas, stadiums, and grandstands, wheelchair spaces complying with 802.1 shall be provided in accordance with Table 221.2.1.1.

Advisory

221.2.1.2 Luxury Boxes, Club Boxes, and Suites in Arenas, Stadiums, and Grandstands. The number of wheelchair spaces required in luxury boxes, club boxes, and suites within an arena, stadium, or grandstand is to be calculated box by box and suite by suite.

221.2.1.3 Other Boxes. In boxes other than those required to comply with 221.2.1.2, the total number of wheelchair spaces required shall be determined in accordance with Table 221.2.1.1. Wheelchair spaces shall be located in not less than 20 percent of all boxes provided. Wheelchair spaces shall comply with 802.1.

Advisory

221.2.1.3 Other Boxes. The provision for seating in "other boxes" includes box seating provided in facilities such as performing arts auditoria where tiered boxes are designed for spatial and acoustical purposes. The number of wheelchair spaces required in boxes covered by 221.2.1.3 is calculated based on the total number of seats provided in these other boxes. The resulting number of wheelchair spaces must be located in no fewer than 20% of the boxes covered by this section. For example, a concert hall has 20 boxes, each of which contains 10 seats, totaling 200 seats. In this example, 5 wheelchair spaces would be required, and they must be placed in at least 4 of the boxes. Additionally, because the wheelchair spaces must also meet the dispersion requirements of 221.2.3, the boxes containing these wheelchair spaces cannot all be located in one area unless an exception to the dispersion requirements applies.

221.2.1.4 Team or Player Seating. At least one wheelchair space complying with 802.1 shall be provided in team or player seating areas serving areas of sport activity.

    EXCEPTION: Wheelchair spaces shall not be required in team or player seating areas serving bowling lanes not required to comply with 206.2.11.

221.2.2 Integration. Wheelchair spaces shall be an integral part of the seating plan.

Advisory

221.2.2 Integration. The requirement that wheelchair spaces be an "integral part of the seating plan" means that wheelchair spaces must be placed within the footprint of the seating area. Wheelchair spaces cannot be segregated from seating areas. For example, it would be unacceptable to place only the wheelchair spaces, or only the wheelchair spaces and their associated companion seats, outside the seating areas defined by risers in an assembly area.

221.2.3 Lines of Sight and Dispersion. Wheelchair spaces shall provide lines of sight complying with 802.2 and shall comply with 221.2.3. In providing lines of sight, wheelchair spaces shall be dispersed. Wheelchair spaces shall provide spectators with choices of seating locations and viewing angles that are substantially equivalent to, or better than, the choices of seating locations and viewing angles available to all other spectators. When the number of wheelchair spaces required by 221.2.1 has been met, further dispersion shall not be required.

EXCEPTION: Wheelchair spaces in team or player seating areas serving areas of sport activity shall not be required to comply with 221.2.3.

Advisory

221.2.3 Lines of Sight and Dispersion. Consistent with the overall intent of the ADA, individuals who use wheelchairs must be provided equal access so that their experience is substantially equivalent to that of other members of the audience. Thus, while individuals who use wheelchairs need not be provided with the best seats in the house, neither may they be relegated to the worst.

221.2.3.1 Horizontal Dispersion. Wheelchair spaces shall be dispersed horizontally.
EXCEPTIONS:
1. Horizontal dispersion shall not be required in assembly areas with 300 or fewer seats if the companion seats required by 221.3 and wheelchair spaces are located within the 2nd or 3rd quartile of the total row length. Intermediate aisles shall be included in determining the total row length. If the row length in the 2nd and 3rd quartile of a row is insufficient to accommodate the required number of companion seats and wheelchair spaces, the additional companion seats and wheelchair spaces shall be permitted to be located in the 1st and 4th quartile of the row.
2. In row seating, two wheelchair spaces shall be permitted to be located side-by-side.

Advisory

221.2.3.1 Horizontal Dispersion. Horizontal dispersion of wheelchair spaces is the placement of spaces in an assembly facility seating area from side-to-side or, in the case of an arena or stadium, around the field of play or performance area.

221.2.3.2 Vertical Dispersion. Wheelchair spaces shall be dispersed vertically at varying distances from the screen, performance area, or playing field. In addition, wheelchair spaces shall be located in each balcony or mezzanine that is located on an accessible route.
EXCEPTIONS:
1. Vertical dispersion shall not be required in assembly areas with 300 or fewer seats if the wheelchair spaces provide viewing angles that are equivalent to, or better than, the average viewing angle provided in the facility.
2. In bleachers, wheelchair spaces shall not be required to be provided in rows other than rows at points of entry to bleacher seating.

Advisory

221.2.3.2 Vertical Dispersion. When wheelchair spaces are dispersed vertically in an assembly facility they are placed at different locations within the seating area from front-to-back so that the distance from the screen, stage, playing field, area of sports activity, or other focal point is varied among wheelchair spaces.

221.2.3.2 Vertical Dispersion Exception 2. Points of entry to bleacher seating may include, but are not limited to, cross aisles, concourses, vomitories, and entrance ramps and stairs. Vertical, center, or side aisles adjoining bleacher seating that are stepped or tiered are not considered entry points.

221.3 Companion Seats. At least one companion seat complying with 802.3 shall be provided for each wheelchair space required by 221.2.1.

221.4 Designated Aisle Seats. At least 5 percent of the total number of aisle seats provided shall comply with 802.4 and shall be the aisle seats located closest to accessible routes.

EXCEPTION: Team or player seating areas serving areas of sport activity shall not be required to comply with 221.4.

Advisory

221.4 Designated Aisle Seats. When selecting which aisle seats will meet the requirements of 802.4, those aisle seats which are closest to, not necessarily on, accessible routes must be selected first. For example, an assembly area has two aisles (A and B) serving seating areas with an accessible route connecting to the top and bottom of Aisle A only. The aisle seats chosen to meet 802.4 must be those at the top and bottom of Aisle A, working toward the middle. Only when all seats on Aisle A would not meet the five percent minimum would seats on Aisle B be designated.

221.5 Lawn Seating. Lawn seating areas and exterior overflow seating areas, where fixed seats are not provided, shall connect to an accessible route.

Guidance

Wheelchair Spaces/Companion Seats. Owners of large assembly areas have historically complained to the Department that the requirement for one percent (1%) of seating to be wheelchair seating is excessive and that wheelchair seats are not being sold. At the same time, advocates have traditionally argued that persons who use wheelchairs will increasingly participate in activities at assembly areas once they become accessible and that at least one percent (1%) of seats should be accessible.

The 1991 Standards, at sections 4.1.3(19)(a) and 4.33.3, require assembly areas to provide wheelchair and companion seats. In assembly areas with a capacity of more than five hundred seats, accessible seating at a ratio of one percent (1%) (plus one seat) of the number of traditional fixed seats must be provided. The 2010 Standards, at section 221.2, require assembly areas with 501 to 5000 seats to provide at least six wheelchair spaces and companion seats plus one additional wheelchair space for each additional 150 seats (or fraction thereof) between 501 through 5000. In assembly areas with more than 5000 seats at least 36 wheelchair spaces and companion seats plus one additional wheelchair space for each 200 seats (or fraction thereof) more than 5000 are required. See sections 221.1 and 221.2 of the 2010 Standards.

Commenters questioned why scoping requirements for large assembly areas are being reduced. During the development of the 2004 ADAAG, industry providers, particularly those representing larger stadium-style assembly areas, supplied data to the Access Board demonstrating the current scoping requirements for large assembly areas often exceed the demand. Based on the data provided to the Access Board, the Department believes the reduced scoping requirements will adequately meet the needs of individuals with disabilities, while balancing concerns of the industry.

Commenters representing assembly areas supported the reduced scoping. One commenter asked that scoping requirements for larger assembly areas be reduced even further. Although the commenter referenced data demonstrating that wheelchair spaces in larger facilities with seating capacities of 70,000 or more may not be used by individuals with disabilities, the data was not based on actual results, but was calculated at least in part based on probability assumptions. The Department is not convinced that further reductions should be made based upon those projections and that further reductions would not substantially limit accessibility at assembly areas for persons who use wheelchairs.

Section 221.2.1.3 of the 2010 Standards clarifies that the scoping requirements for wheelchair spaces and companion seats are to be applied separately to general seating areas and to each luxury box, club box, and suite in arenas, stadiums, and grandstands. In assembly areas other than arenas, stadiums, and grandstands, the scoping requirements will not be applied separately. Thus, in performing arts facilities with tiered boxes designed for spatial and acoustical purposes, the scoping requirement is to be applied to the seats in the tiered boxes. The requisite number of wheelchair spaces and companion seats required in the tiered boxes are to be dispersed among at least twenty percent (20%) of the tiered boxes. For example, if a performing arts facility has 20 tiered boxes with 10 fixed seats in each box, for a total of 200 seats, at least five wheelchair spaces and companion seats must be provided in the boxes, and they must be dispersed among at least four of the 20 boxes.

Commenters raised concerns that the 2010 Standards should clarify requirements for scoping of seating areas and that requiring accessible seating in each luxury box, club box, and suite in arenas, stadiums and grandstands could result in no wheelchair and companion spaces available for individuals with disabilities in

---

the general seating area(s). These comments appear to misunderstand the requirements. The 2010 Standards require each luxury box, club box, and suite in an arena, stadium or grandstand to be accessible and to contain wheelchair spaces and companion seats as required by sections 221.2.1.1, 221.2.1.2 and 221.3. In addition, the remaining seating areas not located in boxes must also contain the number of wheelchair and companion seating locations specified in the 2010 Standards based on the total number of seats in the entire facility excluding luxury boxes, club boxes and suites.

Wheelchair Space Overlap in Assembly Areas. Section 4.33.3 of the 1991 Standards and the 2010 Standards, at sections 402, 403.5.1, 802.1.4, and 802.1.5, require walkways that are part of an accessible route to have a 36-inch minimum clear width. Section 802.1.5 of the 2010 Standards specifically prohibits accessible routes from overlapping wheelchair spaces. This change is consistent with the technical requirements for accessible routes, since the clear width of accessible routes cannot be obstructed by any object. The 2010 Standards also specifically prohibit wheelchair spaces from overlapping circulation paths. An advisory note clarifies that this prohibition applies only to the circulation path width required by applicable building codes and fire and life safety codes since the codes prohibit obstructions in the required width of assembly aisles.

Section 802.1.5 of the 2010 Standards provides that where a main circulation path is located in front of a row of seats that contains a wheelchair space and the circulation path is wider than required by applicable building codes and fire and life safety codes, the wheelchair space may overlap the"extra" circulation path width. Where a main circulation path is located behind a row of seats that contains a wheelchair space and the wheelchair space is entered from the rear, the aisle in front of the row may need to be wider in order not to block the required circulation path to the other seats in the row, or a mid-row opening may need to be provided to access the required circulation path to the other seats.

Line of Sight and Dispersion of Wheelchair Spaces in Assembly Areas. Section 4.33.3 of the 1991 Standards requires wheelchair spaces and companion seats to be an integral part of any fixed seating plan in assembly areas and to provide individuals with disabilities a choice of admission prices and lines of sight comparable to those available to other spectators. Section 4.33.3 also requires wheelchair spaces and companion seats to be dispersed in assembly areas with more than 300 seats. Under the 1991 Standards, sports facilities typically located some wheelchair spaces and companion seats on each accessible level of the facility. In 1994, the Department issued official guidance interpreting the requirement for comparable lines of sight in the 1991 Standards to mean wheelchair spaces and companion seats in sports stadia and arenas must provide patrons with disabilities and their companions with lines of sight over standing spectators to the playing field or performance area, where spectators were expected to stand during events. See"Accessible Stadiums," www.ada.gov/stadium.pdf. The Department also interpreted the section 4.33.3 comparable lines of sight requirement to mean that wheelchair spaces and companion seats in stadium-style movie theaters must provide patrons with disabilities and their companions with viewing angles comparable to those provided to other spectators.

Sections 221.2.3 and 802.2 of the 2010 Standards add specific technical requirements for providing lines of sight over seated and standing spectators and also require wheelchair spaces and companion seats (per section 221.3) to provide individuals with disabilities choices of seating locations and viewing angles that are substantially equivalent to, or better than, the choices of seating locations and viewing angles available to other spectators. This applies to all types of assembly areas, including stadium-style movie theaters, sports arenas, and concert halls. These rules are expected to have minimal impact since they are consistent with the Department's longstanding interpretation of the 1991 Standards and technical assistance.

Commenters stated that the qualitative viewing angle language contained in section 221.2.3 is not appropriate for an enforceable regulatory standard unless the terms of such language are defined. Other commenters requested definitions for viewing angles, an explanation for precisely how viewing angles are measured, and an explanation for precisely how to evaluate whether one viewing angle is better than another viewing angle. The Department is convinced that the regulatory language in the 2010 Standards is sufficient to provide a performance-based standard for designers, architects, and other professionals to design facilities that provide comparable lines of sight for wheelchair seating in assembly areas, including viewing angles. The

Department believes that as a general rule, the vast variety of sizes and configurations in assembly areas requires it to establish a performance standard for designers to adapt to the specific circumstances of the venue that is being designed. The Department has implemented more explicit requirements for stadium-style movie theaters in 28 CFR 36.406(f) and 35.151(g) of the final regulations based on experience and expertise gained after several major enforcement actions.

Another commenter inquired as to what determines whether a choice of seating locations or viewing angles is better than that available to all other spectators. The answer to this question varies according to each assembly area that is being designed, but designers and venue operators understand which seats are better and that understanding routinely drives design choices made to maximize profit and successful operation of the facility, among other things. For example, an "equivalent or better" line of sight in a major league football stadium would be different than for a 350-seat lecture hall. This performance standard is based upon the underlying principle of equal opportunity for a good viewing experience for everyone, including persons with disabilities. The Department believes that for each specific facility that is designed, the owner, operator, and design professionals will be able to distinguish easily between seating locations and the quality of the associated lines of sight from those seating locations in order to decide which ones are better than others. The wheelchair locations do not have to be exclusively among the seats with the very best lines of sight nor may they be exclusively among the seats with the worst lines of sight. Rather, wheelchair seating locations should offer a choice of viewing experiences and be located among the seats where most of the audience chooses to sit.

Section 4.33.3 of the 1991 Standards requires wheelchair spaces and companion seating to be offered at a choice of admission prices, but section 221.2.3.2 of the 2010 Standards no longer requires wheelchair spaces and companion seats to be dispersed based on admission prices. Venue owners and operators commented during the 2004 ADAAG rulemaking process that pricing is not always established at the design phase and may vary from event to event within the same facility, making it difficult to determine where to place wheelchair seats during the design and construction phase. Their concern was that a failure by the venue owner or operator to provide a choice of ticket prices for wheelchair seating as required by the 1991 Standards governing new construction could somehow unfairly subject parties involved in the design and construction to liability unknowingly.

Sections 221.2.3.2 and 221.3 of the 2010 Standards require wheelchair spaces and companion seats to be vertically dispersed at varying distances from the screen, performance area, or playing field. The 2010 Standards, at section 221.2.3.2, also require wheelchair spaces and companion seats to be located in each balcony or mezzanine served by an accessible route. The final regulations at 28 CFR 35.151(g)(1) and 36.406(f)(1) also require assembly areas to locate wheelchair spaces and companion seats at all levels of the facility that include seating and that are served by an accessible route. The Department interprets that requirement to mean that wheelchair and companion seating must be provided in a particular area even if the accessible route may not be the same route that other individuals use to reach their seats. For example, if other patrons reach their seats on the field by an inaccessible route (e.g., by stairs), but there is an accessible route that complies with section 206.3 that could be connected to seats on the field, accessible seats must be placed on the field even if that route is not generally available to the public. The 2010 Standards, at section 221.2.3.2, provide an exception for vertical dispersion in assembly areas with 300 or fewer seats if the wheelchair spaces and companion seats provide viewing angles that are equivalent to, or better than, the average viewing angle provided in the facility.

Section 221.3 of the 2010 Standards requires wheelchair spaces and companion seats to be dispersed horizontally. In addition, 28 CFR 35.151(g)(2) and 36.406(f)(2) require assembly areas that have seating around the field of play or performance area to place wheelchair spaces and companion seating all around that field of play or performance area.

Stadium-Style Movie Theaters

Pursuant to 28 CFR 35.151(g) and 36.406(f), in addition to other obligations, stadium-style movie theaters must meet horizontal and vertical dispersion requirements set forth in sections 221.2.3.1 and 221.2.3.2 of the 2010 Standards; placement of wheelchair and companion seating must be on a riser or cross-aisle in the stadium section of the theater; and placement of such seating must satisfy at least one of the following criteria: (i) it is located within the rear sixty percent (60%) of the seats provided in the auditorium; or (ii) it is located within the area of the auditorium where the vertical viewing angles are between the 40th and 100th percentile of vertical viewing angles for all seats in that theater as ranked from the first row (1st percentile) to the back row (100th percentile). The line-of-sight requirements recognize the importance to the movie-going experience of viewing angles, and the final regulations ensure that movie patrons with disabilities are provided views of the movie screen comparable to other theater patrons. Some commenters supported regulatory language that would require stadium-style theaters to meet standards of accessibility equal to those of non-stadium-style theaters, with larger theaters being required to provide accessible seating locations and viewing angles equal to those offered to individuals without disabilities.

One commenter noted that stadium-style movie theaters, sports arenas, music venues, theaters, and concert halls each pose unique conditions that require separate and specific standards to accommodate patrons with disabilities, and recommended that the Department provide more specific requirements for sports arenas, music venues, theaters, and concert halls. The Department has concluded that the 2010 Standards will provide sufficient flexibility to adapt to the wide variety of assembly venues covered.

Companion Seats. Section 4.33.3 of the 1991 Standards required at least one fixed companion seat to be provided next to each wheelchair space. The 2010 Standards at sections 221.3 and 802.3 permit companion seats to be movable. Several commenters urged the Department to ensure that companion seats are positioned in a manner that places the user at the same shoulder height as their companions using mobility devices. The Department recognizes that some facilities have created problems by locating the wheelchair space and companion seat on different floor elevations (often a difference of one riser height). Section 802.3.1 of the 2010 Standards addresses this problem by requiring the wheelchair space and the companion seat to be on the same floor elevation. This solution should prevent any vertical discrepancies that are not the direct result of differences in the sizes and configurations of wheelchairs.

Designated Aisle Seats. Section 4.1.3(19)(a) of the 1991 Standards requires one percent (1%) of fixed seats in assembly areas to be designated aisle seats with either no armrests or folding or retractable armrests on the aisle side of the seat. The 2010 Standards, at sections 221.4 and 802.4, base the number of required designated aisle seats on the total number of aisle seats, instead of on all of the seats in an assembly area as the 1991 Standards require. At least five percent (5%) of the aisle seats are required to be designated aisle seats and to be located closest to accessible routes. This option will almost always result in fewer aisle seats being designated aisle seats compared to the 1991 Standards. The Department is aware that sports facilities typically locate designated aisle seats on, or as near to, accessible routes as permitted by the configuration of the facility.

One commenter recommended that section 221.4, Designated Aisle Seats, be changed to require that aisle seats be on an accessible route, and be integrated and dispersed throughout an assembly area. Aisle seats, by their nature, typically are located within the general seating area, and integration occurs almost automatically. The issue of dispersing aisle seats or locating them on accessible routes is much more challenging. During the separate rulemaking on the 2004 ADAAG the Access Board specifically requested public comment on the question of whether aisle seats should be required to be located on accessible routes. After reviewing the comments submitted during the 2004 Access Board rulemaking, the Access Board concluded that this could not be done without making significant and costly changes in the design of most assembly areas. However, section 221.4 of the 2004 ADAAG required that designated aisle seats be the aisle seats closest to accessible routes. The Department proposed the same provision and concurs in the Access Board's conclusion and declines to implement further changes.

Team or Player Seating Areas. Section 221.2.1.4 of the 2010 Standards requires that at least one wheelchair space compliant with section 802.1 be provided in each team or player seating area serving areas of sport activity. For bowling lanes, the requirement for a wheelchair space in player seating areas is limited to lanes required to be accessible.

Lawn Seating. The 1991 Standards, at section 4.1.1(1), require all areas of newly constructed facilities to be accessible, but do not contain a specific scoping requirement for lawn seating in assembly areas. The 2010 Standards, at section 221.5, specifically require lawn seating areas and exterior overflow seating areas without fixed seats to connect to an accessible route.

Aisle Stairs and Ramps in Assembly Areas. Sections 4.1.3 and 4.1.3(4) of the 1991 Standards require that interior and exterior stairs connecting levels that are not connected by an elevator, ramp, or other accessible means of vertical access must comply with the technical requirements for stairs set out in section 4.9 of the 1991 Standards. Section 210.1 of the 2010 Standards requires that stairs that are part of a means of egress shall comply with section 504's technical requirements for stairs. The 1991 Standards do not contain any exceptions for aisle stairs in assembly areas. Section 210.1, Exception 3 of the 2010 Standards adds a new exception that exempts aisle stairs in assembly areas from section 504's technical requirements for stairs, including section 505's technical requirements for handrails.

Section 4.8.5 of the 1991 Standards exempts aisle ramps that are part of an accessible route from providing handrails on the side adjacent to seating. The 2010 Standards, at section 405.1, exempt aisle ramps adjacent to seating in assembly areas and not serving elements required to be on an accessible route, from complying with all of section 405's technical requirements for ramps. Where aisle ramps in assembly areas serve elements required to be on an accessible route, the 2010 Standards require that the aisle ramps comply with section 405's technical requirements for ramps. Sections 505.2 and 505.3 of the 2010 Standards provide exceptions for aisle ramp handrails. Section 505.2 states that in assembly areas, a handrail may be provided at either side or within the aisle width when handrails are not provided on both sides of aisle ramps. Section 505.3 states that, in assembly areas, handrails need not be continuous in aisles serving seating.

222 Dressing, Fitting, and Locker Rooms

222.1 General. Where dressing rooms, fitting rooms, or locker rooms are provided, at least 5 percent, but no fewer than one, of each type of use in each cluster provided shall comply with 803.

> **EXCEPTION:** In alterations, where it is technically infeasible to provide rooms in accordance with 222.1, one room for each sex on each level shall comply with 803. Where only unisex rooms are provided, unisex rooms shall be permitted.

Advisory

222.1 General. A "cluster" is a group of rooms proximate to one another. Generally, rooms in a cluster are within sight of, or adjacent to, one another. Different styles of design provide users varying levels of privacy and convenience. Some designs include private changing facilities that are close to core areas of the facility, while other designs use space more economically and provide only group dressing facilities. Regardless of the type of facility, dressing, fitting, and locker rooms should provide people with disabilities rooms that are equally private and convenient to those provided others. For example, in a physician's office, if people without disabilities must traverse the full length of the office suite in clothing other than their street clothes, it is acceptable for people with disabilities to be asked to do the same.

222.2 Coat Hooks and Shelves. Where coat hooks or shelves are provided in dressing, fitting or locker rooms without individual compartments, at least one of each type shall comply with 803.5. Where coat hooks or shelves are provided in individual compartments at least one of each type complying with 803.5 shall be provided in individual compartments in dressing, fitting, or locker rooms required to comply with 222.1.

Guidance

Dressing rooms, fitting rooms, and locker rooms are required to comply with the accessibility requirements of sections 222 and 803 of the 2010 Standards. Where these types of rooms are provided in clusters, five percent (5%) but at least one room in each cluster must comply. Some commenters stated that clothing and retail stores would have to expand and reconfigure accessible dressing, fitting and locker rooms to meet the changed provision for clear floor space alongside the end of the bench. Commenters explained that meeting the new requirement would result in a loss of sales and inventory space. Other commenters also expressed opposition to the changed requirement in locker rooms for similar reasons.

> The Department reminds the commenters that the requirements in the 2010 Standards for the clear floor space to be beside the short axis of the bench in an accessible dressing, fitting, or locker room apply only to new construction and alterations. The requirements for alterations in the 2010 Standards at section 202.3 do not include the requirement from the 1991 Standards at section 4.1.6(1)(c) that if alterations to single elements, when considered together, amount to an alteration of a room or space in a building or facility, the entire space shall be made accessible. Therefore, under the 2010 Standards, the alteration requirements only apply to specific elements or spaces that are being altered. So providing the clear floor space at the end of the bench as required by the 2010 Standards instead of in front of the bench as is allowed by the 1991 Standards would only be required when the bench in the accessible dressing room is altered or when the entire dressing room area is altered.

223 Medical Care and Long-Term Care Facilities

223.1 General. In licensed medical care facilities and licensed long-term care facilities where the period of stay exceeds twenty-four hours, patient or resident sleeping rooms shall be provided in accordance with 223.

[See additional requirements at 28 CFR 35.151(h) and 28 CFR 36.406(g).]

EXCEPTION: Toilet rooms that are part of critical or intensive care patient sleeping rooms shall not be required to comply with 603.

Advisory

223.1 General. Because medical facilities frequently reconfigure spaces to reflect changes in medical specialties, Section 223.1 does not include a provision for dispersion of accessible patient or resident sleeping rooms. The lack of a design requirement does not mean that covered entities are not required to provide services to people with disabilities where accessible rooms are not dispersed in specialty areas. Locate accessible rooms near core areas that are less likely to change over time. While dispersion is not required, the flexibility it provides can be a critical factor in ensuring cost effective compliance with applicable civil rights laws, including titles II and III of the ADA and Section 504 of the Rehabilitation Act of 1973, as amended. Additionally, all types of features and amenities should be dispersed among accessible sleeping rooms to ensure equal access to and a variety of choices for all patients and residents.

223.1.1 Alterations. Where sleeping rooms are altered or added, the requirements of 223 shall apply only to the sleeping rooms being altered or added until the number of sleeping rooms complies with the minimum number required for new construction.

Advisory

223.1.1 Alterations. In alterations and additions, the minimum required number is based on the total number of sleeping rooms altered or added instead of on the total number of sleeping rooms provided in a facility. As a facility is altered over time, every effort should be made to disperse accessible sleeping rooms among patient care areas such as pediatrics, cardiac care, maternity, and other units. In this way, people with disabilities can have access to the full-range of services provided by a medical care facility.

223.2 Hospitals, Rehabilitation Facilities, Psychiatric Facilities and Detoxification Facilities. Hospitals, rehabilitation facilities, psychiatric facilities and detoxification facilities shall comply with 223.2.

223.2.1 Facilities Not Specializing in Treating Conditions That Affect Mobility. In facilities not specializing in treating conditions that affect mobility, at least 10 percent, but no fewer than one, of the patient sleeping rooms shall provide mobility features complying with 805.

223.2.2 Facilities Specializing in Treating Conditions That Affect Mobility. In facilities specializing in treating conditions that affect mobility, 100 percent of the patient sleeping rooms shall provide mobility features complying with 805.

Advisory

223.2.2 Facilities Specializing in Treating Conditions That Affect Mobility. Conditions that affect mobility include conditions requiring the use or assistance of a brace, cane, crutch, prosthetic device, wheelchair, or powered mobility aid; arthritic, neurological, or orthopedic conditions that severely limit one's ability to walk; respiratory diseases and other conditions which may require the use of portable oxygen; and cardiac conditions that impose significant functional limitations. Facilities that may provide treatment for, but that do not specialize in treatment of such conditions, such as general rehabilitation hospitals, are not subject to this requirement but are subject to Section 223.2.1.

223.3 Long-Term Care Facilities. In licensed long-term care facilities, at least 50 percent, but no fewer than one, of each type of resident sleeping room shall provide mobility features complying with 805.

224 Transient Lodging Guest Rooms

224.1 General. Transient lodging facilities shall provide guest rooms in accordance with 224.

[See additional requirements for places of lodging at 28 CFR 36.406(c) and for housing at a place of education at 28 CFR 35.151(f) and 28 CFR 36.406(e).]

Advisory

224.1 General. Certain facilities used for transient lodging, including time shares, dormitories, and town homes may be covered by both these requirements and the Fair Housing Amendments Act. The Fair Housing Amendments Act requires that certain residential structures having four or more multi-family dwelling units, regardless of whether they are privately owned or federally assisted, include certain features of accessible and adaptable design according to guidelines established by the U.S. Department of Housing and Urban Development (HUD). This law and the appropriate regulations should be consulted before proceeding with the design and construction of residential housing.

224.1.1 Alterations. Where guest rooms are altered or added, the requirements of 224 shall apply only to the guest rooms being altered or added until the number of guest rooms complies with the minimum number required for new construction.

Advisory

224.1.1 Alterations. In alterations and additions, the minimum required number of accessible guest rooms is based on the total number of guest rooms altered or added instead of the total number of guest rooms provided in a facility. Typically, each alteration of a facility is limited to a particular portion of the facility. When accessible guest rooms are added as a result of subsequent alterations, compliance with 224.5 (Dispersion) is more likely to be achieved if all of the accessible guest rooms are not provided in the same area of the facility.

224.1.2 Guest Room Doors and Doorways. Entrances, doors, and doorways providing user passage into and within guest rooms that are not required to provide mobility features complying with 806.2 shall comply with 404.2.3.

EXCEPTION: Shower and sauna doors in guest rooms that are not required to provide mobility features complying with 806.2 shall not be required to comply with 404.2.3.

Advisory

224.1.2 Guest Room Doors and Doorways. Because of the social interaction that often occurs in lodging facilities, an accessible clear opening width is required for doors and doorways to and within all guest rooms, including those not required to be accessible. This applies to all doors, including bathroom doors, that allow full user passage. Other requirements for doors and doorways in Section 404 do not apply to guest rooms not required to provide mobility features.

224.2 Guest Rooms with Mobility Features. In transient lodging facilities, guest rooms with mobility features complying with 806.2 shall be provided in accordance with Table 224.2.

Table 224.2 Guest Rooms with Mobility Features (text version)			
Total Number of Guest Rooms Provided	Minimum Number of Required Rooms Without Roll-in Showers	Minimum Number of Required Rooms With Roll-in Showers	Total Number of Required Rooms
1 to 25	1	0	1
26 to 50	2	0	2
51 to 75	3	1	4
76 to 100	4	1	5
101 to 150	5	2	7
151 to 200	6	2	8
201 to 300	7	3	10
301 to 400	8	4	12
401 to 500	9	4	13
501 to 1000	2 percent of total	1 percent of total	3 percent of total
1001 and over	20, plus 1 for each 100, or fraction thereof, over 1000	10, plus 1 for each 100, or fraction thereof, over 1000	30, plus 2 for each 100, or fraction thereof, over 1000

224.3 Beds. In guest rooms having more than 25 beds, 5 percent minimum of the beds shall have clear floor space complying with 806.2.3.

224.4 Guest Rooms with Communication Features. In transient lodging facilities, guest rooms with communication features complying with 806.3 shall be provided in accordance with Table 224.4.

Table 224.4 Guest Rooms with Communication Features	
Total Number of Guest Rooms Provided	Minimum Number of Required Guest Rooms With Communication Features
2 to 25	2
26 to 50	4
51 to 75	7
76 to 100	9
101 to 150	12
151 to 200	14
201 to 300	17
301 to 400	20
401 to 500	22
501 to 1000	5 percent of total
1001 and over	50, plus 3 for each 100 over 1000

224.5 Dispersion. Guest rooms required to provide mobility features complying with 806.2 and guest rooms required to provide communication features complying with 806.3 shall be dispersed among the various classes of guest rooms, and shall provide choices of types of guest rooms, number of beds, and other amenities comparable to the choices provided to other guests. Where the minimum number of guest rooms required to comply with 806 is not sufficient to allow for complete dispersion, guest rooms shall be dispersed in the following priority: guest room type, number of beds, and amenities. At least one guest room required to provide mobility features complying with 806.2 shall also provide communication features complying with 806.3. Not more than 10 percent of guest rooms required to provide mobility features complying with 806.2 shall be used to satisfy the minimum number of guest rooms required to provide communication features complying with 806.3.

Advisory

224.5 Dispersion. Factors to be considered in providing an equivalent range of options may include, but are not limited to, room size, bed size, cost, view, bathroom fixtures such as hot tubs and spas, smoking and nonsmoking, and the number of rooms provided.

Guidance

Scoping. The minimum number of guest rooms required to be accessible in transient lodging facilities is covered by section 224 of the 2010 Standards. Scoping requirements for guest rooms with mobility features and guest rooms with communication features are addressed at section 224.2 and section 224.4, respectively. Under the 1991 Standards all newly constructed guest rooms with mobility features must provide communication features. Under the 2010 Standards, in section 224.5, at least one guest room with mobility features must also provide communication features. Additionally, not more than ten percent (10%) of the guest rooms required to provide mobility features and also equipped with communication features can be used to satisfy the minimum number of guest rooms required to provide communication features.

Some commenters opposed requirements for guest rooms accessible to individuals with mobility disabilities stating that statistics provided by the industry demonstrate that all types of accessible guest rooms are unused. They further claimed that the requirements of the 2010 Standards are too burdensome to meet in new construction, and that the requirements will result in a loss of living space in places of transient lodging. Other commenters urged the Department to increase the number of guest rooms required to be accessible. The number of guest rooms accessible to individuals with mobility disabilities and the number accessible to persons who are deaf or who are hard of hearing in the 2010 Standards are consistent with the 1991 Standards and with the IBC. The Department continues to receive complaints about the lack of accessible guest rooms throughout the country. Accessible guest rooms are used not only by individuals using mobility devices such as wheelchairs and scooters, but also by individuals with other mobility disabilities including persons who use walkers, crutches, or canes.

Data provided by the Disability Statistics Center at the University of California, San Francisco demonstrated that the number of adults who use wheelchairs has been increasing at the rate of six percent (6%) per year from 1969 to 1999; and by 2010, it was projected that two percent (2%) of the adult population would use wheelchairs. In addition to persons who use wheelchairs, three percent (3%) of adults used crutches, canes, walkers, and other mobility devices in 1999; and the number was projected to increase to four percent (4%) by 2010. Thus, in 2010, up to six percent (6%) of the population may need accessible guest rooms.

Dispersion. The 2010 Standards, in section 224.5, set scoping requirements for dispersion in facilities covered by the transient lodging provisions. This section covers guest rooms with mobility features and guest rooms with communication features and applies in new construction and alterations. The primary requirement is to provide choices of types of guest rooms, number of beds, and other amenities comparable to the choices provided to other guests. An advisory in section 224.5 provides guidance that "factors to be considered in providing an equivalent range of options may include, but are not limited to, room size, bed size, cost, view, bathroom fixtures such as hot tubs and spas, smoking and nonsmoking, and the number of rooms provided."

Commenters asked the Department to clarify what is meant by various terms used in section 224.5 such as "classes," "types," "options," and "amenities." Other commenters asked the Department to clarify and simplify the dispersion requirements set forth in section 224.5 of the 2010 Standards, in particular the scope of the term

---

"amenities." One commenter expressed concern that views, if considered an amenity, would further complicate room categories and force owners and operators to make an educated guess. Other commenters stated that views should only be a dispersion criteria if view is a factor for pricing room rates.

These terms are not to be considered terms of art, but should be used as in their normal course. For example, "class" is defined by Webster's Dictionary as "a division by quality." "Type" is defined as "a group of * * * things that share common traits or characteristics distinguishing them as an identifiable group or class." Accordingly, these terms are not intended to convey different concepts, but are used as synonyms. In the 2010 Standards, section 224.5 and its advisory require dispersion in such a varied range of hotels and lodging facilities that the Department believes that the chosen terms are appropriate to convey what is intended. Dispersion required by this section is not "one size fits all" and it is imperative that each covered entity consider its individual circumstance as it applies this requirement. For example, a facility would consider view as an amenity if some rooms faced mountains, a beach, a lake, or other scenery that was considered to be a premium. A facility where view was not marketed or requested by guests would not factor the view as an amenity for purposes of meeting the dispersion requirement.

Section 224.5 of the 2010 Standards requires that guest rooms with mobility features and guest rooms with communication features "shall be dispersed among the various classes of guest rooms, and shall provide choices of types of guest rooms, number of beds, and other amenities comparable to the choices provided to other guests. When the minimum number of guest rooms required is not sufficient to allow for complete dispersion, guest rooms shall be dispersed in the following priority: guest room type, number of beds and amenities."

This general dispersion requirement is intended to effectuate Congress' directive that a percentage of each class of hotel rooms is to be fully accessible to persons with disabilities. See H.R. Rep. No. 101-485 (II) at 391. Accordingly, the promise of the ADA in this instance is that persons with disabilities will have an equal opportunity to benefit from the various options available to hotel guests without disabilities, from single occupancy guest rooms with limited features (and accompanying limited price tags) to luxury suites with lavish features and choices. The inclusion of section 224.5 of the 2010 Standards is not new. Substantially similar language is contained in section 9.1.4 of the 1991 Standards.

Commenters raised concerns that the factors included in the advisory to section 224.5 of the 2010 Standards have been expanded. The advisory provides: "[f]actors to be considered in providing an equivalent range of options may include, but are not limited to, room size, bed size, cost, view, bathroom fixtures such as hot tubs and spas, smoking and nonsmoking, and the number of rooms provided."

As previously discussed, the advisory materials provided in the 2010 Standards are meant to be illustrative and do not set out specific requirements. In this particular instance, the advisory materials for section 224.5 set out some of the common types of amenities found at transient lodging facilities, and include common sense concepts such as view, bathroom fixtures, and smoking status. The intention of these factors is to indicate to the hospitality industry the sorts of considerations that the Department, in its enforcement efforts since the enactment of the ADA, has considered as amenities that should be made available to persons with disabilities, just as they are made available to guests without disabilities.

Commenters offered several suggestions for addressing dispersion. One option included the flexibility to use an equivalent facilitation option similar to that provided in section 9.1.4(2) of the 1991 Standards.

The 2010 Standards eliminated all specific references to equivalent facilitation. Since Congress made it clear that each class of hotel room is to be available to individuals with disabilities, the Department declines to adopt such a specific limitation in favor of the specific requirement for new construction and alterations found in section 224.5 of the 2010 Standards.

In considering the comments of the hospitality industry from the ANPRM and the Department's enforcement efforts in this area, the Department sought comment in the NPRM on whether the dispersion requirements should be applied proportionally, or whether the requirements of section 224.5 of the 2010 Standards would be complied with if access to at least one guest room of each type were to be provided.

One commenter expressed concern about requiring different guest room types to be proportionally represented in the accessible guest room pool as opposed to just having each type represented. Some commenters also expressed concern about accessible guest rooms created in pre-1993 facilities and they requested that such accessible guest rooms be safe harbored just as they are safe harbored under the 1991 Standards. In addition, one commenter requested that the proposed dispersion requirements in section 224.5 of the 2010 Standards not be applied to pre-1993 facilities even when they are altered. Some commenters also offered a suggestion for limitations to the dispersion requirements as an alternative to safe harboring pre-1993 facilities. The suggestion included: (1) Guest rooms´ interior or exterior footprints may remain unchanged in order to meet the dispersion requirements; (2) Dispersion should only be required among the types of rooms affected by an alteration; and (3) Subject to (1) and (2) above and technical feasibility, a facility would need to provide only one guest room in each guest room type such as single, double and suites. One commenter requested an exception to the dispersion criteria that applies to both existing and new multi-story timeshare facilities. This requested exception waives dispersion based on views to the extent that up to eight units may be vertically stacked in a single location.

Section 224.1.1 of the 2010 Standards sets scoping requirements for alterations to transient lodging guest rooms. The advisory to section 224.1.1 further explains that compliance with 224.5 is more likely to be achieved if all of the accessible guest rooms are not provided in the same area of the facility, when accessible guest rooms are added as a result of subsequent alterations.

Some commenters requested a specific exemption for small hotels of 300 or fewer guest rooms from dispersion regarding smoking rooms. The ADA requires that individuals with disabilities be provided with the same range of options as persons without disabilities, and, therefore, the Department declines to add such an exemption. It is noted, however, that the existence of this language in the advisory does not require a place of transient lodging that does not offer smoking guest rooms at its facility to do so only for individuals with disabilities.

Guest Rooms with Mobility Features. Scoping provisions for guest rooms with mobility features are provided in section 224.2 of the 2010 Standards. Scoping requirements for alterations are included in 224.1.1. These scoping requirements in the 2010 Standards are consistent with the 1991 Standards.

One commenter expressed opposition to the new scoping provisions for altered guest rooms, which, according to the commenter, require greater numbers of accessible guest rooms with mobility features.

Section 224.1.1 of the 2010 Standards provides scoping requirements for alterations to guest rooms in existing facilities. Section 224.1.1 modifies the scoping requirements for new construction in section 224 by limiting the application of section 224 requirements only to those guest rooms being altered or added until the number of such accessible guest rooms complies with the minimum number required for new construction in section 224.2 of the 2010 Standards. The minimum required number of accessible guest rooms is based on the total number of guest rooms altered or added instead of the total number of guest rooms provided. These requirements are consistent with the requirements in the 1991 Standards. Language in the 2010 Standards clarifies the provision of section 104.2 of the 2010 Standards which requires rounding up values to the next whole number for calculations of percentages in scoping.

Guest Rooms with Communication Features. The revisions at section 224.4 of the 2010 Standards effect no substantive change from the 1991 Standards with respect to the number of guest rooms required to provide communication features. The scoping requirement is consolidated into a single table, instead of appearing in three sections as in the 1991 Standards. The revised provisions also limit the overlap between guest rooms required to provide mobility features and guest rooms required to provide communication features. Section 224.5 of the 2010 Standards requires that at least one guest room providing mobility features must also provide communications features. At least one, but not more than ten percent (10%), of the guest rooms required to provide mobility features can also satisfy the minimum number of guest rooms required to provide communication features.

Commenters suggested that the requirements for scoping and dispersion of guest rooms for persons with mobility impairments and guest rooms with communication features are too complex for the industry to effectively implement.

The Department believes the requirements for guest rooms with communications features in the 2010 Standards clarify the requirements necessary to provide equal opportunity for travelers with disabilities. Additional technical assistance will be made available to address questions before the rule goes into effect.

Visible Alarms in Guest Rooms with Communication Features. The 1991 Standards at sections 9.3.1 and 4.28.4 require transient lodging guest rooms with communication features to provide either permanently installed visible alarms that are connected to the building fire alarm system or portable visible alarms that are connected to a standard

110-volt electrical outlet and are both activated by the building fire alarm system and provide a visible alarm when the single station smoke detector is activated. Section 215.4 of the 2010 Standards no longer includes the portable visible alarm option and instead requires that transient lodging guest rooms with communication features be equipped with a fire alarm system which includes permanently installed audible and visible alarms in accordance with NFPA 72 National Fire Alarm Code (1999 or 2002 edition). Such guest rooms with communication features are also required by section 806.3.2 of the 2010 Standards to be equipped with visible notification devices that alert room occupants of incoming telephone calls and a door knock or bell.

The 2010 Standards add a new exception for alterations to existing facilities that exempts existing fire alarm systems from providing visible alarms, unless the fire alarm system itself is upgraded or replaced, or a new fire alarm system is installed. Transient lodging facilities that alter guest rooms are not required to provide permanently installed visible alarms complying with the NFPA 72 if the existing fire alarm system has not been upgraded or replaced, or a new fire alarm system has not been installed.

Commenters representing small providers of transient lodging raised concerns about the proposed changes to prohibit the use of portable visible alarms used in transient lodging guest rooms. These commenters recommended retaining requirements that allow the use of portable visible alarms.

Persons who are deaf or hard of hearing have reported that portable visible alarms used in transient lodging guest rooms are deficient because the alarms are not activated by the building fire alarm system, and the alarms do not work when the building power source goes out in emergencies. The 2010 Standards are consistent with the model building, fire, and life safety codes as applied to newly constructed transient lodging facilities. One commenter sought confirmation of its understanding of visible alarm requirements from the Department. This commenter interpreted the exception to section 215.1 of the 2010 Standards and the Department's commentary to the NPRM to mean that if a transient lodging facility does not have permanently installed visible alarms in its communication accessible guest rooms, it will not be required to provide such alarms until such time that its fire alarm system is upgraded or replaced, or a new fire alarm system is installed. In addition, this commenter also understood that, if a hotel already has permanently installed visible alarms in all of its mobility accessible guest rooms, it would not have to relocate such visible alarms and other communication features in those rooms to other guest rooms to comply with the ten percent (10%) overlap requirement until the alarm system is upgraded or replaced.

This commenter's interpretation and understanding are consistent with the Department's position in this matter. Section 215.4 of the 2010 Standards requires that guest rooms required to have communication features be equipped with a fire alarm system complying with section 702. Communication accessible guest rooms are required to have all of the communication features described in section 806.3 of the 2010 Standards including a fire alarm system which provides both audible and visible alarms. The exception to section 215.1 of the 2010 Standards, which applies only to fire alarm requirements for guest rooms with communication features in existing facilities, exempts the visible alarm requirement until such time as the existing fire alarm system is upgraded or replaced, or a new fire alarm system is installed. If guest rooms in existing facilities are altered and they are required by section 224 of the 2010 Standards to have communication features, such guest rooms are required by section 806.3 to have all other communication features including notification devices.

Vanity Counter Space. Section 806.2.4.1 of the 2010 Standards requires that if vanity countertop space is provided in inaccessible transient lodging guest bathrooms, comparable vanity space must be provided in accessible transient lodging guest bathrooms.

A commenter questioned whether in existing facilities vanity countertop space may be provided through the addition of a shelf. Another commenter found the term "comparable" vague and expressed concern about confusion the new requirement would cause. This commenter suggested that the phrase "equal area in square inches" be used instead of comparable vanity space.

In some circumstances, the addition of a shelf in an existing facility may be a reasonable way to provide a space for travelers with disabilities to use their toiletries and other personal items. However, this is a determination that must be made on a case-by-case basis. Comparable vanity countertop space need not be one continuous surface and need not be exactly the same size as the countertops in comparable guest bathrooms. For example, accessible shelving within reach of the lavatory could be stacked to provide usable surfaces for toiletries and other personal items.

Shower and Sauna Doors in Transient Lodging Facilities. Section 9.4 of the 1991 Standards and section 206.5.3 of the 2010 Standards both require passage doors in transient lodging guest rooms that do not provide mobility features to provide at least 32 inches of clear width. Congress directed this requirement to be included so that individuals with disabilities could visit guests in other rooms. *See* H. Rept. 101-485, pt. 2, at 118 (1990); S. Rept. 101-116, at 70 (1989). Section 224.1.2 of the 2010 Standards adds a new exception to clarify that shower and sauna doors in such inaccessible guest rooms are exempt from the requirement for passage doors to provide at least 32 inches of clear width. Two commenters requested that saunas and steam rooms in existing facilities be exempt from the section 224.1.2 requirement and that the requirement be made applicable to new construction only.

The exemption to the section 224.1.2 requirement for a 32-inch wide clearance at doors to shower and saunas applies only to those showers and saunas in guest rooms which are not required to have mobility features. Showers and saunas in other locations, including those in common use areas and guest rooms with mobility features, are required to comply with the 32-inch clear width standard as well as other applicable accessibility standards. Saunas come in a variety of types: portable, pre-built, pre-cut, and custom-made. All saunas except for custom-made saunas are made to manufacturers' standard dimensions. The Department is aware that creating the required 32-inch clearance at existing narrower doorways may not always be technically feasible. However, the Department believes that owners and operators will have an opportunity to provide the required doorway clearance, unless doing so is technically infeasible, when an alteration to an existing sauna is undertaken. Therefore, the Department has retained these requirements.

Platform Lifts in Transient Lodging Guest Rooms and Dwelling Units. The 1991 Standards, at section 4.1.3(5), exception 4, and the 2010 Standards, at sections 206.7 and 206.7.6, both limit the locations where platform lifts are permitted to be used as part of an accessible route. The 2010 Standards add a new scoping requirement that permits platform lifts to be used to connect levels within transient lodging guest rooms and dwelling units with mobility features.

225 Storage

225.1 General. Storage facilities shall comply with 225.

225.2 Storage. Where storage is provided in accessible spaces, at least one of each type shall comply with 811.

Advisory

225.2 Storage. Types of storage include, but are not limited to, closets, cabinets, shelves, clothes rods, hooks, and drawers. Where provided, at least one of each type of storage must be within the reach ranges specified in 308; however, it is permissible to install additional storage outside the reach ranges.

225.2.1 Lockers. Where lockers are provided, at least 5 percent, but no fewer than one of each type, shall comply with 811.

Advisory

225.2.1 Lockers. Different types of lockers may include full-size and half-size lockers, as well as those specifically designed for storage of various sports equipment.

225.2.2 Self-Service Shelving. Self-service shelves shall be located on an accessible route complying with 402. Self-service shelving shall not be required to comply with 308.

Advisory

225.2.2 Self-Service Shelving. Self-service shelves include, but are not limited to, library, store, or post office shelves.

225.3 Self-Service Storage Facilities. Self-service storage facilities shall provide individual self-service storage spaces complying with these requirements in accordance with Table 225.3.

Table 225.3 Self-Service Storage Facilities	
Total Spaces in Facility	**Minimum Number of Spaces Required to be Accessible**
1 to 200	5 percent, but no fewer than 1
201 and over	10, plus 2 percent of total number of units over 200

Advisory

225.3 Self-Service Storage Facilities. Although there are no technical requirements that are unique to self-service storage facilities, elements and spaces provided in facilities containing self-service storage spaces required to comply with these requirements must comply with this document where applicable. For example: the number of storage spaces required to comply with these requirements must provide Accessible Routes complying with Section 206; Accessible Means of Egress complying with Section 207; Parking Spaces complying with Section 208; and, where provided, other public use or common use elements and facilities such as toilet rooms, drinking fountains, and telephones must comply with the applicable requirements of this document.

225.3.1 Dispersion. Individual self-service storage spaces shall be dispersed throughout the various classes of spaces provided. Where more classes of spaces are provided than the number required to be accessible, the number of spaces shall not be required to exceed that required by Table 225.3. Self-service storage spaces complying with Table 225.3 shall not be required to be dispersed among buildings in a multi-building facility.

Guidance

Section 225 of the 2010 Standards provides that where storage is provided in accessible spaces, at least one of each type shall comply with the 2010 Standards. Self-service shelving is required to be on an accessible route, but is not required to comply with the reach range requirements. These requirements are consistent with the 1991 Standards.

Section 225.3 adds a new scoping requirement for self-storage facilities. Facilities with 200 or fewer storage spaces will be required to make at least five percent (5%) of the storage spaces accessible. Facilities with more than 200 storage spaces will be required to provide ten accessible storage spaces, plus two percent (2%) of the total storage spaces over 200.

Sections 225.2.1 and 811 of the 2010 Standards require lockers to meet accessibility requirements. Where lockers are provided in clusters, five percent (5%) but at least one locker in each cluster will have to comply. Under the 1991 Standards, only one locker of each type provided must be accessible.

Commenters recommended that the Department adopt language requiring public accommodations to provide access to all self-service shelves and display areas available to customers. Other commenters opposed this requirement as too burdensome to retail and other entities and claimed that significant revenue would be lost if this requirement were to be implemented.

Other commenters raised concerns that section 225.2.2 of the 2010 Standards scopes only self-service shelving whereas section 4.1.3(12)(b) of the 1991 Standards applies to both "shelves or display units."

Although "display units" were not included in the 2010 Standards under the belief that displays are not to be touched and therefore by definition cannot be "self-service," both the 2010 Standards and the 1991 Standards should be read broadly to apply to all types of shelves, racks, hooks, and similar self-service merchandising fittings, including self-service display units. Such fixtures are permitted to be installed above or below the reach ranges possible for many persons with disabilities so that space available for merchandising is used as efficiently as possible.

226 Dining Surfaces and Work Surfaces

226.1 General. Where dining surfaces are provided for the consumption of food or drink, at least 5 percent of the seating spaces and standing spaces at the dining surfaces shall comply with 902. In addition, where work surfaces are provided for use by other than employees, at least 5 percent shall comply with 902.

EXCEPTIONS:

1. Sales counters and service counters shall not be required to comply with 902.

2. Check writing surfaces provided at check-out aisles not required to comply with 904.3 shall not be required to comply with 902.

Advisory

226.1 General. In facilities covered by the ADA, this requirement does not apply to work surfaces used only by employees. However, the ADA and, where applicable, Section 504 of the Rehabilitation Act of 1973, as amended, provide that employees are entitled to "reasonable accommodations." With respect to work surfaces, this means that employers may need to procure or adjust work stations such as desks, laboratory and work benches, fume hoods, reception counters, teller windows, study carrels, commercial kitchen counters, and conference tables to accommodate the individual needs of employees with disabilities on an "as needed" basis. Consider work surfaces that are flexible and permit installation at variable heights and clearances.

226.2 Dispersion. Dining surfaces and work surfaces required to comply with 902 shall be dispersed throughout the space or facility containing dining surfaces and work surfaces.

Guidance

Section 226.1 of the 2010 Standards require that where dining surfaces are provided for the consumption of food or drink, at least five percent (5%) of the seating spaces and standing spaces at the dining surfaces comply with section 902. Section 902.2 requires the provision of accessible knee and toe clearance.

Commenters stated that basing accessible seating on seating spaces and standing spaces potentially represents a significant increase in scoping, particularly given the ambiguity in what represents a "standing space" and urged a return to the 1991 Standard of requiring accessible seating based on fixed dining tables. The scoping change merely takes into account that tables may vary in size so that basing the calculation on the number of tables rather than on the number of individuals that may be accommodated by the tables could unnecessarily restrict opportunities for persons with disabilities. The revised scoping permits greater flexibility by allowing designers to disperse accessible seating and standing spaces throughout the dining area. Human factors data, which is readily available to designers, provides information about the amount of space required for both eating and drinking while seated or standing.

---

227 Sales and Service

227.1 General. Where provided, check-out aisles, sales counters, service counters, food service lines, queues, and waiting lines shall comply with 227 and 904.

227.2 Check-Out Aisles. Where check-out aisles are provided, check-out aisles complying with 904.3 shall be provided in accordance with Table 227.2. Where check-out aisles serve different functions, check-out aisles complying with 904.3 shall be provided in accordance with Table 227.2 for each function. Where check-out aisles are dispersed throughout the building or facility, check-out aisles complying with 904.3 shall be dispersed.

EXCEPTION: Where the selling space is under 5000 square feet (465 m^2) no more than one check-out aisle complying with 904.3 shall be required.

Table 227.2 Check-Out Aisles	
Number of Check-Out Aisles of Each Function	Minimum Number of Check-Out Aisles of Each Function Required to Comply with 904.3
1 to 4	1
5 to 8	2
9 to 15	3
16 and over	3, plus 20 percent of additional aisles

227.2.1 Altered Check-Out Aisles. Where check-out aisles are altered, at least one of each check-out aisle serving each function shall comply with 904.3 until the number of check-out aisles complies with 227.2.

227.3 Counters. Where provided, at least one of each type of sales counter and service counter shall comply with 904.4. Where counters are dispersed throughout the building or facility, counters complying with 904.4 also shall be dispersed.

Advisory

227.3 Counters. Types of counters that provide different services in the same facility include, but are not limited to, order, pick-up, express, and returns. One continuous counter can be used to provide different types of service. For example, order and pick-up are different services. It would not be acceptable to provide access only to the part of the counter where orders are taken when orders are picked-up at a different location on the same counter. Both the order and pick-up section of the counter must be accessible.

227.4 Food Service Lines. Food service lines shall comply with 904.5. Where self-service shelves are provided, at least 50 percent, but no fewer than one, of each type provided shall comply with 308.

227.5 Queues and Waiting Lines. Queues and waiting lines servicing counters or check-out aisles required to comply with 904.3 or 904.4 shall comply with 403.

Guidance

Check-Out Aisles and Sales and Service Counters. The 1991 Standards, at section 7.2, and the 2010 Standards, at section 904.4, contain technical requirements for sales and service counters. The 1991 Standards generally require sales and service counters to provide an accessible portion at least 36 inches long and no higher than 36 inches above the finish floor. The nondiscrimination requirements of the ADA regulations require the level of service provided at the accessible portion of any sales and service counter to be the same as the level of service provided at the inaccessible portions of the counter.

The 2010 Standards specify different lengths for the accessible portion of sales and service counters based on the type of approach provided. Where a forward approach is provided, the accessible portion of the counter must be at least 30 inches long and no higher than 36 inches, and knee and toe space must be provided under the counter. The requirement that knee and toe space be provided where only clear floor space for a forward approach to a sales and service counter is provided is not a new requirement. It is a clarification of the ongoing requirement that part of the sales and service counter be accessible. This requirement applies to the entire accessible part of sales and service counters and requires that the accessible clear floor or ground space adjacent to those counters be kept clear of merchandise, equipment, and other items so that the accessible part of the counter is readily accessible to and usable by individuals with disabilities. The accessible part of the counter must also be staffed and provide an equivalent level of service as that provided to all customers.

Where clear floor space for a parallel approach is provided, the accessible portion of the counter must be at least 36 inches long and no higher than 36 inches above the finish floor. A clear floor or ground space that is at least 48 inches long x 30 inches wide must be provided positioned for a parallel approach adjacent to the 36-inch minimum length of counter.

Section 904.4 of the 2010 Standards includes an exception for alterations to sales and service counters in existing facilities. It permits the accessible portion of the counter to be at least 24 inches long, where providing a longer accessible counter will result in a reduction in the number of existing counters at work stations or existing mailboxes, provided that the required clear floor or ground space is centered on the accessible length of the counter.

Section 904.4 of the 2010 Standards also clarifies that the accessible portion of the counter must extend the same depth as the sales or service counter top. Where the counter is a single-height counter, this requirement applies across the entire depth of the counter top. Where the counter is a split-height counter, this requirement applies only to the customer side of the counter top. The employee-side of the counter top may be higher or lower than the customer-side of the counter top.

Commenters recommended that the Department consider a regulatory alternative exempting small retailers from the new knee and toe clearance requirement and retaining existing wheelchair accessibility standards for sales and service counters. These commenters believed that the knee and toe clearance requirements will cause a reduction in the sales and inventory space at check-out aisles and other sales and service counters.

Both the 1991 and the 2010 Standards permit covered entities to determine whether they will provide a forward or a parallel approach to sales and service counters. So any facility that does not wish to provide the knee or toe clearance required for a front approach to such a counter may avoid that option. However, the Department believes that permitting a forward approach without requiring knee and toe clearance is not adequate to provide accessibility because the person using a wheelchair will be prevented from coming close enough to the counter to see the merchandise or to transact business with a degree of convenience that is comparable to that provided to other customers.

A parallel approach to sales and service counters also can provide the accessibility required by the 2010 Standards. Individuals using wheelchairs can approach sales and service counters from the side, and, assuming the necessary elements, features, or merchandise necessary to complete a business transaction are within the reach range requirements for a side approach, the needs of individuals with disabilities can be met effectively.

Section 227 of the 2010 Standards clarifies the requirements for food service lines. Queues and waiting lines serving counters or check-out aisles, including those for food service, must be accessible to individuals with disabilities.

228 Depositories, Vending Machines, Change Machines, Mail Boxes, and Fuel Dispensers

228.1 General. Where provided, at least one of each type of depository, vending machine, change machine, and fuel dispenser shall comply with 309.

EXCEPTION: Drive-up only depositories shall not be required to comply with 309.

Advisory
228.1 General. Depositories include, but are not limited to, night receptacles in banks, post offices, video stores, and libraries.

228.2 Mail Boxes. Where mail boxes are provided in an interior location, at least 5 percent, but no fewer than one, of each type shall comply with 309. In residential facilities, where mail boxes are provided for each residential dwelling unit, mail boxes complying with 309 shall be provided for each residential dwelling unit required to provide mobility features complying with 809.2 through 809.4.

229 Windows

229.1 General. Where glazed openings are provided in accessible rooms or spaces for operation by occupants, at least one opening shall comply with 309. Each glazed opening required by an administrative authority to be operable shall comply with 309.

EXCEPTION:

1. Glazed openings in residential dwelling units required to comply with 809 shall not be required to comply with 229.

2. Glazed openings in guest rooms required to provide communication features and in guest rooms required to comply with 206.5.3 shall not be required to comply with 229.

Guidance

A new requirement at section 229.1 of the 2010 Standards provides that if operable windows are provided for building users, then at least one window in an accessible space must be equipped with controls that comply with section 309.

Commenters generally supported this provision but some commenters asked whether the maximum five-pounds (5 lbs.) of force requirement of section 309 applies to the window latch itself or only to the force required to open the window. Section 309 applies to all controls and operating mechanisms, so the latch must comply with the requirement to operate with no more than five pounds of force (5 lbf).

---

230 Two-Way Communication Systems

230.1 General. Where a two-way communication system is provided to gain admittance to a building or facility or to restricted areas within a building or facility, the system shall comply with 708.

Advisory

230.1 General. This requirement applies to facilities such as office buildings, courthouses, and other facilities where admittance to the building or restricted spaces is dependent on two-way communication systems.

Guidance

New provisions of the 2010 Standards at sections 230.1 and 708 require two-way communications systems to be equipped with visible as well as audible signals.

---

231 Judicial Facilities

231.1 General. Judicial facilities shall comply with 231.

231.2 Courtrooms. Each courtroom shall comply with 808.

231.3 Holding Cells. Where provided, central holding cells and court-floor holding cells shall comply with 231.3.

231.3.1 Central Holding Cells. Where separate central holding cells are provided for adult male, juvenile male, adult female, or juvenile female, one of each type shall comply with 807.2. Where central holding cells are provided and are not separated by age or sex, at least one cell complying with 807.2 shall be provided.

231.3.2 Court-Floor Holding Cells. Where separate court-floor holding cells are provided for adult male, juvenile male, adult female, or juvenile female, each courtroom shall be served by one cell of each type complying with 807.2. Where court-floor holding cells are provided and are not separated by age or sex, courtrooms shall be served by at least one cell complying with 807.2. Cells may serve more than one courtroom.

231.4 Visiting Areas. Visiting areas shall comply with 231.4.

231.4.1 Cubicles and Counters. At least 5 percent, but no fewer than one, of cubicles shall comply with 902 on both the visitor and detainee sides. Where counters are provided, at least one shall comply with 904.4.2 on both the visitor and detainee sides.

EXCEPTION: The detainee side of cubicles or counters at non-contact visiting areas not serving holding cells required to comply with 231 shall not be required to comply with 902 or 904.4.2.

231.4.2 Partitions. Where solid partitions or security glazing separate visitors from detainees at least one of each type of cubicle or counter partition shall comply with 904.6.

Guidance

Section 231 of the 2010 Standards adds requirements for accessible courtrooms, holding cells, and visiting areas.

Accessible Courtroom Stations. Sections 231.2, 808, 304, 305, and 902 of the 2010 Standards provide increased accessibility at courtroom stations. Clear floor space for a forward approach is required for all courtroom stations (judges' benches, clerks' stations, bailiffs' stations, deputy clerks' stations, court reporters' stations, and litigants' and counsel stations). Other applicable specifications include accessible work surface heights and toe and knee clearance.

Accessible Jury Boxes, Attorney Areas, and Witness Stands. Section 206.2.4 of the 2010 Standards requires, in new construction and alterations, at least one accessible route to connect accessible building or facility entrances with all accessible spaces and elements within the building or facility that are connected by a circulation path unless they are exempted by Exceptions 1 - 7 of section 206.2.3. Advisory 206.2.4 Spaces and Elements Exception 1 explains that the exception allowing raised courtroom stations to be used by court employees, such as judge's benches, to be adaptable does not apply to areas of the courtroom likely to be used by members of the public such as jury areas, attorney areas, or witness stands. These areas must be on an accessible route at the time of initial construction or alteration.

Raised Courtroom Stations Not for Members of the Public. Section 206.2.4, Exception 1 of the 2010 Standards provides that raised courtroom stations that are used by judges, clerks, bailiffs, and court reporters will not have to provide full vertical access when first constructed or altered if they are constructed to be easily adaptable to provide vertical accessibility.

One commenter suggested that a sufficient number of accessible benches for judges with disabilities, in addition to requiring accessible witness stands and attorney areas, be required. The Department believes that the requirements regarding raised benches for judges are easily adaptable to provide vertical access in the event a judge requires an accessible bench. Section 206.2.4 of the 2010 Standards provides that raised courtroom stations used by judges and other judicial staff do not have to provide full vertical access when first constructed or altered as long as the required clear floor space, maneuvering space, and electrical service, where appropriate, is provided at the time of new construction or can be achieved without substantial reconstruction during alterations.

A commenter asserted that there is nothing inherent in clerks' stations, jury boxes, and witness stands that require them to be raised. While it would, of course, be easiest to provide access by eliminating height differences among courtroom elements, the Department recognizes that accessibility is only one factor that must be considered in the design process of a functioning courtroom. The need to ensure the ability of the judge to maintain order, the need to ensure sight lines among the judge, the witness, the jury, and other participants, and the need to maintain the security of the participants all affect the design of the space. The Department believes that the 2010 Standards have been drafted in a way that will achieve accessibility without unduly constraining the ability of a designer to address the other considerations that are unique to courtrooms.

Commenters argued that permitting courtroom stations to be adaptable rather than fully accessible at the time of new construction likely will lead to discrimination in hiring of clerks, court reporters, and other court staff. The Department believes that the provisions will facilitate, not hinder, the hiring of court personnel who have disabilities. All courtroom work stations will be on accessible routes and will be required to have all fixed elements designed in compliance with the 2010 Standards. Elevated work stations for court employees may be designed to add vertical access as needed. Since the original design must provide the proper space and electrical wiring to install vertical access, the change should be easily accomplished.

232 Detention Facilities and Correctional Facilities

232.1 General. Buildings, facilities, or portions thereof, in which people are detained for penal or correction purposes, or in which the liberty of the inmates is restricted for security reasons shall comply with 232.

[See additional requirements at 28 CFR 35.151(k).]

Advisory

232.1 General. Detention facilities include, but are not limited to, jails, detention centers, and holding cells in police stations. Correctional facilities include, but are not limited to, prisons, reformatories, and correctional centers.

232.2 General Holding Cells and General Housing Cells. General holding cells and general housing cells shall be provided in accordance with 232.2.

> **EXCEPTION:** Alterations to cells shall not be required to comply except to the extent determined by the Attorney General.

Advisory

232.2 General Holding Cells and General Housing Cells. Accessible cells or rooms should be dispersed among different levels of security, housing categories, and holding classifications (e.g., male/female and adult/juvenile) to facilitate access. Many detention and correctional facilities are designed so that certain areas (e.g., "shift" areas) can be adapted to serve as different types of housing according to need. For example, a shift area serving as a medium-security housing unit might be redesignated for a period of time as a high-security housing unit to meet capacity needs. Placement of accessible cells or rooms in shift areas may allow additional flexibility in meeting requirements for dispersion of accessible cells or rooms.

232.2 General Holding Cells and General Housing Cells Exception. Although these requirements do not specify that cells be accessible as a consequence of an alteration, Title II of the ADA requires that each service, program, or activity conducted by a public entity, when viewed in its entirety, be readily accessible to and usable by individuals with disabilities. This requirement must be met unless doing so would fundamentally alter the nature of a service, program, or activity or would result in undue financial and administrative burdens.

232.2.1 Cells with Mobility Features. At least 2 percent, but no fewer than one, of the total number of cells in a facility shall provide mobility features complying with 807.2.

232.2.1.1 Beds. In cells having more than 25 beds, at least 5 percent of the beds shall have clear floor space complying with 807.2.3.

232.2.2 Cells with Communication Features. At least 2 percent, but no fewer than one, of the total number of general holding cells and general housing cells equipped with audible emergency alarm systems and permanently installed telephones within the cell shall provide communication features complying with 807.3.

232.3 Special Holding Cells and Special Housing Cells. Where special holding cells or special housing cells are provided, at least one cell serving each purpose shall provide mobility features complying with 807.2. Cells subject to this requirement include, but are not limited to, those used for purposes of orientation, protective custody, administrative or disciplinary detention or segregation, detoxification, and medical isolation.

> **EXCEPTION:** Alterations to cells shall not be required to comply except to the extent determined by the Attorney General.

232.4 Medical Care Facilities. Patient bedrooms or cells required to comply with 223 shall be provided in addition to any medical isolation cells required to comply with 232.3.

232.5 Visiting Areas. Visiting areas shall comply with 232.5.

232.5.1 Cubicles and Counters. At least 5 percent, but no fewer than one, of cubicles shall comply with 902 on both the visitor and detainee sides. Where counters are provided, at least one shall comply with 904.4.2 on both the visitor and detainee or inmate sides.

> **EXCEPTION:** The inmate or detainee side of cubicles or counters at non-contact visiting areas not serving holding cells or housing cells required to comply with 232 shall not be required to comply with 902 or 904.4.2.

232.5.2 Partitions. Where solid partitions or security glazing separate visitors from detainees or inmates at least one of each type of cubicle or counter partition shall comply with 904.6.

Guidance

Section 232 of the 2010 Standards establishes requirements for the design and construction of cells, medical care facilities, and visiting areas in detention facilities and in correctional facilities. Section 35.151(k) of the Department's title II rule provides scoping for newly constructed general holding cells and general housing cells requiring mobility features compliant with section 807.2 of the 2010 Standards in a minimum of three percent (3%) of cells, but no fewer than one cell. Section 232.2 of the 2010 Standards provides scoping for newly constructed cells with communications features requiring a minimum of two percent (2%) of cells, but at least one cell, to have communication features.

The Department's title II rule at § 35.151(k) also specifies scoping for alterations to detention and correctional facilities. Generally a minimum of three percent (3%), but no fewer than one, of the total number of altered cells must comply with section 807.2 of the 2010 Standards and be provided within each facility. Altered cells with mobility features must be provided in each classification level, including administrative and disciplinary segregation, each use and service area, and special program. The Department notes that the three percent (3%), but no fewer than one, requirement is a minimum. As corrections systems plan for new facilities or alterations, the Department urges planners to include in their population estimates a projection of the numbers of inmates with disabilities so as to have sufficient numbers of accessible cells to meet inmate needs.

233 Residential Facilities

233.1 General. Facilities with residential dwelling units shall comply with 233.

[See additional requirements at 28 CFR 35.151(e) and 28 CFR 35.151(f) and 28 CFR 36.406(d) and 28 CFR 36.406(e).]

Advisory

233.1 General. Section 233 outlines the requirements for residential facilities subject to the Americans with Disabilities Act of 1990. The facilities covered by Section 233, as well as other facilities not covered by this section, may still be subject to other Federal laws such as the Fair Housing Act and Section 504 of the Rehabilitation Act of 1973, as amended. For example, the Fair Housing Act requires that certain residential structures having four or more multi-family dwelling units, regardless of whether they are privately owned or federally assisted, include certain features of accessible and adaptable design according to guidelines established by the U.S. Department of Housing and Urban Development (HUD). These laws and the appropriate regulations should be consulted before proceeding with the design and construction of residential facilities.

Residential facilities containing residential dwelling units provided by entities subject to HUD's Section 504 regulations and residential dwelling units covered by Section 233.3 must comply with the technical and scoping requirements in Chapters 1 through 10 included this document. Section 233 is not a stand-alone section; this section only addresses the minimum number of residential dwelling units within a facility required to comply with Chapter 8. However, residential facilities must also comply with the requirements of this document. For example: Section 206.5.4 requires all doors and doorways providing user passage in residential dwelling units providing mobility features to comply with Section 404; Section 206.7.6 permits platform lifts to be used to connect levels within residential dwelling units providing mobility features; Section 208 provides general scoping for accessible parking and Section 208.2.3.1 specifies the required number of accessible parking spaces for each residential dwelling unit providing mobility features; Section 228.2 requires mail boxes to be within reach ranges when they serve residential dwelling units providing mobility features; play areas are addressed in Section 240; and swimming pools are addressed in Section 242. There are special provisions applicable to facilities containing residential dwelling units at: Exception 3 to 202.3; Exception to 202.4; 203.8; and Exception 4 to 206.2.3.

233.2 Residential Dwelling Units Provided by Entities Subject to HUD Section 504 Regulations. Where facilities with residential dwelling units are provided by entities subject to regulations issued by the Department of Housing and Urban Development (HUD) under Section 504 of the Rehabilitation Act of 1973, as amended, such entities shall provide residential dwelling units with mobility features complying with 809.2 through 809.4 in a number required by the applicable HUD regulations. Residential dwelling units required to provide mobility features complying with 809.2 through 809.4 shall be on an accessible route as required by 206. In addition, such entities shall provide residential dwelling units with communication features complying with 809.5 in a number required by the applicable HUD regulations. Entities subject to 233.2 shall not be required to comply with 233.3.

233.2 Residential Dwelling Units Provided by Entities Subject to HUD Section 504 Regulations. Section 233.2 requires that entities subject to HUD's regulations implementing Section 504 of the Rehabilitation Act of 1973, as amended, provide residential dwelling units containing mobility features and residential dwelling units containing communication features complying with these regulations in a number specified in HUD's Section 504 regulations. Further, the residential dwelling units provided must be dispersed according to HUD's Section 504 criteria. In addition, Section 233.2 defers to HUD the specification of criteria by which the technical requirements of this document will apply to alterations of existing facilities subject to HUD's Section 504 regulations.

233.3 Residential Dwelling Units Provided by Entities Not Subject to HUD Section 504 Regulations. Facilities with residential dwelling units provided by entities not subject to regulations issued by the Department of Housing and Urban Development (HUD) under Section 504 of the Rehabilitation Act of 1973, as amended, shall comply with 233.3.

233.3.1 Minimum Number: New Construction. Newly constructed facilities with residential dwelling units shall comply with 233.3.1.

> **EXCEPTION:** Where facilities contain 15 or fewer residential dwelling units, the requirements of 233.3.1.1 and 233.3.1.2 shall apply to the total number of residential dwelling units that are constructed under a single contract, or are developed as a whole, whether or not located on a common site.

233.3.1.1 Residential Dwelling Units with Mobility Features. In facilities with residential dwelling units, at least 5 percent, but no fewer than one unit, of the total number of residential dwelling units shall provide mobility features complying with 809.2 through 809.4 and shall be on an accessible route as required by 206.

233.3.1.2 Residential Dwelling Units with Communication Features. In facilities with residential dwelling units, at least 2 percent, but no fewer than one unit, of the total number of residential dwelling units shall provide communication features complying with 809.5.

233.3.2 Residential Dwelling Units for Sale. Residential dwelling units offered for sale shall provide accessible features to the extent required by regulations issued by Federal agencies under the Americans with Disabilities Act or Section 504 of the Rehabilitation Act of 1973, as amended.

[See additional requirements at 28 CFR 35.151(j).]

233.3.2 Residential Dwelling Units for Sale. A public entity that conducts a program to build housing for purchase by individual home buyers must provide access according to the requirements of the ADA regulations and a program receiving Federal financial assistance must comply with the applicable Section 504 regulation.

233.3.3 Additions. Where an addition to an existing building results in an increase in the number of residential dwelling units, the requirements of 233.3.1 shall apply only to the residential dwelling units that are added until the total number of residential dwelling units complies with the minimum number required by 233.3.1. Residential dwelling units required to comply with 233.3.1.1 shall be on an accessible route as required by 206.

233.3.4 Alterations. Alterations shall comply with 233.3.4.

> **EXCEPTION:** Where compliance with 809.2, 809.3, or 809.4 is technically infeasible, or where it is technically infeasible to provide an accessible route to a residential dwelling unit, the entity shall be permitted to alter or construct a comparable residential dwelling unit to comply with 809.2 through 809.4 provided that the minimum number of residential dwelling units required by 233.3.1.1 and 233.3.1.2, as applicable, is satisfied.

233.3.4 Alterations Exception. A substituted dwelling unit must be comparable to the dwelling unit that is not made accessible. Factors to be considered in comparing one dwelling unit to another should include the number of bedrooms; amenities provided within the dwelling unit; types of common spaces provided within the facility; and location with respect to community resources and services, such as public transportation and civic, recreational, and mercantile facilities.

233.3.4.1 Alterations to Vacated Buildings. Where a building is vacated for the purposes of alteration, and the altered building contains more than 15 residential dwelling units, at least 5 percent of the residential dwelling units shall comply with 809.2 through 809.4 and shall be on an accessible route as required by 206. In addition, at least 2 percent of the residential dwelling units shall comply with 809.5.

Advisory

233.3.4.1 Alterations to Vacated Buildings. This provision is intended to apply where a building is vacated with the intent to alter the building. Buildings that are vacated solely for pest control or asbestos removal are not subject to the requirements to provide residential dwelling units with mobility features or communication features.

233.3.4.2 Alterations to Individual Residential Dwelling Units. In individual residential dwelling units, where a bathroom or a kitchen is substantially altered, and at least one other room is altered, the requirements of 233.3.1 shall apply to the altered residential dwelling units until the total number of residential dwelling units complies with the minimum number required by 233.3.1.1 and 233.3.1.2. Residential dwelling units required to comply with 233.3.1.1 shall be on an accessible route as required by 206.

EXCEPTION: Where facilities contain 15 or fewer residential dwelling units, the requirements of 233.3.1.1 and 233.3.1.2 shall apply to the total number of residential dwelling units that are altered under a single contract, or *are developed as a whole, whether or not located on a common site.*

Advisory

233.3.4.2 Alterations to Individual Residential Dwelling Units. Section 233.3.4.2 uses the terms "substantially altered" and "altered." A substantial alteration to a kitchen or bathroom includes, but is not limited to, alterations that are changes to or rearrangements in the plan configuration, or replacement of cabinetry. Substantial alterations do not include normal maintenance or appliance and fixture replacement, unless such maintenance or replacement requires changes to or rearrangements in the plan configuration, or replacement of cabinetry. The term "alteration" is defined both in Section 106 of these requirements and in the Department of Justice ADA regulations.

233.3.5 Dispersion. Residential dwelling units required to provide mobility features complying with 809.2 through 809.4 and residential dwelling units required to provide communication features complying with 809.5 shall be dispersed among the various types of residential dwelling units in the facility and shall provide choices of residential dwelling units comparable to, and integrated with, those available to other residents.

EXCEPTION: Where multi-story residential dwelling units are one of the types of residential dwelling units provided, one-story residential dwelling units shall be permitted as a substitute for multi-story residential dwelling units where equivalent spaces and amenities are provided in the one-story residential dwelling unit.

Guidance

Homeless Shelters, Group Homes, and Similar Social Service Establishments. Section 233 of the 2010 Standards includes specific scoping and technical provisions that apply to new construction and alteration of residential facilities. In the 1991 Standards scoping and technical requirements for homeless shelters, group homes, and similar social service establishments were included in section 9 Transient Lodging. These types of facilities will be covered by section 233 of the 2010 Standards and by 28 CFR 35.151(e) and 36.406(d) and will be subject to requirements for residential facilities rather than the requirements for transient lodging. This approach will harmonize federal accessibility obligations under both the ADA and section 504 of the Rehabilitation Act of 1973, as amended. In sleeping rooms with more than 25 beds that are covered by § 36.406(d) a minimum of five percent (5%) of the beds must have clear floor space compliant with section 806.2.3 of the 2010 Standards. In large facilities with more than 50 beds, at least one roll-in shower compliant with section 608.2.2 or section 608.2.3 of the 2010 Standards must be provided. Where separate shower facilities are provided for men and for women, at least one roll-in shower must be provided for each gender.

Housing Operated By or On Behalf of Places of Education. Housing at a place of education includes: residence halls, dormitories, suites, apartments, or other places of residence operated by or on behalf of places of education. Residence halls or dormitories operated by or on behalf of places of education are covered by the provisions in sections 224 and 806 of the 2010 Standards. The Department has included in the title III rule at § 36.406(e) requirements that apply to housing at places of education that clarify requirements for residence halls and dormitories and other types of student housing. Requirements for housing at a place of education covered by the title II rule are included at § 35.151(f).

Kitchens and Kitchenettes. Section 4.34.2 of the UFAS requires a clear turning space at least 60 inches in diameter or an equivalent T-shaped turning space in kitchens. Section 4.34.6 requires a clearance between opposing base cabinets, counters, appliances, or walls of at least 40 inches except in a U-shaped kitchen where the minimum clearance is 60 inches.

Section 804 of the 2010 Standards provides technical requirements for kitchens and kitchenettes. Section 804.2.1 requires that pass through kitchens, which have two entries and counters, appliances, or cabinets on two opposite sides or opposite a parallel wall, provide at least 40 inches minimum clearance. Section 804.2.2 requires that U-shaped kitchens, which are enclosed on three continuous sides, provide at least 60 inches minimum clearance between all opposing base cabinets, countertops, appliances, or walls within kitchen work areas. Kitchens that do not have a cooktop or conventional range are exempt from the clearance requirements but still must provide an accessible route.

If a kitchen does not have two entries, the 2010 Standards require the kitchen to have 60 inches minimum clearance between the opposing base cabinets, counters, appliances, or walls.

One commenter supported the provisions of section 804 of the 2010 Standards but sought clarification whether this section applies to residential units only, or to lodging and office buildings as well. Section 212 makes section 804 applicable to all kitchens and kitchenettes in covered buildings.

Residential Facilities. Section 4.1.4(11) of the UFAS contains scoping requirements for the new construction of housing. Under the 1991 title II regulation, state and local governments had the option of complying with the UFAS or the 1991 Standards. After the compliance date for the 2010 Standards, state and local governments will no longer have the option of complying with the UFAS, but will have to use the 2010 Standards for new construction and alterations.

Sections 233.1, 233.2, 233.3, 233.3.1, and 233.3.2 of the 2010 Standards differentiate between entities subject to the United States Department of Housing and Urban Development (HUD) regulations implementing section 504 of the Rehabilitation Act of 1973 and entities not subject to the HUD regulations. The HUD regulations apply to recipients of federal financial assistance through HUD, and require at least five percent (5%) of dwelling units in multi-family projects of five or more dwelling units to provide mobility features and at least two percent (2%) of the dwelling units to provide communication features. The HUD regulations define a project unique to its programs as "one or more residential structures which are covered by a single contract for federal financial assistance or application for assistance, or are treated as a whole for processing purposes, whether or not located on a common site." To avoid any potential conflicts with the HUD regulations, the 2010 Standards require residential dwelling units subject to the HUD regulations to comply with the scoping requirements in the HUD regulations, instead of the scoping requirements in the 2010 Standards.

For entities not subject to the HUD regulations, the 2010 Standards require at least five percent (5%) of the dwelling units in residential facilities to provide mobility features, and at least two percent (2%) of the dwelling units to provide communication features. The 2010 Standards define facilities in terms of buildings located on a site. The 2010 Standards permit facilities that contain 15 or fewer dwelling units to apply the scoping requirements to all the dwelling units that are constructed under a single contract, or are developed as whole, whether or not located on a common site.

Alterations to Residential Facilities. Section 4.1.6 of the UFAS requires federal, state, and local government housing to comply with the general requirements for alterations to facilities. Applying the general requirements for alterations to housing can result in partially accessible dwelling units where single elements or spaces in dwelling units are altered.

The 2010 Standards, at sections 202.3 Exception 3, 202.4, and 233.3, contain specific scoping requirements for alterations to dwelling units. Dwelling units that are not required to be accessible are exempt from the general requirements for alterations to elements and spaces and for alterations to primary function areas.

The scoping requirements for alterations to dwelling units generally are based on the requirements in the UFAS:

• Where a building is vacated for purposes of alterations and has more than 15 dwelling units, at least five percent (5%) of the altered dwelling units are required to provide mobility features and at least two percent (2%) of the dwelling units are required to provide communication features.

• Where a bathroom or a kitchen is substantially altered in an individual dwelling unit and at least one other room is also altered, the dwelling unit is required to comply with the scoping requirements for new construction until the total number of dwelling units in the facility required to provide mobility features and communication features is met.

As with new construction, the 2010 Standards permit facilities that contain 15 or fewer dwelling units to apply the scoping requirements to all the dwelling units that are altered under a single contract, or are developed as a whole, whether or not located on a common site. The 2010 Standards also permit a comparable dwelling unit to provide mobility features where it is not technically feasible for the altered dwelling unit to comply with the technical requirements.

234 Amusement Rides

234.1 General. Amusement rides shall comply with 234.

EXCEPTION: Mobile or portable amusement rides shall not be required to comply with 234.

Advisory

234.1 General. These requirements apply generally to newly designed and constructed amusement rides and attractions. A custom designed and constructed ride is new upon its first use, which is the first time amusement park patrons take the ride. With respect to amusement rides purchased from other entities, new refers to the first permanent installation of the ride, whether it is used off the shelf or modified before it is installed. Where amusement rides are moved after several seasons to another area of the park or to another park, the ride would not be considered newly designed or newly constructed.

Some amusement rides and attractions that have unique designs and features are not addressed by these requirements. In those situations, these requirements are to be applied to the extent possible. An example of an amusement ride not specifically addressed by these requirements includes "virtual reality" rides where the device does not move through a fixed course within a defined area. An accessible route must be provided to these rides. Where an attraction or ride has unique features for which there are no applicable scoping provisions, then a reasonable number, but at least one, of the features must be located on an accessible route. Where there are appropriate technical provisions, they must be applied to the elements that are covered by the scoping provisions.

234.1 General Exception. Mobile or temporary rides are those set up for short periods of time such as traveling carnivals, State and county fairs, and festivals. The amusement rides that are covered by 234.1 are ones that are not regularly assembled and disassembled.

234.2 Load and Unload Areas. Load and unload areas serving amusement rides shall comply with 1002.3.

234.3 Minimum Number. Amusement rides shall provide at least one wheelchair space complying with 1002.4, or at least one amusement ride seat designed for transfer complying with 1002.5, or at least one transfer device complying with 1002.6.

EXCEPTIONS:

1. Amusement rides that are controlled or operated by the rider shall not be required to comply with 234.3.

2. Amusement rides designed primarily for children, where children are assisted on and off the ride by an adult, shall not be required to comply with 234.3.

3. Amusement rides that do not provide amusement ride seats shall not be required to comply with 234.3.

Advisory

234.3 Minimum Number Exceptions 1 through 3. Amusement rides controlled or operated by the rider, designed for children, or rides without ride seats are not required to comply with 234.3. These rides are not exempt from the other provisions in 234 requiring an accessible route to the load and unload areas and to the ride. The exception does not apply to those rides where patrons may cause the ride to make incidental movements, but where the patron otherwise has no control over the ride.

234.3 Minimum Number Exception 2. The exception is limited to those rides designed "primarily" for children, where children are assisted on and off the ride by an adult. This exception is limited to those rides designed for children and not for the occasional adult user. An accessible route to and turning space in the load and unload area will provide access for adults and family members assisting children on and off these rides.

234.4 Existing Amusement Rides. Where existing amusement rides are altered, the alteration shall comply with 234.4.

Advisory

234.4 Existing Amusement Rides. Routine maintenance, painting, and changing of theme boards are examples of activities that do not constitute an alteration subject to this section.

234.4.1 Load and Unload Areas. Where load and unload areas serving existing amusement rides are newly designed and constructed, the load and unload areas shall comply with 1002.3.

234.4.2 Minimum Number. Where the structural or operational characteristics of an amusement ride are altered to the extent that the amusement ride's performance differs from that specified by the manufacturer or the original design, the amusement ride shall comply with 234.3.

Guidance

New and Altered Permanently Installed Amusement Rides. Section 234 of the 2010 Standards sets out scoping requirements and section 1002 sets out the technical requirements for the accessibility of permanently installed amusement rides. These requirements apply to newly designed and constructed amusement rides and used rides when certain alterations are made.

A commenter raised concerns that smaller amusement parks tend to purchase used rides more frequently than new rides, and that the conversion of a used ride to provide the required accessibility may be difficult to ensure because of the possible complications in modifying equipment to provide accessibility.

The Department agrees with this commenter. The Department notes, however, that the 2010 Standards will require modifications to existing amusement rides when a ride's structural and operational characteristics are altered to the extent that the ride's performance differs from that specified by the manufacturer or the original design. Such an extensive alteration to an amusement ride may well require that new load and unload areas be designed and constructed. When load and unload areas serving existing amusement rides are newly designed and constructed they must be level, provide wheelchair turning space, and be on an accessible route compliant with Chapter 4 of the 2010 Standards except as modified by section 1002.2 of the 2010 Standards.

Mobile or Portable Amusement Rides. The exception in section 234.1 of the 2010 Standards exempts mobile or portable amusement rides, such as those set up for short periods of time at carnivals, fairs or festivals, from having to comply with the 2010 Standards. However, even though the mobile/portable ride itself is not subject to the Standards, these facilities are still subject to the ADA's general requirement to ensure that individuals with disabilities have an equal opportunity to enjoy the services and amenities of these facilities.

Subject to these general requirements, mobile or portable amusement rides should be located on an accessible route and the load and unload areas serving a ride should provide a level wheelchair turning space to provide equal opportunity for individuals with disabilities to be able to participate on the amusement ride to the extent feasible.

One commenter noted that the exception in Section 234.1 of the 2010 Standards for mobile or portable amusement rides limits the opportunities of persons with disabilities to participate on amusement rides because traveling or temporary amusement rides by their nature come to their customers' town or a nearby town rather than the customer having to go to them and so are less expensive than permanent amusement parks. While the Department understands the commenter's concerns, the Department notes that most amusement rides are too complex to be reasonably modified or re-engineered to accommodate the majority of individuals with disabilities and that additional complexities and safety concerns are added when the rides are mobile or portable.

A commenter asked that section 234 of the 2010 Standards make clear that the requirements for accessible routes include the routes leading up to and including the loading and unloading areas of amusement rides. Sections 206.2.9 and 1002.2 of the 2010 Standards clarify that the requirements for accessible routes include the routes leading up to and including the loading and unloading areas of amusement rides.

A commenter requested that the final rule specifically allow for wheelchair access through the exit or other routes, or alternate means of wheelchair access routes to amusement rides. The commenter stated that the concept of wheelchair access through the exit or alternate routes was a base assumption for the 2010 Standards. The commenter noted that the concept is apparent in the signage and load/unload area provisions in Section 216.12 (" * * * where accessible unload areas also serve as accessible load areas, signs indicating the location of the accessible load and unload areas shall be provided at entries to queues and waiting lines"). The Department agrees with the commenter that accessible load and unload areas may be the same where signs that comply with section 216.12 are provided.

Wheelchair Space or Transfer Seat or Transfer Device. Sections 234.3 and 1002.4 - 1002.6 of the 2010 Standards provide that each new and altered amusement ride, except for mobile/portable rides and a few additional excepted rides, will be required to provide at least one type of access by means of one wheelchair space or one transfer seat or one transfer device (the design of the transfer device is not specified).

Commenters urged the Department to revise the requirements for wheelchair spaces and transfer seats and devices because most amusement rides are too complex to be reasonably modified or re-engineered to accommodate the majority of individuals with disabilities. They argued that the experience of amusement rides will be significantly reduced if the proposed requirements are implemented.

The 2004 ADAAG, which the Department adopted as part of the 2010 Standards, was developed with the assistance of an advisory committee that included representation from the design staffs of major amusement venues and from persons with disabilities. The Department believes that the resulting 2004 ADAAG reflected sensitivity to the complex problems posed in adapting existing rides by focusing on new rides that can be designed from the outset to be accessible.

To permit maximum design flexibility, the 2010 Standards permit designers to determine whether it is more appropriate to permit individuals who use wheelchairs to remain in their chairs on the ride, or to provide for transfer access.

Maneuvering Space in Load and Unload Areas. Sections 234.2 and 1002.3 of the 2010 Standards require that a level wheelchair turning space be provided at the load and unload areas of each amusement ride. The turning space must comply with sections 304.2 and 304.3.

Signs Required at Waiting Lines to Amusement Rides. Section 216.12 of the 2010 Standards requires signs at entries to queues and waiting lines identifying type and location of access for the amusement ride.

235 Recreational Boating Facilities

235.1 General. Recreational boating facilities shall comply with 235.

235.2 Boat Slips. Boat slips complying with 1003.3.1 shall be provided in accordance with Table 235.2. Where the number of boat slips is not identified, each 40 feet (12 m) of boat slip edge provided along the perimeter of the pier shall be counted as one boat slip for the purpose of this section.

Table 235.2 Boat Slips

Total Number of Boat Slips Provided in Facility	Minimum Number of Required Accessible Boat Slips
1 to 25	1
26 to 50	2
51 to 100	3
101 to 150	4
151 to 300	5
301 to 400	6
401 to 500	7
501 to 600	8
601 to 700	9
701 to 800	10
801 to 900	11
901 to 1000	12
1001 and over	12, plus 1 for every 100, or fraction thereof, over 1000

Advisory

235.2 Boat Slips. The requirement for boat slips also applies to piers where boat slips are not demarcated. For example, a single pier 25 feet (7620 mm) long and 5 feet (1525 mm) wide (the minimum width specified by Section 1003.3) allows boats to moor on three sides. Because the number of boat slips is not demarcated, the total length of boat slip edge (55 feet, 17 m) must be used to determine the number of boat slips provided (two). This number is based on the specification in Section 235.2 that each 40 feet (12 m) of boat slip edge, or fraction thereof, counts as one boat slip. In this example, Table 235.2 would require one boat slip to be accessible.

235.2.1 Dispersion. Boat slips complying with 1003.3.1 shall be dispersed throughout the various types of boat slips provided. Where the minimum number of boat slips required to comply with 1003.3.1 has been met, no further dispersion shall be required.

Advisory

235.2.1 Dispersion. Types of boat slips are based on the size of the boat slips; whether single berths or double berths, shallow water or deep water, transient or longer-term lease, covered or uncovered; and whether slips are equipped with features such as telephone, water, electricity or cable connections. The term "boat slip" is intended to cover any pier area other than launch ramp boarding piers where recreational boats are moored for purposes of berthing, embarking, or disembarking. For example, a fuel pier may contain boat slips, and this type of short term slip would be included in determining compliance with 235.2.

235.3 Boarding Piers at Boat Launch Ramps. Where boarding piers are provided at boat launch ramps, at least 5 percent, but no fewer than one, of the boarding piers shall comply with 1003.3.2.

Guidance

These sections require that accessible boat slips and boarding piers be provided. Most commenters approved of the requirements for recreational boating facility accessibility and urged the Department to keep regulatory language consistent with those provisions. They commented that the requirements appropriately reflect industry conditions. Individual commenters and disability organizations agreed that the 2010 Standards achieve acceptable goals for recreational boating facility access.

Accessible Route. Sections 206.2.10 and 1003.2 of the 2010 Standards require an accessible route to all accessible boating facilities, including boat slips and boarding piers at boat launch ramps. Section 1003.2.1 provides a list of exceptions applicable to structures such as gangways, transition plates, floating piers, and structures containing combinations of these elements that are affected by water level changes. The list of exceptions specifies alternate design requirements applicable to these structures which, because of water level variables, cannot comply with the slope, cross slope, and handrail requirements for fixed ramps contained in sections 403.3, 405.2, 405.3, 405.6, and 405.7 of the 2010 Standards. Exceptions 3 and 4 in Section 1003.2.1, which permit a slope greater than that specified in Section 405.2, are available for structures that meet specified length requirements. Section 206.7.10 permits the use of platform lifts as an alternative to gangways that are part of accessible routes.

Commenters raised concerns that because of water level fluctuations it may be difficult to provide accessible routes to all accessible boating facilities, including boat slips and boarding piers at boat launch ramps. One of the specific concerns expressed by several commenters relates to the limits for running slope permitted on gangways that are part of an accessible route as gangways may periodically have a steeper slope than is permitted for a fixed ramp. The exceptions contained in section 1003.2 of the 2010 Standards modify the requirements of Chapter 4. For example, where the total length of a gangway or series of gangways serving as an accessible route is 80 feet or more an exception permits the slope on gangways to exceed the maximum slope in section 405.2.

Some commenters suggested that permissible slope variations could be reduced further by introducing a formula that ties required gangway length to anticipated water level fluctuations. Such a formula would incorporate predictions of tidal level changes such as those issued by the National Oceanographic and Atmospheric Administration (NOAA) and the United States Geologic Survey (USGS). This suggested approach would be an alternative to the gangway length exceptions and limits in section 1003.2.1 of the 2010 Standards. These commenters noted that contemporary building materials and techniques make gangways of longer length and alternative configurations achievable. These commenters provided at least one example of a regional regulatory authority using this type of formula. While this approach may be successfully implemented and consistent with the goals of the ADA, the example provided was applied in a highly developed area containing larger facilities. The Department has considered that many facilities do not have sufficient resources available to take advantage of the latest construction materials and design innovations. Other commenters supported compliance exceptions for facilities that are subject to extreme tidal conditions. One commenter noted that if a facility is located in an area with limited space and extreme tidal variations, a disproportionately long gangway might intrude into water travel routes. The Department has considered a wide range of boating facility characteristics including size, water surface areas, tidal fluctuations, water conditions, variable resources, whether the facility is in a highly developed or remote location, and other factors. The Department has determined that the 2010 Standards provide sufficient flexibility for such broad application. Additionally, the length requirement for accessible routes in section 1003.2.1 provides an easily determinable compliance standard.

Accessible Boarding Piers. Where boarding piers are provided at boat launch ramps, sections 235.3 and 1003.3.2 of the 2010 Standards require that at least five percent (5%) of boarding piers, but at least one, must be accessible.

Accessible Boat Slips. Sections 235.2 and 1003.3.1 of the 2010 Standards require that a specified number of boat slips in each recreational boating facility meet specified accessibility standards. The number of accessible boat slips required by the 2010 Standards is set out in a chart in section 235.2. One accessible boat slip is required for facilities containing 25 or fewer total slips. The number of required accessible boat slips increases with the total number of slips at the facility. Facilities containing more than one thousand (1000) boat slips are required to provide twelve (12) accessible boat slips plus one for each additional one hundred slips at the facility.

One commenter asserted the need for specificity in the requirement for dispersion of accessible slips. Section 235.2.1 of the 2010 Standards addresses dispersion and requires that boat slips "shall be dispersed throughout the various types of boat slips provided." The commenter was concerned that if a marina could not put accessible slips all on one pier, it would have to reconstruct the entire facility to accommodate accessible piers, gangways, docks and walkways. The provision permits required accessible boat slips to be grouped together. The Department recognizes that economical and structural feasibility may produce this result. The 2010 Standards do not require the dispersion of the physical location of accessible boat slips. Rather, the dispersion must be among the various types of boat slips offered by the facility. Section 235.2.1 of the 2010 Standards specifies that if the required number has been met, no further dispersion is required. For example, if a facility offers five different ´types´ of boat slips but is only required to provide three according to the table in Section 235.2, that facility is not required to provide more than three accessible boat slips, but the three must be varied among the five ´types´ of boat slips available at the facility.

236 Exercise Machines and Equipment

236.1 General. At least one of each type of exercise machine and equipment shall comply with 1004.

Guidance

Accessible Route to Exercise Machines and Equipment. Section 206.2.13 of the 2010 Standards requires an accessible route to serve accessible exercise machines and equipment.

Commenters raised concerns that the requirement to provide accessible routes to serve accessible exercise machines and equipment will be difficult for some facilities to provide, especially some transient lodging facilities that typically locate exercise machines and equipment in a single room. The Department believes that this requirement is a reasonable one in new construction and alterations because accessible exercise machines and equipment can be located so that an accessible route can serve more than one piece of equipment.

Exercise Machines and Equipment. Section 236 of the 2010 Standards requires at least one of each type of exercise machine to meet clear floor space requirements of section 1004.1. Types of machines are generally defined according to the muscular groups exercised or the kind of cardiovascular exercise provided.

Several commenters were concerned that existing facilities would have to reduce the number of available exercise equipment and machines in order to comply with the 2010 Standards. One commenter submitted prototype drawings showing equipment and machine layouts with and without the required clearance specified in the 2010 Standards. The accessible alternatives all resulted in a loss of equipment and machines. However, because these prototype layouts included certain possibly erroneous assumptions about the 2010 Standards, the Department wishes to clarify the requirements.

Section 1004.1 of the 2010 Standards requires a clear floor space "positioned for transfer or for use by an individual seated in a wheelchair" to serve at least one of each type of exercise machine and equipment. This requirement provides the designer greater flexibility regarding the location of the clear floor space than was employed by the commenter who submitted prototype layouts. The 2010 Standards do not require changes to exercise machines or equipment in order to make them more accessible to persons with disabilities. Even where machines or equipment do not have seats and typically are used by individuals in a standing position, at least one of each type of machine or equipment must have a clear floor space. Therefore, it is reasonable to assume that persons with disabilities wishing to use this type of machine or equipment can stand or walk, even if they use wheelchairs much of the time. As indicated in Advisory 1004.1, "the position of the clear floor space may vary greatly depending on the use of the equipment or machine." Where exercise equipment or machines require users to stand on them, the clear floor space need not be located parallel to the length of the machine or equipment in order to provide a lateral seat-to-platform transfer. It is permissible to locate the clear floor space for such machines or equipment in the aisle behind the device and to overlap the clear floor space and the accessible route.

Commenters were divided in response to the requirement for accessible exercise machines and equipment. Some supported requirements for accessible machines and equipment; others urged the Department not to require accessible machines and equipment because of the costs involved. The Department believes that the requirement strikes an appropriate balance in ensuring that persons with disabilities, particularly those who use wheelchairs, will have the opportunity to use the exercise equipment. Providing access to exercise machines and equipment recognizes the need and desires of individuals with disabilities to have the same opportunity as other patrons to enjoy the advantages of exercise and maintaining health.

237 Fishing Piers and Platforms

237.1 General. Fishing piers and platforms shall comply with 1005.

Guidance

Accessible Route. Sections 206.2.14 and 1005.1 of the 2010 Standards require an accessible route to each accessible fishing pier and platform. The exceptions described under Recreational Boating above also apply to gangways and floating piers. All commenters supported the requirements for accessible routes to fishing piers and platforms.

Accessible Fishing Piers and Platforms. Sections 237 and 1005 of the 2010 Standards require at least twenty-five percent (25%) of railings, guards, or handrails (if provided) to be at a 34-inch maximum height (so that a person seated in a wheelchair can cast a fishing line over the railing) and to be located in a variety of locations on the fishing pier or platform to give people a variety of locations to fish. An exception allows a guard required to comply with the IBC to have a height greater than 34 inches. If railings, guards, or handrails are provided, accessible edge protection and clear floor or ground space at accessible railings are required. Additionally, at least one turning space complying with section 304.3 of the 2010 Standards is required to be provided on fishing piers and platforms.

Commenters expressed concerns about the provision for fishing piers and platforms at the exception in section 1005.2.1 of the 2010 Standards that allows a maximum height of 42 inches for a guard when the pier or platform is covered by the IBC. Two commenters stated that allowing a 42-inch guard or railing height for facilities covered by another building code would be difficult to enforce. They also thought that this would hinder access for persons with disabilities because the railing height would be too high for a person seated in a wheelchair to reach over with their fishing pole in order to fish. The Department understands these concerns but believes that the railing height exception is necessary in order to avoid confusion resulting from conflicting accessibility requirements, and therefore has retained this exception.

238 Golf Facilities

238.1 General. Golf facilities shall comply with 238.

238.2 Golf Courses. Golf courses shall comply with 238.2.

238.2.1 Teeing Grounds. Where one teeing ground is provided for a hole, the teeing ground shall be designed and constructed so that a golf car can enter and exit the teeing ground. Where two teeing grounds are provided for a hole, the forward teeing ground shall be designed and constructed so that a golf car can enter and exit the teeing ground. Where three or more teeing grounds are provided for a hole, at least two teeing grounds, including the forward teeing ground, shall be designed and constructed so that a golf car can enter and exit each teeing ground.

> **EXCEPTION:** In existing golf courses, the forward teeing ground shall not be required to be one of the teeing grounds on a hole designed and constructed so that a golf car can enter and exit the teeing ground where compliance is not feasible due to terrain.

238.2.2 Putting Greens. Putting greens shall be designed and constructed so that a golf car can enter and exit the putting green.

238.2.3 Weather Shelters. Where provided, weather shelters shall be designed and constructed so that a golf car can enter and exit the weather shelter and shall comply with 1006.4.

238.3 Practice Putting Greens, Practice Teeing Grounds, and Teeing Stations at Driving Ranges. At least 5 percent, but no fewer than one, of practice putting greens, practice teeing grounds, and teeing stations at driving ranges shall be designed and constructed so that a golf car can enter and exit the practice putting greens, practice teeing grounds, and teeing stations at driving ranges.

Guidance

Accessible Route. Sections 206.2.15, 1006.2, and 1006.3 of the 2010 Standards require an accessible route to connect all accessible elements within the boundary of the golf course and, in addition, to connect golf car rental areas, bag drop areas, teeing grounds, putting greens, and weather shelters. An accessible route also is required to connect any practice putting greens, practice teeing grounds, and teeing stations at driving ranges that are required to be accessible. An exception permits the accessible route requirements to be met, within the boundaries of the golf course, by providing a "golf car passage" (the path typically used by golf cars) if specifications for width and curb cuts are met.

Most commenters expressed the general viewpoint that nearly all golf courses provide golf cars and have either well-defined paths or permit the cars to drive on the course where paths are not present, and thus meet the accessible route requirement.

The Department received many comments requesting clarification of the term "golf car passage." Some commenters recommended additional regulatory language specifying that an exception from a pedestrian route requirement should be allowed only when a golf car passage provides unobstructed access onto the teeing ground, putting green, or other accessible element of the course so that an accessible golf car can have full access to those elements. These commenters cautioned that full and equal access would not be provided if a golfer were required to navigate a steep slope up or down a hill or a flight of stairs in order to get to the teeing ground, putting green, or other accessible element of the course.

Conversely, another commenter requesting clarification of the term "golf car passage" argued that golf courses typically do not provide golf car paths or pedestrian paths up to actual tee grounds or greens, many of which are higher or lower than the car path. This commenter argued that if golf car passages were required to extend onto teeing grounds and greens in order to qualify for an exception, then some golf courses would have to substantially regrade teeing grounds and greens at a high cost.

Some commenters argued that older golf courses, small nine-hole courses, and executive courses that do not have golf car paths would be unable to comply with the accessible route requirements because of the excessive cost involved. A commenter noted that, for those older courses that have not yet created an accessible pedestrian route or golf car passage, the costs and impacts to do so should be considered.

A commenter argued that an accessible route should not be required where natural terrain makes it infeasible to create an accessible route. Some commenters cautioned that the 2010 Standards would jeopardize the integrity of golf course designs that utilize natural terrain elements and elevation changes to set up shots and create challenging golf holes.

The Department has given careful consideration to the comments and has decided to adopt the 2010 Standards requiring that at least one accessible route connect accessible elements and spaces within the boundary of the golf course including teeing grounds, putting greens, and weather shelters, with an exception provided that golf car passages shall be permitted to be used for all or part of required accessible routes. In response to requests for clarification of the term "golf car passage," the Department points out that golf car passage is merely a pathway on which a motorized golf car can operate and includes identified or paved paths, teeing grounds, fairways, putting greens, and other areas of the course. Golf cars cannot traverse steps and exceedingly steep slopes. A nine-hole golf course or an executive golf course that lacks an identified golf car path but provides golf car passage to teeing grounds, putting greens, and other elements throughout the course may utilize the exception for all or part of the accessible pedestrian route. The exception in section 206.2.15 of the 2010 Standards does not exempt golf courses from their obligation to provide access to necessary elements of the golf course; rather, the exception allows a golf course to use a golf car passage for part or all of the accessible pedestrian route to ensure that persons with mobility disabilities can fully and equally participate in the recreational activity of playing golf.

Accessible Teeing Grounds, Putting Greens, and Weather Shelters. Sections 238.2 and 1006.4 of the 2010 Standards require that golf cars be able to enter and exit each putting green and weather shelter. Where two teeing grounds are provided, the forward teeing ground is required to be accessible (golf car can enter and exit). Where three or more teeing grounds are provided, at least two, including the forward teeing ground, must be accessible.

A commenter supported requirements for teeing grounds, particularly requirements for accessible teeing grounds, noting that accessible teeing grounds are essential to the full and equal enjoyment of the golfing experience.

A commenter recommended that existing golf courses be required to provide access to only one teeing ground per hole. The majority of commenters reported that most public and private golf courses already provide golf car passage to teeing grounds and greens. The Department has decided that it is reasonable to maintain the requirement. The 2010 Standards provide an exception for existing golf courses with three or more teeing grounds not to provide golf car passage to the forward teeing ground where terrain makes such passage infeasible.

Section 1006.3.2 of the 2010 Standards requires that where curbs or other constructed barriers prevent golf cars from entering a fairway, openings 60 inches wide minimum shall be provided at intervals not to exceed 75 yards.

A commenter disagreed with the requirement that openings 60 inches wide minimum be installed at least every 75 yards, arguing that a maximum spacing of 75 yards may not allow enough flexibility for terrain and hazard placements. To resolve this problem, the commenter recommended that the standards be modified to require that each golf car passage include one 60-inch wide opening for an accessible golf car to reach the tee, and that one opening be provided where necessary for an accessible golf car to reach a green. The requirement for openings where curbs or other constructed barriers may otherwise prevent golf cars from entering a fairway allows the distance between openings to be less than every 75 yards. Therefore, the Department believes that the language in section 1006.3.2 of the 2010 Standards allows appropriate flexibility. Where a paved path with curbs or other constructed barrier exists, the Department believes that it is essential that openings be provided to enable golf car passages to access teeing grounds, fairways and putting greens, and other required elements. Golf car passage is not restricted to a paved path with curbs. Golf car passage also includes fairways, teeing grounds, putting greens, and other areas on which golf cars operate.

Accessible Practice Putting Greens, Practice Teeing Grounds, and Teeing Stations at Driving Ranges. Section 238.3 of the 2010 Standards requires that five percent (5%) but at least one of each of practice putting greens, practice teeing grounds, and teeing stations at driving ranges must permit golf cars to enter and exit.

239 Miniature Golf Facilities

239.1 General. Miniature golf facilities shall comply with 239.

239.2 Minimum Number. At least 50 percent of holes on miniature golf courses shall comply with 1007.3.

239.3 Miniature Golf Course Configuration. Miniature golf courses shall be configured so that the holes complying with 1007.3 are consecutive. Miniature golf courses shall provide an accessible route from the last hole complying with 1007.3 to the course entrance or exit without requiring travel through any other holes on the course.

EXCEPTION: One break in the sequence of consecutive holes shall be permitted provided that the last hole on the miniature golf course is the last hole in the sequence.

Guidance

Accessible Route to Miniature Golf Course Holes. Sections 206.2.16, 239.3, and 1007.2 of the 2010 Standards require an accessible route to connect accessible miniature golf course holes and the last accessible hole on the course directly to the course entrance or exit. Accessible holes are required to be consecutive with an exception permitting one break in the sequence of consecutive holes provided that the last hole on the miniature golf course is the last hole in the sequence.

Many commenters supported expanding the exception from one to multiple breaks in the sequence of accessible holes. One commenter noted that permitting accessible holes with breaks in the sequence would enable customers with disabilities to enjoy the landscaping, water and theme elements of the miniature golf course. Another commenter wrote in favor of allowing multiple breaks in accessible holes with a connecting accessible route.

Other commenters objected to allowing multiple breaks in the sequence of miniature golf holes. Commenters opposed to this change argued that allowing any breaks in the sequence of accessible holes at a miniature golf course would disrupt the flow of play for persons with disabilities and create a less socially integrated experience. A commenter noted that multiple breaks in sequence would not necessarily guarantee the provision of access to holes that are most representative of those with landscaping, water elements, or a fantasy-like experience.

The Department has decided to retain the exception without change. Comments did not provide a sufficient basis on which to conclude that allowing multiple breaks in the sequence of accessible holes would necessarily increase integration of accessible holes with unique features of miniature golf courses. Some designs of accessible holes with multiple breaks in the sequence might provide equivalent facilitation where persons with disabilities gain access to landscaping, water or theme elements not otherwise represented in a consecutive configuration of accessible holes. A factor that might contribute to equivalent facilitation would be an accessible route designed to bring persons with disabilities to a unique feature, such as a waterfall, that would otherwise not be served by an accessible route connecting consecutive accessible holes.

Specified exceptions are permitted for accessible route requirements when located on the playing surfaces near holes.

Accessible Miniature Golf Course Holes. Sections 239.2 and 1007.3 of the 2010 Standards require at least fifty percent (50%) of golf holes on miniature golf courses to be accessible, including providing a clear floor or ground space that is 48 inches minimum by 60 inches minimum with slopes not steeper than 1:48 at the start of play.

240 Play Areas

240.1 General. Play areas for children ages 2 and over shall comply with 240. Where separate play areas are provided within a site for specific age groups, each play area shall comply with 240.

EXCEPTIONS:

1. Play areas located in family child care facilities where the proprietor actually resides shall not be required to comply with 240.

2. In existing play areas, where play components are relocated for the purposes of creating safe use zones and the ground surface is not altered or extended for more than one use zone, the play area shall not be required to comply with 240.

3. Amusement attractions shall not be required to comply with 240.

4. Where play components are altered and the ground surface is not altered, the ground surface shall not be required to comply with 1008.2.6 unless required by 202.4.

Advisory

240.1 General. Play areas may be located on exterior sites or within a building. Where separate play areas are provided within a site for children in specified age groups (e.g., preschool (ages 2 to 5) and school age (ages 5 to 12)), each play area must comply with this section. Where play areas are provided for the same age group on a site but are geographically separated (e.g., one is located next to a picnic area and another is located next to a softball field), they are considered separate play areas and each play area must comply with this section.

240.1.1 Additions. Where play areas are designed and constructed in phases, the requirements of 240 shall apply to each successive addition so that when the addition is completed, the entire play area complies with all the applicable requirements of 240.

Advisory

240.1.1 Additions. These requirements are to be applied so that when each successive addition is completed, the entire play area complies with all applicable provisions. For example, a play area is built in two phases. In the first phase, there are 10 elevated play components and 10 elevated play components are added in the second phase for a total of 20 elevated play components in the play area. When the first phase was completed, at least 5 elevated play components, including at least 3 different types, were to be provided on an accessible route. When the second phase is completed, at least 10 elevated play components must be located on an accessible route, and at least 7 ground level play components, including 4 different types, must be provided on an accessible route. At the time the second phase is complete, ramps must be used to connect at least 5 of the elevated play components and transfer systems are permitted to be used to connect the rest of the elevated play components required to be located on an accessible route.

240.2 Play Components. Where provided, play components shall comply with 240.2.

240.2.1 Ground Level Play Components. Ground level play components shall be provided in the number and types required by 240.2.1. Ground level play components that are provided to comply with 240.2.1.1 shall be permitted to satisfy the additional number required by 240.2.1.2 if the minimum required types of play components are satisfied. Where two or more required ground level play components are provided, they shall be dispersed throughout the play area and integrated with other play components.

Advisory

240.2.1 Ground Level Play Components. Examples of ground level play components may include spring rockers, swings, diggers, and stand-alone slides. When distinguishing between the different types of ground level play components, consider the general experience provided by the play component. Examples of different types of experiences include, but are not limited to, rocking, swinging, climbing, spinning, and sliding. A spiral slide may provide a slightly different experience from a straight slide, but sliding is the general experience and therefore a spiral slide is not considered a different type of play component from a straight slide.

Ground level play components accessed by children with disabilities must be integrated into the play area. Designers should consider the optimal layout of ground level play components accessed by children with disabilities to foster interaction and socialization among all children. Grouping all ground level play components accessed by children with disabilities in one location is not considered integrated.

Where a stand-alone slide is provided, an accessible route must connect the base of the stairs at the entry point to the exit point of the slide. A ramp or transfer system to the top of the slide is not required. Where a sand box is provided, an accessible route must connect to the border of the sand box. Accessibility to the sand box would be enhanced by providing a transfer system into the sand or by providing a raised sand table with knee clearance complying with 1008.4.3.

Ramps are preferred over transfer systems since not all children who use wheelchairs or other mobility devices may be able to use, or may choose not to use, transfer systems. Where ramps connect elevated play components, the maximum rise of any ramp run is limited to 12 inches (305 mm). Where possible, designers and operators are encouraged to provide ramps with a slope less than the 1:12 maximum. Berms or sculpted dirt may be used to provide elevation and may be part of an accessible route to composite play structures.

Platform lifts are permitted as a part of an accessible route. Because lifts must be independently operable, operators should carefully consider the appropriateness of their use in unsupervised settings.

240.2.1.1 Minimum Number and Types. Where ground level play components are provided, at least one of each type shall be on an accessible route and shall comply with 1008.4.

240.2.1.2 Additional Number and Types. Where elevated play components are provided, ground level play components shall be provided in accordance with Table 240.2.1.2 and shall comply with 1008.4.

EXCEPTION: If at least 50 percent of the elevated play components are connected by a ramp and at least 3 of the elevated play components connected by the ramp are different types of play components, the play area shall not be required to comply with 240.2.1.2.

Table 240.2.1.2 Number and Types of Ground Level Play Components Required to be on Accessible Routes (text version)		
Number of Elevated Play Components Provided	**Minimum Number of Ground Level Play Components Required to be on an Accessible Route**	**Minimum Number of Different Types of Ground Level Play Components Required to be on an Accessible Route**
1	Not applicable	Not applicable
2 to 4	1	1
5 to 7	2	2
8 to 10	3	3
11 to 13	4	3
14 to 16	5	3
17 to 19	6	3
20 to 22	7	4
23 to 25	8	4
26 and over	8, plus 1 for each additional 3, or fraction thereof, over 25	5

Advisory

240.2.1.2 Additional Number and Types. Where a large play area includes two or more composite play structures designed for the same age group, the total number of elevated play components on all the composite play structures must be added to determine the additional number and types of ground level play components that must be provided on an accessible route.

240.2.2 Elevated Play Components. Where elevated play components are provided, at least 50 percent shall be on an accessible route and shall comply with 1008.4.

Advisory

240.2.2 Elevated Play Components. A double or triple slide that is part of a composite play structure is one elevated play component. For purposes of this section, ramps, transfer systems, steps, decks, and roofs are not considered elevated play components. Although socialization and pretend play can occur on these elements, they are not primarily intended for play.

Some play components that are attached to a composite play structure can be approached or exited at the ground level or above grade from a platform or deck. For example, a climber attached to a composite play structure can be approached or exited at the ground level or above grade from a platform or deck on a composite play structure. Play components that are attached to a composite play structure and can be approached from a platform or deck (e.g., climbers and overhead play components) are considered elevated play components. These play components are not considered ground level play components and do not count toward the requirements in 240.2.1.2 regarding the number of ground level play components that must be located on an accessible route.

Guidance

Section 240 of the 2010 Standards provides scoping for play areas and section 1008 provides technical requirements for play areas. Section 240.1 of the 2010 Standards sets requirements for play areas for children ages 2 and over and covers separate play areas within a site for specific age groups. Section 240.1 also provides four exceptions to the requirements that apply to family child care facilities, relocation of existing play components in existing play areas, amusement attractions, and alterations to play components where the ground surface is not altered.

Ground Surfaces. Section 1008.2.6 of the 2010 Standards provides technical requirements for accessible ground surfaces for play areas on accessible routes, clear floor or ground spaces, and turning spaces. These ground surfaces must follow special rules, incorporated by reference from nationally recognized standards for accessibility and safety in play areas, including those issued by the American Society for Testing and Materials (ASTM).

A commenter recommended that the Department closely examine the requirements for ground surfaces at play areas. The Department is aware that there is an ongoing controversy about play area ground surfaces arising from a concern that some surfaces that meet the ASTM requirements at the time of installation will become inaccessible if they do not receive constant maintenance. The Access Board is also aware of this issue and is working to develop a portable field test that will provide more relevant information on installed play surfaces. The Department would caution covered entities selecting among the ground surfacing materials that comply with the ASTM requirements that they must anticipate the maintenance costs that will be associated with some of the products. Permitting a surface to deteriorate so that it does not meet the 2010 Standards would be an independent violation of the Department's ADA regulations.

Accessible Route to Play Components. Section 206.2.17 of the 2010 Standards provides scoping requirements for accessible routes to ground level and elevated play components and to soft contained play structures. Sections 240.2 and 1008 of the 2010 Standards require that accessible routes be provided for play components. The accessible route must connect to at least one ground level play component of each different type provided (e.g., for different experiences such as rocking, swinging, climbing, spinning, and sliding). Table 240.2.1.2 sets requirements for the number and types of ground level play components required to be on accessible routes. When elevated play components are provided, an accessible route must connect at least fifty percent (50%) of the elevated play components. Section 240.2.1.2, provides an exception to the requirements for ground level play components if at least fifty percent (50%) of the elevated play components are connected by a ramp and at least three of the elevated play components connected by the ramp are different types of play components.

The technical requirements at section 1008 include provisions where if three or fewer entry points are provided to a soft contained play structure, then at least one entry point must be on an accessible route. In addition, where four or more entry points are provided to a soft contained play structure, then at least two entry points must be served by an accessible route.

If elevated play components are provided, fifty percent (50%) of the elevated components are required to be accessible. Where 20 or more elevated play components are provided, at least twenty five percent (25%) will have to be connected by a ramp. The remaining play components are permitted to be connected by a transfer system. Where

---

less than 20 elevated play components are provided, a transfer system is permitted in lieu of a ramp.

A commenter noted that the 2010 Standards allow for the provision of transfer steps to elevated play structures based on the number of elevated play activities, but asserted that transfer steps have not been documented as an effective means of access.

The 2010 Standards recognize that play structures are designed to provide unique experiences and opportunities for children. The 2010 Standards provide for play components that are accessible to children who cannot transfer from their wheelchair, but they also provide opportunities for children who are able to transfer. Children often interact with their environment in ways that would be considered inappropriate for adults. Crawling and climbing, for example, are integral parts of the play experience for young children. Permitting the use of transfer platforms in play structures provides some flexibility for creative playground design.

Accessible Play Components. Accessible play components are required to be on accessible routes, including elevated play components that are required to be connected by ramps. These play components must also comply with other accessibility requirements, including specifications for clear floor space and seat heights (where provided).

A commenter expressed concerns that the general requirements of section 240.2.1 of the 2010 Standards and the advisory accompanying section 240.2.1 conflict. The comment asserts that section 240.2.1 of the 2010 Standards provides that the only requirement for integration of equipment is where there are two or more required ground level play components, while the advisory appears to suggest that all accessible components must be integrated.

The commenter misinterprets the requirement. The ADA mandates that persons with disabilities be able to participate in programs or activities in the most integrated setting appropriate to their needs. Therefore, all accessible play components must be integrated into the general playground setting. Section 240.2.1 of the 2010 Standards specifies that where there is more than one accessible ground level play component, the components must be both dispersed and integrated.

241 Saunas and Steam Rooms

241 General. Where provided, saunas and steam rooms shall comply with 612.

EXCEPTION: Where saunas or steam rooms are clustered at a single location, no more than 5 percent of the saunas and steam rooms, but no fewer than one, of each type in each cluster shall be required to comply with 612.

Guidance

Section 241 of the 2010 Standards sets scoping for saunas and steam rooms and section 612 sets technical requirements including providing accessible turning space and an accessible bench. Doors are not permitted to swing into the clear floor or ground space for the accessible bench. The exception in section 612.2 of the 2010 Standards permits a readily removable bench to obstruct the required wheelchair turning space and the required clear floor or ground space. Where they are provided in clusters, five percent (5%) but at least one sauna or steam room in each cluster must be accessible.

Commenters raised concerns that the safety of individuals with disabilities outweighs the usefulness in providing accessible saunas and steam rooms. The Department believes that there is an element of risk in many activities available to the general public. One of the major tenets of the ADA is that individuals with disabilities should have the same opportunities as other persons to decide what risks to take. It is not appropriate for covered entities to prejudge the abilities of persons with disabilities.

242 Swimming Pools, Wading Pools, and Spas

242.1 General. Swimming pools, wading pools, and spas shall comply with 242.

242.2 Swimming Pools. At least two accessible means of entry shall be provided for swimming pools. Accessible means of entry shall be swimming pool lifts complying with 1009.2; sloped entries complying with 1009.3; transfer walls complying with 1009.4; transfer systems complying with 1009.5; and pool stairs complying with 1009.6. At least one accessible means of entry provided shall comply with 1009.2 or 1009.3.

EXCEPTIONS:

1. Where a swimming pool has less than 300 linear feet (91 m) of swimming pool wall, no more than one accessible means of entry shall be required provided that the accessible means of entry is a swimming pool lift complying with 1009.2 or sloped entry complying with 1009.3.

2. Wave action pools, leisure rivers, sand bottom pools, and other pools where user access is limited to one area shall not be required to provide more than one accessible means of entry provided that the accessible means of entry is a swimming pool lift complying with 1009.2, a sloped entry complying with 1009.3, or a transfer system complying with 1009.5.

3. Catch pools shall not be required to provide an accessible means of entry provided that the catch pool edge is on an accessible route.

Advisory

242.2 Swimming Pools. Where more than one means of access is provided into the water, it is recommended that the means be different. Providing different means of access will better serve the varying needs of people with disabilities in getting into and out of a swimming pool. It is also recommended that where two or more means of access are provided, they not be provided in the same location in the pool. Different locations will provide increased options for entry and exit, especially in larger pools.

242.2 Swimming Pools Exception 1. Pool walls at diving areas and areas along pool walls where there is no pool entry because of landscaping or adjacent structures are to be counted when determining the number of accessible means of entry required.

242.3 Wading Pools. At least one accessible means of entry shall be provided for wading pools. Accessible means of entry shall comply with sloped entries complying with 1009.3.

242.4 Spas. At least one accessible means of entry shall be provided for spas. Accessible means of entry shall comply with swimming pool lifts complying with1009.2; transfer walls complying with 1009.4; or transfer systems complying with 1009.5.

EXCEPTION: Where spas are provided in a cluster, no more than 5 percent, but no fewer than one, spa in each cluster shall be required to comply with 242.4.

Guidance

Accessible Means of Entry to Pools. Section 242 of the 2010 Standards requires at least two accessible means of entry for larger pools (300 or more linear feet) and at least one accessible entry for smaller pools. This section requires that at least one entry will have to be a sloped entry or a pool lift; the other could be a sloped entry, pool lift, a transfer wall, or a transfer system (technical specifications for each entry type are included at section 1009).

Many commenters supported the scoping and technical requirements for swimming pools. Other commenters stated that the cost of requiring facilities to immediately purchase a pool lift for each indoor and outdoor swimming pool would be very significant especially considering the large number of swimming pools at lodging facilities. One commenter requested that the Department clarify what would be an "alteration" to a swimming pool that would trigger the obligation to comply with the accessible means of entry in the 2010 Standards.

Alterations are covered by section 202.3 of the 2010 Standards and the definition of "alteration" is provided at section 106.5. A physical change to a swimming pool which affects or could affect the usability of the pool is considered to be an alteration. Changes to the mechanical and electrical systems, such as filtration and chlorination systems, are not alterations. Exception 2 to section 202.3 permits an altered swimming pool to comply with applicable requirements to the maximum extent feasible if full compliance is technically infeasible. "Technically infeasible" is also defined in section 106.5 of the 2010 Standards.

The Department also received comments suggesting that it is not appropriate to require two accessible means of entry to wave pools, lazy rivers, sand bottom pools, and other water amusements where there is only one point of entry. Exception 2 of Section 242.2 of the 2010 Standards exempts pools of this type from having to provide more than one accessible means of entry provided that the one accessible means of entry is a swimming pool lift compliant with section 1009.2, a sloped entry compliant with section 1009.3, or a transfer system compliant with section 1009.5 of the 2010 Standards.

Accessible Means of Entry to Wading Pools. Sections 242.3 and 1009.3 of the 2010 Standards require that at least one sloped means of entry is required into the deepest part of each wading pool.

Accessible Means of Entry to Spas. Sections 242.4 and 1009.2, 1009.4, and 1009.5 of the 2010 Standards require spas to meet accessibility requirements, including an accessible means of entry. Where spas are provided in clusters, five percent (5%) but at least one spa in each cluster must be accessible. A pool lift, a transfer wall, or a transfer system will be permitted to provide the required accessible means of entry.

243 Shooting Facilities with Firing Positions

243.1 General. Where shooting facilities with firing positions are designed and constructed at a site, at least 5 percent, but no fewer than one, of each type of firing position shall comply with 1010.

Guidance

Sections 243 and 1010 of the 2010 Standards require an accessible turning space for each different type of firing position at a shooting facility if designed and constructed on a site. Where firing positions are provided in clusters, five percent (5%), but at least one position of each type in each cluster must be accessible.

CHAPTER 3: BUILDING BLOCKS

301 General

301.1 Scope. The provisions of Chapter 3 shall apply where required by Chapter 2 or where referenced by a requirement in this document.

302 Floor or Ground Surfaces

302.1 General. Floor and ground surfaces shall be stable, firm, and slip resistant and shall comply with 302.

EXCEPTIONS:

1. Within animal containment areas, floor and ground surfaces shall not be required to be stable, firm, and slip resistant.

2. Areas of sport activity shall not be required to comply with 302.

Advisory

302.1 General. A stable surface is one that remains unchanged by contaminants or applied force, so that when the contaminant or force is removed, the surface returns to its original condition. A firm surface resists deformation by either indentations or particles moving on its surface. A slip-resistant surface provides sufficient frictional counterforce to the forces exerted in walking to permit safe ambulation.

Guidance

Both section 4.5.1 of the 1991 Standards and section 302.2 of the 2010 Standards require that floor or ground surfaces along accessible routes and in accessible rooms and spaces be stable, firm, slip-resistant, and comply with either section 4.5 in the case of the 1991 Standards or section 302 in the case of the 2010 Standards.

Commenters recommended that the Department apply an ASTM Standard (with modifications) to assess whether a floor surface is "slip resistant" as required by section 302.1 of the 2010 Standards. The Department declines to accept this recommendation since, currently, there is no generally accepted test method for the slip-resistance of all walking surfaces under all conditions.

302.2 Carpet. Carpet or carpet tile shall be securely attached and shall have a firm cushion, pad, or backing or no cushion or pad. Carpet or carpet tile shall have a level loop, textured loop, level cut pile, or level cut/uncut pile texture. Pile height shall be 1/2 inch (13 mm) maximum. Exposed edges of carpet shall be fastened to floor surfaces and shall have trim on the entire length of the exposed edge. Carpet edge trim shall comply with 303.

Advisory

302.2 Carpet. Carpets and permanently affixed mats can significantly increase the amount of force (roll resistance) needed to propel a wheelchair over a surface. The firmer the carpeting and backing, the lower the roll resistance. A pile thickness up to 1/2 inch (13 mm) (measured to the backing, cushion, or pad) is allowed, although a lower pile provides easier wheelchair maneuvering. If a backing, cushion or pad is used, it must be firm. Preferably, carpet pad should not be used because the soft padding increases roll resistance.

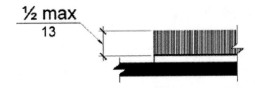

Figure 302.2 Carpet Pile Height

302.3 Openings. Openings in floor or ground surfaces shall not allow passage of a sphere more than 1/2 inch (13 mm) diameter except as allowed in 407.4.3, 409.4.3, 410.4, 810.5.3 and 810.10. Elongated openings shall be placed so that the long dimension is perpendicular to the dominant direction of travel.

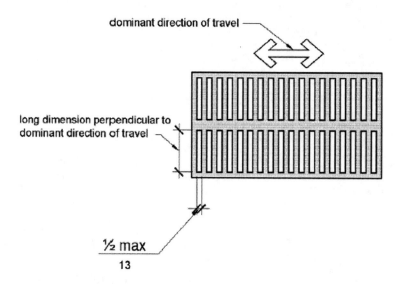

Figure 302.3 Elongated Openings in Floor or Ground Surfaces

303 Changes in Level

303.1 General. Where changes in level are permitted in floor or ground surfaces, they shall comply with 303.

EXCEPTIONS:

1. Animal containment areas shall not be required to comply with 303.

2. Areas of sport activity shall not be required to comply with 303.

303.2 Vertical. Changes in level of 1/4 inch (6.4 mm) high maximum shall be permitted to be vertical.

Figure 303.2 Vertical Change in Level

303.3 Beveled. Changes in level between 1/4 inch (6.4 mm) high minimum and 1/2 inch (13 mm) high maximum shall be beveled with a slope not steeper than 1:2.

Advisory

303.3 Beveled. A change in level of 1/2 inch (13 mm) is permitted to be 1/4 inch (6.4 mm) vertical plus 1/4 inch (6.4 mm) beveled. However, in no case may the combined change in level exceed 1/2 inch (13 mm). Changes in level exceeding 1/2 inch (13 mm) must comply with 405 (Ramps) or 406 (Curb Ramps).

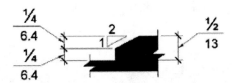

Figure 303.3 Beveled Change in Level

303.4 Ramps. Changes in level greater than 1/2 inch (13 mm) high shall be ramped, and shall comply with 405 or 406.

304 Turning Space

304.1 General. Turning space shall comply with 304.

304.2 Floor or Ground Surfaces. Floor or ground surfaces of a turning space shall comply with 302. Changes in level are not permitted.

EXCEPTION: Slopes not steeper than 1:48 shall be permitted.

Advisory

304.2 Floor or Ground Surface Exception. As used in this section, the phrase "changes in level" refers to surfaces with slopes and to surfaces with abrupt rise exceeding that permitted in Section 303.3. Such changes in level are prohibited in required clear floor and ground spaces, turning spaces, and in similar spaces where people using wheelchairs and other mobility devices must park their mobility aids such as in wheelchair spaces, or maneuver to use elements such as at doors, fixtures, and telephones. The exception permits slopes not steeper than 1:48.

304.3 Size. Turning space shall comply with 304.3.1 or 304.3.2.

304.3.1 Circular Space. The turning space shall be a space of 60 inches (1525 mm) diameter minimum. The space shall be permitted to include knee and toe clearance complying with 306.

304.3.2 T-Shaped Space. The turning space shall be a T-shaped space within a 60 inch (1525 mm) square minimum with arms and base 36 inches (915 mm) wide minimum. Each arm of the T shall be clear of obstructions 12 inches (305 mm) minimum in each direction and the base shall be clear of obstructions 24 inches (610 mm) minimum. The space shall be permitted to include knee and toe clearance complying with 306 only at the end of either the base or one arm.

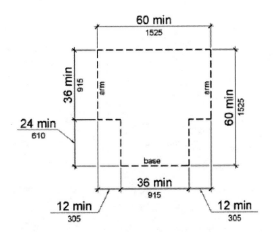

Figure 304.3.2 T-Shaped Turning Space

304.4 Door Swing. Doors shall be permitted to swing into turning spaces.

Guidance

Section 4.2.3 of the 1991 Standards and Section 304.3 of the 2010 Standards allow turning space to be either a circular space or a T-shaped space. Section 304.3 permits turning space to include knee and toe clearance complying with section 306. Section 4.2.3 of the 1991 Standards did not specifically permit turning space to include knee and toe clearance. Commenters urged the Department to retain the turning space requirement, but exclude knee and toe clearance from being permitted as part of this space. They argued that wheelchairs and other mobility devices are becoming larger and that more individuals with disabilities are using electric three and four-wheeled scooters which cannot utilize knee clearance.

The Department recognizes that the technical specifications for T-shaped and circular turning spaces in the 1991 and 2010 Standards, which are based on manual wheelchair dimensions, may not adequately meet the needs of individuals using larger electric scooters. However, there is no consensus about the appropriate dimension on which to base revised requirements. The Access Board is conducting research to study this issue in order to determine if new requirements are warranted. For more information, see the Access Board's website at http://www.access-board.gov/research/current-projects.htm#suny. The Department plans to wait for the results of this study and action by the Access Board before considering any changes to the Department's rules. Covered entities may wish to consider providing more than the minimum amount of turning space in confined spaces where a turn will be required. Appendix section A4.2.3 and Fig. A2 of the 1991 Standards provide guidance on additional space for making a smooth turn without bumping into surrounding objects.

---

305 Clear Floor or Ground Space

305.1 General. Clear floor or ground space shall comply with 305.

305.2 Floor or Ground Surfaces. Floor or ground surfaces of a clear floor or ground space shall comply with 302. Changes in level are not permitted.

EXCEPTION: Slopes not steeper than 1:48 shall be permitted.

305.3 Size. The clear floor or ground space shall be 30 inches (760 mm) minimum by 48 inches (1220 mm) minimum.

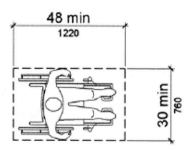

Figure 305.3 Clear Floor or Ground Space

305.4 Knee and Toe Clearance. Unless otherwise specified, clear floor or ground space shall be permitted to include knee and toe clearance complying with 306.

305.5 Position. Unless otherwise specified, clear floor or ground space shall be positioned for either forward or parallel approach to an element.

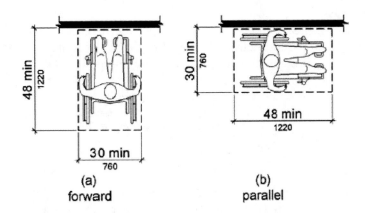

Figure 305.5 Position of Clear Floor or Ground Space

305.6 Approach. One full unobstructed side of the clear floor or ground space shall adjoin an accessible route or adjoin another clear floor or ground space.

305.7 Maneuvering Clearance. Where a clear floor or ground space is located in an alcove or otherwise confined on all or part of three sides, additional maneuvering clearance shall be provided in accordance with 305.7.1 and 305.7.2.

305.7.1 Forward Approach. Alcoves shall be 36 inches (915 mm)wide minimum where the depth exceeds 24 inches (610 mm).

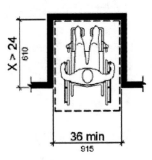

Figure 305.7.1 Maneuvering Clearance in an Alcove, Forward Approach

305.7.2 Parallel Approach. Alcoves shall be 60 inches (1525 mm) wide minimum where the depth exceeds 15 inches (380 mm).

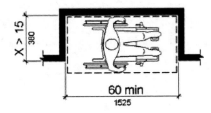

Figure 305.7.2 Maneuvering Clearance in an Alcove, Parallel Approach

306 Knee and Toe Clearance

306.1 General. Where space beneath an element is included as part of clear floor or ground space or turning space, the space shall comply with 306. Additional space shall not be prohibited beneath an element but shall not be considered as part of the clear floor or ground space or turning space.

Advisory

306.1 General. Clearances are measured in relation to the usable clear floor space, not necessarily to the vertical support for an element. When determining clearance under an object for required turning or maneuvering space, care should be taken to ensure the space is clear of any obstructions.

306.2 Toe Clearance.

306.2.1 General. Space under an element between the finish floor or ground and 9 inches (230 mm) above the finish floor or ground shall be considered toe clearance and shall comply with 306.2.

306.2.2 Maximum Depth. Toe clearance shall extend 25 inches (635 mm) maximum under an element.

306.2.3 Minimum Required Depth. Where toe clearance is required at an element as part of a clear floor space, the toe clearance shall extend 17 inches (430 mm) minimum under the element.

306.2.4 Additional Clearance. Space extending greater than 6 inches (150 mm) beyond the available knee clearance at 9 inches (230 mm) above the finish floor or ground shall not be considered toe clearance.

306.2.5 Width. Toe clearance shall be 30 inches (760 mm) wide minimum.

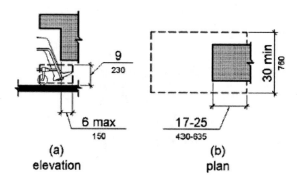

Figure 306.2 Toe Clearance

306.3 Knee Clearance.

306.3.1 General. Space under an element between 9 inches (230 mm) and 27 inches (685 mm) above the finish floor or ground shall be considered knee clearance and shall comply with 306.3.

306.3.2 Maximum Depth. Knee clearance shall extend 25 inches (635 mm) maximum under an element at 9 inches (230 mm) above the finish floor or ground.

306.3.3 Minimum Required Depth. Where knee clearance is required under an element as part of a clear floor space, the knee clearance shall be 11 inches (280 mm) deep minimum at 9 inches (230 mm) above the finish floor or ground, and 8 inches (205 mm) deep minimum at 27 inches (685 mm) above the finish floor or ground.

306.3.4 Clearance Reduction. Between 9 inches (230 mm) and 27 inches (685 mm) above the finish floor or ground, the knee clearance shall be permitted to reduce at a rate of 1 inch (25 mm) in depth for each 6 inches (150 mm) in height.

306.3.5 Width. Knee clearance shall be 30 inches (760 mm) wide minimum.

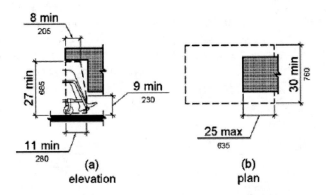

Figure 306.3 Knee Clearance

307 Protruding Objects

307.1 General. Protruding objects shall comply with 307.

307.2 Protrusion Limits. Objects with leading edges more than 27 inches (685 mm) and not more than 80 inches (2030 mm) above the finish floor or ground shall protrude 4 inches (100 mm) maximum horizontally into the circulation path.

> **EXCEPTION:** Handrails shall be permitted to protrude 4 1/2 inches (115 mm) maximum.

Advisory

307.2 Protrusion Limits. When a cane is used and the element is in the detectable range, it gives a person sufficient time to detect the element with the cane before there is body contact. Elements located on circulation paths, including operable elements, must comply with requirements for protruding objects. For example, awnings and their supporting structures cannot reduce the minimum required vertical clearance. Similarly, casement windows, when open, cannot encroach more than 4 inches (100 mm) into circulation paths above 27 inches (685 mm).

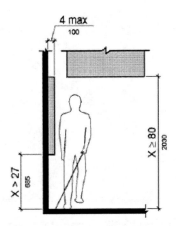

Figure 307.2 Limits of Protruding Objects

307.3 Post-Mounted Objects. Free-standing objects mounted on posts or pylons shall overhang circulation paths 12 inches (305 mm) maximum when located 27 inches (685 mm) minimum and 80 inches (2030 mm) maximum above the finish floor or ground. Where a sign or other obstruction is mounted between posts or pylons and the clear distance between the posts or pylons is greater than 12 inches (305 mm), the lowest edge of such sign or obstruction shall be 27 inches (685 mm) maximum or 80 inches (2030 mm) minimum above the finish floor or ground.

EXCEPTION: The sloping portions of handrails serving stairs and ramps shall not be required to comply with 307.3.

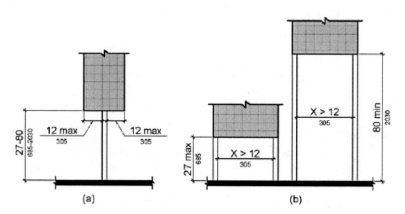

Figure 307.3 Post-Mounted Protruding Objects

307.4 Vertical Clearance. Vertical clearance shall be 80 inches (2030 mm) high minimum. Guardrails or other barriers shall be provided where the vertical clearance is less than 80 inches (2030 mm) high. The leading edge of such guardrail or barrier shall be located 27 inches (685 mm) maximum above the finish floor or ground.

EXCEPTION: Door closers and door stops shall be permitted to be 78 inches (1980 mm) minimum above the finish floor or ground.

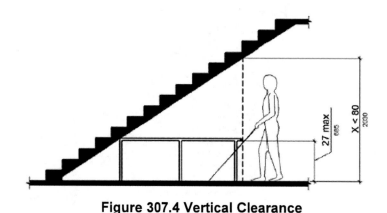

Figure 307.4 Vertical Clearance

307.5 Required Clear Width. Protruding objects shall not reduce the clear width required for accessible routes.
308 Reach Ranges

308.1 General. Reach ranges shall comply with 308.

Advisory

308.1 General. The following table provides guidance on reach ranges for children according to age where building elements such as coat hooks, lockers, or operable parts are designed for use primarily by children. These dimensions apply to either forward or side reaches. Accessible elements and operable parts designed for adult use or children over age 12 can be located outside these ranges but must be within the adult reach ranges required by 308.

Children's Reach Ranges			
Forward or Side Reach	Ages 3 and 4	Ages 5 through 8	Ages 9 through 12
High (maximum)	36 in (915 mm)	40 in (1015 mm)	44 in (1120 mm)
Low (minimum)	20 in (510 mm)	18 in (455 mm)	16 in (405 mm)

308.2 Forward Reach.

308.2.1 Unobstructed. Where a forward reach is unobstructed, the high forward reach shall be 48 inches (1220 mm) maximum and the low forward reach shall be 15 inches (380 mm) minimum above the finish floor or ground.

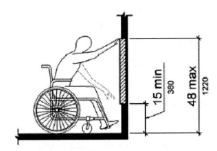

Figure 308.2.1 Unobstructed Forward Reach

308.2.2 Obstructed High Reach. Where a high forward reach is over an obstruction, the clear floor space shall extend beneath the element for a distance not less than the required reach depth over the obstruction. The high forward reach shall be 48 inches (1220 mm) maximum where the reach depth is 20 inches (510 mm) maximum. Where the reach depth exceeds 20 inches (510 mm), the high forward reach shall be 44 inches (1120 mm) maximum and the reach depth shall be 25 inches (635 mm) maximum.

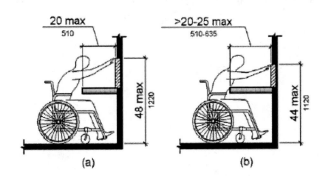

Figure 308.2.2 Obstructed High Forward Reach

308.3 Side Reach.

308.3.1 Unobstructed. Where a clear floor or ground space allows a parallel approach to an element and the side reach is unobstructed, the high side reach shall be 48 inches (1220 mm) maximum and the low side reach shall be 15 inches (380 mm) minimum above the finish floor or ground.

EXCEPTIONS:

1. An obstruction shall be permitted between the clear floor or ground space and the element where the depth of the obstruction is 10 inches (255 mm) maximum.

2. Operable parts of fuel dispensers shall be permitted to be 54 inches (1370 mm) maximum measured from the surface of the vehicular way where fuel dispensers are installed on existing curbs.

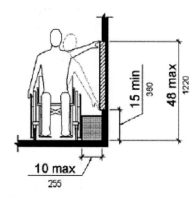

Figure 308.3.1 Unobstructed Side Reach

308.3.2 Obstructed High Reach. Where a clear floor or ground space allows a parallel approach to an element and the high side reach is over an obstruction, the height of the obstruction shall be 34 inches (865 mm) maximum and the depth of the obstruction shall be 24 inches (610 mm) maximum. The high side reach shall be 48 inches (1220 mm) maximum for a reach depth of 10 inches (255 mm) maximum. Where the reach depth exceeds 10 inches (255 mm), the high side reach shall be 46 inches (1170 mm) maximum for a reach depth of 24 inches (610 mm) maximum.

EXCEPTIONS:

1. The top of washing machines and clothes dryers shall be permitted to be 36 inches (915 mm) maximum above the finish floor.

2. Operable parts of fuel dispensers shall be permitted to be 54 inches (1370 mm) maximum measured from the surface of the vehicular way where fuel dispensers are installed on existing curbs.

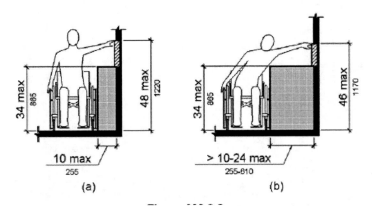

Figure 308.3.2 Obstructed High Side Reach

309 Operable Parts

309.1 General. Operable parts shall comply with 309.

309.2 Clear Floor Space. A clear floor or ground space complying with 305 shall be provided.

309.3 Height. Operable parts shall be placed within one or more of the reach ranges specified in 308.

309.4 Operation. Operable parts shall be operable with one hand and shall not require tight grasping, pinching, or twisting of the wrist. The force required to activate operable parts shall be 5 pounds (22.2 N) maximum.

> **EXCEPTION:** Gas pump nozzles shall not be required to provide operable parts that have an activating force of 5 pounds (22.2 N) maximum.

Guidance

Section 4.1.3, and more specifically sections 4.1.3(13), 4.27.3, and 4.27.4 of the 1991 Standards, require operable parts on accessible elements, along accessible routes, and in accessible rooms and spaces to comply with the technical requirements for operable parts, including height and operation. The 1991 Standards, at section 4.27.3, contain an exception, " * * * where the use of special equipment dictates otherwise or where electrical and communications systems receptacles are not normally intended for use by building occupants," from the technical requirement for the height of operable parts. Section 205.1 of the 2010 Standards divides this exception into three exceptions covering operable parts intended only for use by service or maintenance personnel, electrical or communication receptacles serving a dedicated use, and floor electrical receptacles. Operable parts covered by these new exceptions are exempt from all of the technical requirements for operable parts in section 309. The 2010 Standards also add exceptions that exempt certain outlets at kitchen counters; heating, ventilating and air conditioning diffusers; redundant controls provided for a single element, other than light switches; and exercise machines and equipment from all of the technical requirements for operable parts. Exception 7, in section 205.1 of the 2010 Standards, exempts cleats and other boat securement devices from the accessible height requirement. Similarly, section 309.4 of the 2010 Standards exempts gas pump nozzles, but only from the technical requirement for activating force.

Reach Ranges. The 1991 Standards set the maximum height for side reach at 54 inches above the floor. The 2010 Standards, at section 308.3, lower that maximum height to 48 inches above the finish floor or ground. The 2010 Standards also add exceptions, as discussed above, to the scoping requirement for operable parts for certain elements that, among other things, will exempt them from the reach range requirements in section 308.

The 1991 Standards, at sections 4.1.3, 4.27.3, and 4.2.6, and the 2010 Standards, at sections 205.1, 228.1, 228.2, 308.3, and 309.3, require operable parts of accessible elements, along accessible routes, and in accessible rooms and spaces to be placed within the forward or side-reach ranges specified in section 308. The 2010 Standards also require at least five percent (5%) of mailboxes provided in an interior location and at least one of each type of depository, vending machine, change machine, and gas pump to meet the technical requirements for a forward or a side reach.

Section 4.2.6 of the 1991 Standards specifies a maximum 54-inch high side reach and a minimum 9-inch low side reach for an unobstructed reach depth of 10 inches maximum. Section 308.3.1 of the 2010 Standards specifies a maximum 48-inch high side reach and a minimum 15-inch low side reach where the element being reached for is unobstructed. Section 308.3.1, Exception 1, permits an obstruction that is no deeper than 10 inches between the edge of the clear floor or ground space and the element that the individual with a disability is trying to reach. Changes in the side-reach range for new construction and alterations in the 2010 Standards will affect a variety of building elements such as light switches, electrical outlets, thermostats, fire alarm pull stations, card readers, and keypads.

Commenters were divided in their views about the changes to the unobstructed side-reach range. Disability advocacy groups and others, including individuals of short stature, supported the modifications to the proposed reach range requirements. Other commenters stated that the new reach range requirements will be burdensome for small businesses to comply with. These comments argued that the new reach range requirements restrict design options, especially in residential housing.

The Department continues to believe that data submitted by advocacy groups and others provides compelling evidence that lowered reach range requirements will better serve significantly greater numbers of individuals with disabilities, including individuals of short stature, persons with limited upper body strength, and others with limited use of their arms and fingers. The change to the side-reach range was developed by the Access Board over a prolonged period in which there was extensive public participation. This process did not produce any significant data to indicate that applying the new unobstructed side-reach range requirement in new construction or during alterations would impose a significant burden.

CHAPTER 4: ACCESSIBLE ROUTES

Guidance

Chapter 4 Accessible Routes

Slope. The 2010 Standards provide, at section 403.3, that the cross slope of walking surfaces not be steeper than 1:48. The 1991 Standards´ cross slope requirement was that it not exceed 1:50. A commenter recommended increasing the cross slope requirement to allow a maximum of 1/2 inch per foot (1:24) to prevent imperfections in concrete surfaces from ponding water. The Department continues to believe that the requirement that a cross slope not be steeper than 1:48 adequately provides for water drainage in most situations. The suggested changes would double the allowable cross slope and create a significant impediment for many wheelchair users and others with a mobility disability.

Accessible Routes from Site Arrival Points and Within Sites. The 1991 Standards, at sections 4.1.2(1) and (2), and the 2010 Standards, at sections 206.2.1 and 206.2.2, require that at least one accessible route be provided within the site from site arrival points to an accessible building entrance and that at least one accessible route connect accessible facilities on the same site. The 2010 Standards also add two exceptions that exempt site arrival points and accessible facilities within a site from the accessible route requirements where the only means of access between them is a vehicular way that does not provide pedestrian access.

Commenters urged the Department to eliminate the exception that exempts site arrival points and accessible facilities from the accessible route requirements where the only means of access between them is a vehicular way not providing pedestrian access. The Department declines to accept this recommendation because the Department believes that its use will be limited. If it can be reasonably anticipated that the route between the site arrival point and the accessible facilities will be used by pedestrians, regardless of whether a pedestrian route is provided, then this exception will not apply. It will apply only in the relatively rare situations where the route between the site arrival point and the accessible facility dictates vehicular access – for example, an office complex on an isolated site that has a private access road, or a self-service storage facility where all users are expected to drive to their storage units.

Another commenter suggested that the language of section 406.1 of the 2010 Standards is confusing because it states that curb ramps on accessible routes shall comply with 406, 405.2 through 405.5, and 405.10. The 1991 Standards require that curb ramps be provided wherever an accessible route crosses a curb.

The Department declines to change this language because the change is purely editorial, resulting from the overall changes in the format of the 2010 Standards. It does not change the substantive requirement. In the 2010 Standards all elements on a required accessible route must be accessible; therefore, if the accessible route crosses a curb, a curb ramp must be provided.

Areas of Sport Activity. Section 206.2.2 of the 2010 Standards requires at least one accessible route to connect accessible buildings, facilities, elements, and spaces on the same site. Advisory section 206.2.2 adds the explanation that an accessible route must connect the boundary of each area of sport activity (e.g., courts and playing fields, whether indoor or outdoor). Section 206.2.12 of the 2010 Standards further requires that in court sports the accessible route must directly connect both sides of the court.

Limited-Use/Limited-Application Elevators, Destination-Oriented Elevators and Private Residence Elevators. The 1991 Standards, at section 4.1.3(5), and the 2010 Standards, at sections 206.2 and 206.6, include exceptions to the scoping requirement for accessible routes that exempt certain facilities from connecting each story with an elevator. If a facility is exempt from the scoping requirement, but nonetheless installs an elevator, the 1991 Standards require the elevator to comply with the technical requirements for elevators. The 2010 Standards add a new exception that allows a facility that is exempt from the scoping requirement to install a limited-use/limited-application (LULA) elevator. LULA elevators are also permitted in the 1991 Standards and the 2010 Standards as an alternative to platform lifts. The 2010 Standards also add a new exception that permits private residence elevators in multi-story dwelling and transient lodging units. The 2010 Standards contain technical requirements for LULA elevators at section 408 and private residence elevators at section 409.

Section 407.2.1.4 of the 2010 Standards includes an exception to the technical requirements for locating elevator call buttons for destination-oriented elevators. The advisory at section 407.2.1.4 describes lobby controls for destination-oriented elevator systems. Many elevator manufacturers have recently developed these new "buttonless" elevator control systems. These new, more efficient elevators are usually found in high-rise buildings that have several elevators. They require passengers to enter their destination floor on an entry device, usually a keypad, in the elevator lobby. The system then sends the most efficient car available to take all of the passengers going to the sixth floor, for example, only to the sixth floor, without making stops at the third, fourth, and fifth floors on the way to the sixth floor. The challenge for individuals who are blind or have low vision is how to know which elevator car to enter, after they have entered their destination floor into the keypad.

Commenters requested that the Department impose a moratorium on the installation of destination-oriented elevators arguing that this new technology presents wayfinding challenges for persons who are blind or have low vision.

Section 407.2.1.5 of the 2010 Standards allows destination-oriented elevators to not provide call buttons with visible signals to indicate when each call is registered and when each call is answered *provided* that visible and audible signals, compliant with 407.2.2 of the 2010 Standards, indicating which elevator car to enter, are provided. This will require the responding elevator car to automatically provide audible and visible communication so that the system will always verbally and visually indicate which elevator car to enter.

As with any new technology, all users must have time to become acquainted with how to use destination-oriented elevators. The Department will monitor the use of this new technology and work with the Access Board so that there is not a decrease in accessibility as a result of permitting this new technology to be installed.

Accessible Routes to Tiered Dining Areas in Sports Facilities. The 1991 Standards, at sections 4.1.3(1) and 5.4, and section 206.2.5 of the 2010 Standards require an accessible route to be provided to all dining areas in new construction, including raised or sunken dining areas. The 2010 Standards add a new exception for tiered dining areas in sports facilities. Dining areas in sports facilities are typically integrated into the seating bowl and are tiered to provide adequate lines of sight for individuals with disabilities. The new exception requires accessible routes to be provided to at least 25 percent (25%) of the tiered dining areas in sports facilities. Each tier must have the same services and the accessible routes must serve the accessible seating.

Accessible Routes to Press Boxes. The 1991 Standards, at sections 4.1.1(1) and 4.1.3(1), cover all areas of newly constructed facilities required to be accessible, and require an accessible route to connect accessible entrances with all accessible spaces and elements within the facility. Section 201.1 of the 2010 Standards requires that all areas of newly designed and constructed buildings and facilities and altered portions of existing buildings and facilities be accessible. Sections 206.2.7(1) and (2) of the 2010 Standards add two exceptions that exempt small press boxes that are located in bleachers with entrances on only one level, and small press boxes that are free-standing structures elevated 12 feet or more above grade, from the accessible route requirement when the aggregate area of all press boxes in a sports facility does not exceed 500 square feet. The Department anticipates that this change will significantly reduce the economic impact on smaller sports facilities, such as those associated with high schools or community colleges.

Public Entrances. The 1991 Standards, at sections 4.1.3(8) and 4.1.6(1)(h), require at least fifty percent (50%) of public entrances to be accessible. Additionally, the 1991 Standards require the number of accessible public entrances to be equivalent to the number of exits required by applicable building and fire codes. With very few exceptions, building and fire codes require at least two exits to be provided from spaces within a building and from the building itself. Therefore, under the 1991 Standards where two public entrances are planned in a newly constructed facility, both entrances are required to be accessible.

Instead of requiring accessible entrances based on the number of public entrances provided or the number of exits required (whichever is greater), section 206.4.1 of the 2010 Standards requires at least sixty percent (60%) of public entrances to be accessible. The revision is intended to achieve the same result as the 1991 Standards. Thus, under the 2010 Standards where two public entrances are planned in a newly constructed facility, both entrances must be accessible.

Where multiple public entrances are planned to serve different site arrival points, the 1991 Standards, at section

4.1.2(1), and section 206.2.1 of the 2010 Standards require at least one accessible route to be provided from each type of site arrival point provided, including accessible parking spaces, accessible passenger loading zones, public streets and sidewalks, and public transportation stops, to an accessible public entrance that serves the site arrival point.

Commenters representing small businesses recommended retaining the 1991 requirement for fifty percent (50%) of public entrances of covered entities to be accessible. These commenters also raised concerns about the impact upon existing facilities of the new sixty percent (60%) requirement.

The Department believes that these commenters misunderstand the 1991 Standards. As explained above, the requirements of the 1991 Standards generally require more than fifty percent (50%) of entrances in small facilities to be accessible. Model codes require that most buildings have more than one means of egress. Most buildings have more than one entrance, and the requirements of the 1991 Standards typically resulted in these buildings having more than one accessible entrance. Requiring at least sixty percent (60%) of public entrances to be accessible is not expected to result in a substantial increase in the number of accessible entrances compared to the requirements of the 1991 Standards. In some very large facilities this change may result in fewer accessible entrances being required by the 2010 Standards. However, the Department believes that the realities of good commercial design will result in more accessible entrances being provided for the convenience of all users.

The 1991 Standards and the 2010 Standards also contain exceptions that limit the number of accessible entrances required in alterations to existing facilities. When entrances to an existing facility are altered and the facility has an accessible entrance, the entrance being altered is not required to be accessible, unless a primary function area also is altered and then an accessible path of travel must be provided to the primary function area to the extent that the cost to do so is not disproportionate to the overall cost of the alteration.

Alterations to Existing Elevators. When a single space or element is altered, the 1991 Standards, at sections 4.1.6(1)(a) and (b), require the space or element to be made accessible. When an element in one elevator is altered, the 2010 Standards, at section 206.6.1, require the same element to be altered in all elevators that are programmed to respond to the same call button as the altered elevator.

The 2010 Standards, at sections 407.2.1 - 407.4.7.1.2, also contain exceptions to the technical requirements for elevators when existing elevators are altered that minimize the impact of this change.

Commenters expressed concerns about the requirement that when an element in one elevator is altered, the 2010 Standards, at section 206.6.1, will require the same element to be altered in all elevators that are programmed to respond to the same call button as the altered elevator. Commenters noted that such a requirement is burdensome and will result in costly efforts without significant benefit to individuals with disabilities.

The Department believes that this requirement is necessary to ensure that when an individual with a disability presses a call button, an accessible elevator will arrive. Without this requirement, individuals with disabilities would have to wait unnecessarily for an accessible elevator to make its way to them arbitrarily. The Department also believes that the effort required to meet this provision is minimal in the majority of situations because it is typical to upgrade all of the elevators in a bank at the same time.

Accessible Routes in Dwelling Units with Mobility Features. Sections 4.34.1 and 4.34.2 of the UFAS require the living area, kitchen and dining area, bedroom, bathroom, and laundry area, where provided, in covered dwelling units with mobility features to be on an accessible route. Where covered dwelling units have two or more bedrooms, at least two bedrooms are required to be on an accessible route.

The 2010 Standards at sections 233.3.1.1, 809.1, 809.2, 809.2.1, and 809.4 will require all spaces and elements within dwelling units with mobility features to be on an accessible route. These changes exempt unfinished attics and unfinished basements from the accessible route requirement. Section 233.3.5 of the 2010 Standards also includes an exception to the dispersion requirement that permits accessible single-story dwelling units to be constructed, where multi-story dwelling units are one of the types of units provided.

Location of Accessible Routes. Section 4.3.2(1) of the 1991 Standards requires accessible routes connecting site arrival points and accessible building entrances to coincide with general circulation paths, to the maximum extent feasible. The 2010 Standards require all accessible routes to coincide with or be located in the same general area as general circulation paths. Additionally, a new provision specifies that where a circulation path is interior, the required accessible route must also be located in the interior of the facility. The change affects a limited number of buildings.

Section 206.3 of the 2010 Standards requires all accessible routes to coincide with or be located in the same general area as general circulation paths. Designing newly constructed interior accessible routes to coincide with or to be located in the same area as general circulation paths will not typically present a difficult design challenge and is expected to impose limited design constraints. The change will have no impact on exterior accessible routes. The 1991 Standards and the 2010 Standards also require accessible routes to be located in the interior of the facility where general circulation paths are located in the interior of the facility. The revision affects a limited number of buildings.

Location of Accessible Routes to Stages. The 1991 Standards at section 4.33.5 require an accessible route to connect the accessible seating and the performing area.

Section 206.2.6 of the 2010 Standards requires the accessible route to directly connect the seating area and the accessible seating, stage, and all areas of the stage, where a circulation path directly connects the seating area and the stage. Both the 1991 Standards and the 2010 Standards also require an accessible route to connect the stage and ancillary areas, such as dressing rooms, used by performers. The 2010 Standards do not require an additional accessible route to be provided to the stage. Rather, the changes specify where the accessible route to the stage, which is required by the 1991 Standards, must be located.

401 General

401.1 Scope. The provisions of Chapter 4 shall apply where required by Chapter 2 or where referenced by a requirement in this document.

402 Accessible Routes

402.1 General. Accessible routes shall comply with 402.

402.2 Components. Accessible routes shall consist of one or more of the following components: walking surfaces with a running slope not steeper than 1:20, doorways, ramps, curb ramps excluding the flared sides, elevators, and platform lifts. All components of an accessible route shall comply with the applicable requirements of Chapter 4.

Advisory

402.2 Components. Walking surfaces must have running slopes not steeper than 1:20, see 403.3. Other components of accessible routes, such as ramps (405) and curb ramps (406), are permitted to be more steeply sloped.

403 Walking Surfaces

403.1 General. Walking surfaces that are a part of an accessible route shall comply with 403.

403.2 Floor or Ground Surface. Floor or ground surfaces shall comply with 302.

403.3 Slope. The running slope of walking surfaces shall not be steeper than 1:20. The cross slope of walking surfaces shall not be steeper than 1:48.

403.4 Changes in Level. Changes in level shall comply with 303.

403.5 Clearances. Walking surfaces shall provide clearances complying with 403.5.

EXCEPTION: Within employee work areas, clearances on common use circulation paths shall be permitted to be decreased by work area equipment provided that the decrease is essential to the function of the work being performed.

403.5.1 Clear Width. Except as provided in 403.5.2 and 403.5.3, the clear width of walking surfaces shall be 36 inches (915 mm) minimum.

EXCEPTION: The clear width shall be permitted to be reduced to 32 inches (815 mm) minimum for a length of 24 inches (610 mm) maximum provided that reduced width segments are separated by segments that are 48 inches (1220 mm) long minimum and 36 inches (915 mm) wide minimum.

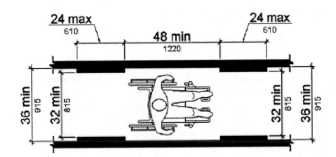

Figure 403.5.1 Clear Width of an Accessible Route

403.5.2 Clear Width at Turn. Where the accessible route makes a 180 degree turn around an element which is less than 48 inches (1220 mm) wide, clear width shall be 42 inches (1065 mm) minimum approaching the turn, 48 inches (1220 mm) minimum at the turn and 42 inches (1065 mm) minimum leaving the turn.

   EXCEPTION: Where the clear width at the turn is 60 inches (1525 mm) minimum compliance with 403.5.2 shall not be required.

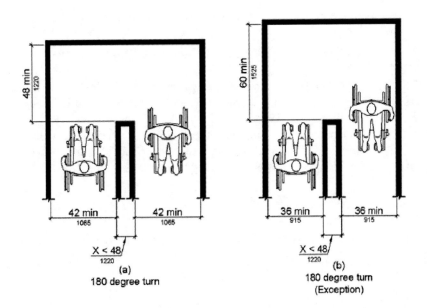

Figure 403.5.2 Clear Width at Turn

403.5.3 Passing Spaces. An accessible route with a clear width less than 60 inches (1525 mm) shall provide passing spaces at intervals of 200 feet (61 m) maximum. Passing spaces shall be either: a space 60 inches (1525 mm) minimum by 60 inches (1525 mm) minimum; or, an intersection of two walking surfaces providing a T-shaped space complying with 304.3.2 where the base and arms of the T-shaped space extend 48 inches (1220 mm) minimum beyond the intersection.

403.6 Handrails. Where handrails are provided along walking surfaces with running slopes not steeper than 1:20 they shall comply with 505.

Advisory

403.6 Handrails. Handrails provided in elevator cabs and platform lifts are not required to comply with the requirements for handrails on walking surfaces.

404 Doors, Doorways, and Gates

404.1 General. Doors, doorways, and gates that are part of an accessible route shall comply with 404.

EXCEPTION: Doors, doorways, and gates designed to be operated only by security personnel shall not be required to comply with 404.2.7, 404.2.8, 404.2.9, 404.3.2 and 404.3.4 through 404.3.7.

Advisory

404.1 General Exception. Security personnel must have sole control of doors that are eligible for the Exception at 404.1. It would not be acceptable for security personnel to operate the doors for people with disabilities while allowing others to have independent access.

404.2 Manual Doors, Doorways, and Manual Gates. Manual doors and doorways and manual gates intended for user passage shall comply with 404.2.

404.2.1 Revolving Doors, Gates, and Turnstiles. Revolving doors, revolving gates, and turnstiles shall not be part of an accessible route.

404.2.2 Double-Leaf Doors and Gates. At least one of the active leaves of doorways with two leaves shall comply with 404.2.3 and 404.2.4.

404.2.3 Clear Width. Door openings shall provide a clear width of 32 inches (815 mm) minimum. Clear openings of doorways with swinging doors shall be measured between the face of the door and the stop, with the door open 90 degrees. Openings more than 24 inches (610 mm) deep shall provide a clear opening of 36 inches (915 mm) minimum. There shall be no projections into the required clear opening width lower than 34 inches (865 mm) above the finish floor or ground. Projections into the clear opening width between 34 inches (865 mm) and 80 inches (2030 mm) above the finish floor or ground shall not exceed 4 inches (100 mm).

EXCEPTIONS:

1. In alterations, a projection of 5/8 inch (16 mm) maximum into the required clear width shall be permitted for the latch side stop.

2. Door closers and door stops shall be permitted to be 78 inches (1980 mm) minimum above the finish floor or ground.

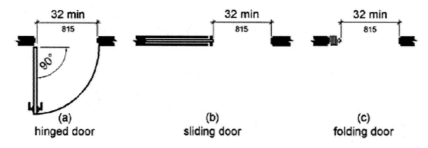

Figure 404.2.3 Clear Width of Doorways

404.2.4 Maneuvering Clearances. Minimum maneuvering clearances at doors and gates shall comply with 404.2.4. Maneuvering clearances shall extend the full width of the doorway and the required latch side or hinge side clearance.

 EXCEPTION: Entry doors to hospital patient rooms shall not be required to provide the clearance beyond the latch side of the door.

404.2.4.1 Swinging Doors and Gates. Swinging doors and gates shall have maneuvering clearances complying with Table 404.2.4.1.

Table 404.2.4.1 Maneuvering Clearances at Manual Swinging Doors and Gates (text version)			
Type of Use		**Minimum Maneuvering Clearance**	
Approach Direction	**Door or Gate Side**	**Perpendicular to Doorway**	**Parallel to Doorway (beyond latch side unless noted)**
From front	Pull	60 inches (1525 mm)	18 inches (455 mm)
From front	Push	48 inches (1220 mm)	0 inches (0 mm)[1]
From hinge side	Pull	60 inches (1525 mm)	36 inches (915 mm)
From hinge side	Pull	54 inches (1370 mm)	42 inches (1065 mm)
From hinge side	Push	42 inches (1065 mm)[2]	22 inches (560 mm)[3]
From latch side	Pull	48 inches (1220 mm)[4]	24 inches (610 mm)
From latch side	Push	42 inches (1065 mm)[4]	24 inches (610 mm)

[1.] Add 12 inches (305 mm) if closer and latch are provided.

[2.] Add 6 inches (150 mm) if closer and latch are provided.

[3.] Beyond hinge side.

[4.] Add 6 inches (150 mm) if closer is provided.

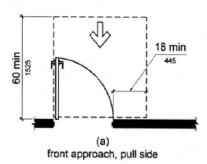

(a)
front approach, pull side

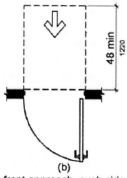

(b)
front approach, push side

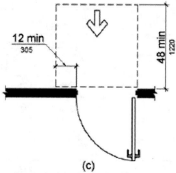

(c)
front approach, push side, door
provided with both closer and latch

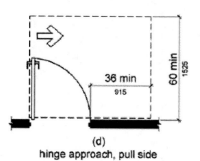

(d)
hinge approach, pull side

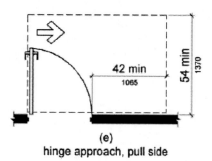

(e)
hinge approach, pull side

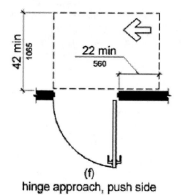

(f)
hinge approach, push side

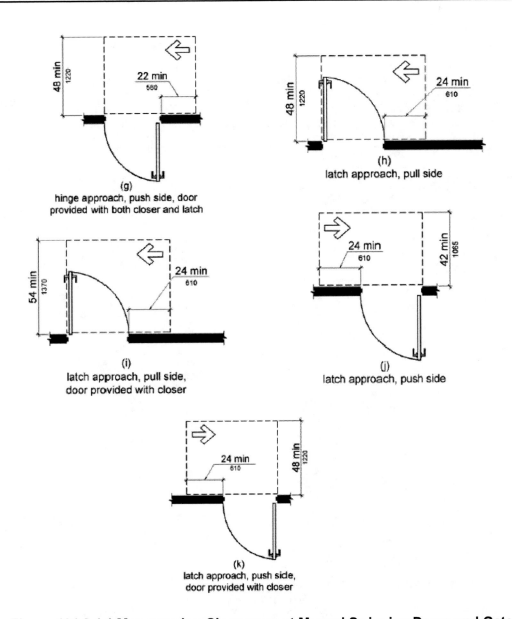

(g)
hinge approach, push side, door
provided with both closer and latch

(h)
latch approach, pull side

(i)
latch approach, pull side,
door provided with closer

(j)
latch approach, push side

(k)
latch approach, push side,
door provided with closer

Figure 404.2.4.1 Maneuvering Clearances at Manual Swinging Doors and Gates

404.2.4.2 Doorways without Doors or Gates, Sliding Doors, and Folding Doors. Doorways less than 36 inches (915 mm) wide without doors or gates, sliding doors, or folding doors shall have maneuvering clearances complying with Table 404.2.4.2.

Table 404.2.4.2 Maneuvering Clearances at Doorways without Doors or Gates, Manual Sliding Doors, and Manual Folding Doors		
	Minimum Maneuvering Clearance	
Approach Direction	**Perpendicular to Doorway**	**Parallel to Doorway (beyond stop/latch side unless noted)**
From Front	48 inches (1220 mm)	0 inches (0 mm)
From side[1]	42 inches (1065 mm)	0 inches (0 mm)
From pocket/hinge side	42 inches (1065 mm)	22 inches (560 mm)[2]
From stop/latch side	42 inches (1065 mm)	24 inches (610 mm)

[1.] Doorway with no door only.
[2.] Beyond pocket/hinge side.

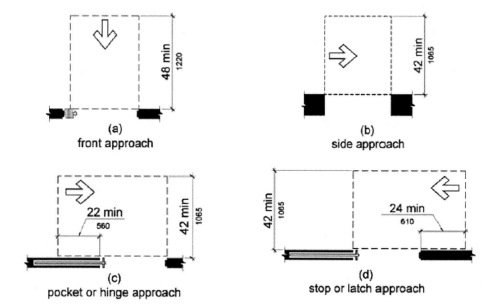

(a) front approach

(b) side approach

(c) pocket or hinge approach

(d) stop or latch approach

Figure 404.2.4.2 Maneuvering Clearances at Doorways without Doors, Sliding Doors, Gates, and Folding Doors

404.2.4.3 Recessed Doors and Gates. Maneuvering clearances for forward approach shall be provided when any obstruction within 18 inches (455 mm) of the latch side of a doorway projects more than 8 inches (205 mm) beyond the face of the door, measured perpendicular to the face of the door or gate.

Advisory

404.2.4.3 Recessed Doors and Gates. A door can be recessed due to wall thickness or because of the placement of casework and other fixed elements adjacent to the doorway. This provision must be applied wherever doors are recessed.

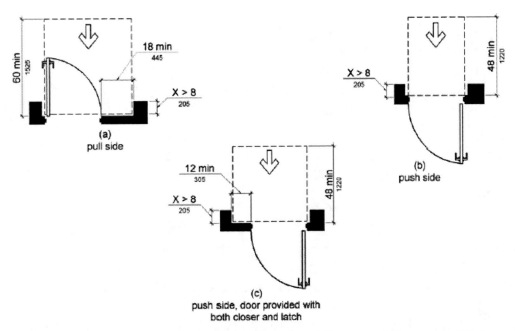

Figure 404.2.4.3 Maneuvering Clearances at Recessed Doors and Gates

404.2.4.4 Floor or Ground Surface. Floor or ground surface within required maneuvering clearances shall comply with 302. Changes in level are not permitted.

EXCEPTIONS:

1. Slopes not steeper than 1:48 shall be permitted.

2. Changes in level at thresholds complying with 404.2.5 shall be permitted.

404.2.5 Thresholds. Thresholds, if provided at doorways, shall be 1/2 inch (13 mm) high maximum. Raised thresholds and changes in level at doorways shall comply with 302 and 303.

EXCEPTION: Existing or altered thresholds 3/4 inch (19 mm) high maximum that have a beveled edge on each side with a slope not steeper than 1:2 shall not be required to comply with 404.2.5.

404.2.6 Doors in Series and Gates in Series. The distance between two hinged or pivoted doors in series and gates in series shall be 48 inches (1220 mm) minimum plus the width of doors or gates swinging into the space.

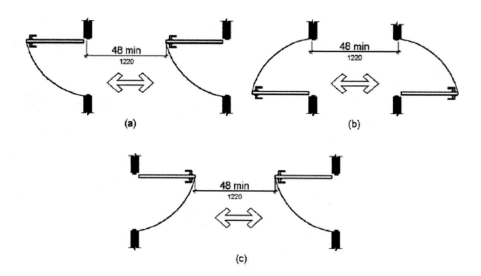

Figure 404.2.6 Doors in Series and Gates in Series

404.2.7 Door and Gate Hardware. Handles, pulls, latches, locks, and other operable parts on doors and gates shall comply with 309.4. Operable parts of such hardware shall be 34 inches (865 mm) minimum and 48 inches (1220 mm) maximum above the finish floor or ground. Where sliding doors are in the fully open position, operating hardware shall be exposed and usable from both sides.

EXCEPTIONS:

1. Existing locks shall be permitted in any location at existing glazed doors without stiles, existing overhead rolling doors or grilles, and similar existing doors or grilles that are designed with locks that are activated only at the top or bottom rail.

2. Access gates in barrier walls and fences protecting pools, spas, and hot tubs shall be permitted to have operable parts of the release of latch on self-latching devices at 54 inches (1370 mm) maximum above the finish floor or ground provided the self-latching devices are not also self-locking devices and operated by means of a key, electronic opener, or integral combination lock.

Advisory

404.2.7 Door and Gate Hardware. Door hardware that can be operated with a closed fist or a loose grip accommodates the greatest range of users. Hardware that requires simultaneous hand and finger movements require greater dexterity and coordination, and is not recommended.

404.2.8 Closing Speed. Door and gate closing speed shall comply with 404.2.8.

404.2.8.1 Door Closers and Gate Closers. Door closers and gate closers shall be adjusted so that from an open position of 90 degrees, the time required to move the door to a position of 12 degrees from the latch is 5 seconds minimum.

404.2.8.2 Spring Hinges. Door and gate spring hinges shall be adjusted so that from the open position of 70 degrees, the door or gate shall move to the closed position in 1.5 seconds minimum.

404.2.9 Door and Gate Opening Force. Fire doors shall have a minimum opening force allowable by the appropriate administrative authority. The force for pushing or pulling open a door or gate other than fire doors shall be as follows:

1. Interior hinged doors and gates: 5 pounds (22.2 N) maximum.

2. Sliding or folding doors: 5 pounds (22.2 N) maximum.

These forces do not apply to the force required to retract latch bolts or disengage other devices that hold the door or gate in a closed position.

Advisory

404.2.9 Door and Gate Opening Force. *The maximum force pertains to the continuous application of force necessary to fully open a door, not the initial force needed to overcome the inertia of the door. It does not apply to the force required to retract bolts or to disengage other devices used to keep the door in a closed position.*

404.2.10 Door and Gate Surfaces. Swinging door and gate surfaces within 10 inches (255 mm) of the finish floor or ground measured vertically shall have a smooth surface on the push side extending the full width of the door or gate. Parts creating horizontal or vertical joints in these surfaces shall be within 1/16 inch (1.6 mm) of the same plane as the other. Cavities created by added kick plates shall be capped.

EXCEPTIONS:

1. Sliding doors shall not be required to comply with 404.2.10.

2. Tempered glass doors without stiles and having a bottom rail or shoe with the top leading edge tapered at 60 degrees minimum from the horizontal shall not be required to meet the 10 inch (255 mm) bottom smooth surface height requirement.

3. Doors and gates that do not extend to within 10 inches (255 mm) of the finish floor or ground shall not be required to comply with 404.2.10.

4. Existing doors and gates without smooth surfaces within 10 inches (255 mm) of the finish floor or ground shall not be required to provide smooth surfaces complying with 404.2.10 provided that if added kick plates are installed, cavities created by such kick plates are capped

404.2.11 Vision Lights. Doors, gates, and side lights adjacent to doors or gates, containing one or more glazing panels that permit viewing through the panels shall have the bottom of at least one glazed panel located 43 inches (1090 mm) maximum above the finish floor.

EXCEPTION: Vision lights with the lowest part more than 66 inches (1675 mm) from the finish floor or ground shall not be required to comply with 404.2.11.

404.3 Automatic and Power-Assisted Doors and Gates. Automatic doors and automatic gates shall comply with 404.3. Full-powered automatic doors shall comply with ANSI/BHMA A156.10 (incorporated by reference, see "Referenced Standards" in Chapter 1). Low-energy and power-assisted doors shall comply with ANSI/BHMA A156.19 (1997 or 2002 edition) (incorporated by reference, see "Referenced Standards" in Chapter 1).

404.3.1 Clear Width. Doorways shall provide a clear opening of 32 inches (815 mm) minimum in power-on and power-off mode. The minimum clear width for automatic door systems in a doorway shall be based on the clear opening provided by all leaves in the open position.

404.3.2 Maneuvering Clearance. Clearances at power-assisted doors and gates shall comply with 404.2.4. Clearances at automatic doors and gates without standby power and serving an accessible means of egress shall comply with 404.2.4.

EXCEPTION: Where automatic doors and gates remain open in the power-off condition, compliance with 404.2.4 shall not be required.

404.3.3 Thresholds. Thresholds and changes in level at doorways shall comply with 404.2.5.

404.3.4 Doors in Series and Gates in Series. Doors in series and gates in series shall comply with 404.2.6.

404.3.5 Controls. Manually operated controls shall comply with 309. The clear floor space adjacent to the control shall be located beyond the arc of the door swing.

404.3.6 Break Out Opening. Where doors and gates without standby power are a part of a means of egress, the clear break out opening at swinging or sliding doors and gates shall be 32 inches (815 mm) minimum when operated in emergency mode.

> **EXCEPTION:** Where manual swinging doors and gates comply with 404.2 and serve the same means of egress compliance with 404.3.6 shall not be required.

404.3.7 Revolving Doors, Revolving Gates, and Turnstiles. Revolving doors, revolving gates, and turnstiles shall not be part of an accessible route.

Guidance

Automatic Door Break Out Openings. The 1991 Standards do not contain any technical requirement for automatic door break out openings. The 2010 Standards at sections 404.1, 404.3, 404.3.1, and 404.3.6 require automatic doors that are part of a means of egress and that do not have standby power to have a 32-inch minimum clear break out opening when operated in emergency mode. The minimum clear opening width for automatic doors is measured with all leaves in the open position. Automatic bi-parting doors or pairs of swinging doors that provide a 32-inch minimum clear break out opening in emergency mode when both leaves are opened manually meet the technical requirement. Section 404.3.6 of the 2010 Standards includes an exception that exempts automatic doors from the technical requirement for break out openings when accessible manual swinging doors serve the same means of egress.

Maneuvering Clearance or Standby Power for Automatic Doors. Section 4.13.6 of the 1991 Standards does not require maneuvering clearance at automatic doors. Section 404.3.2 of the 2010 Standards requires automatic doors that serve as an accessible means of egress to either provide maneuvering clearance or to have standby power to operate the door in emergencies. This provision has limited application and will affect, among others, in-swinging automatic doors that serve small spaces.

Commenters urged the Department to reconsider provisions that would require maneuvering clearance or standby power for automatic doors. They assert that these requirements would impose unreasonable financial and administrative burdens on all covered entities, particularly smaller entities. The Department declines to change these provisions because they are fundamental life-safety issues. The requirement applies only to doors that are part of a means of egress that must be accessible in an emergency. If an emergency-related power failure prevents the operation of the automatic door, a person with a disability could be trapped unless there is either adequate maneuvering room to open the door manually or a back-up power source.

Thresholds at Doorways. The 1991 Standards, at section 4.13.8, require the height of thresholds at doorways not to exceed 1/2 inch and thresholds at exterior sliding doors not to exceed 3/4 inch. Sections 404.1 and 404.2.5 of the 2010 Standards require the height of thresholds at all doorways that are part of an accessible route not to exceed 1/2 inch. The 1991 Standards and the 2010 Standards require raised thresholds that exceed ¼ inch in height to be beveled on each side with a slope not steeper than 1:2. The 2010 Standards include an exception that exempts existing and altered thresholds that do not exceed 3/4 inch in height and are beveled on each side from the requirement.

---

405 Ramps

405.1 General. Ramps on accessible routes shall comply with 405.

> **EXCEPTION:** In assembly areas, aisle ramps adjacent to seating and not serving elements required to be on an accessible route shall not be required to comply with 405.

405.2 Slope. Ramp runs shall have a running slope not steeper than 1:12.

> **EXCEPTION:** In existing sites, buildings, and facilities, ramps shall be permitted to have running slopes steeper than 1:12 complying with Table 405.2 where such slopes are necessary due to space limitations.

Table 405.2 Maximum Ramp Slope and Rise for Existing Sites, Buildings, and Facilities	
Slope[1]	Maximum Rise
Steeper than 1:10 but not steeper than 1:8	3 inches (75 mm)
Steeper than 1:12 but not steeper than 1:10	6 inches (150 mm)
[1]. A slope steeper than 1:8 is prohibited.	

Advisory

405.2 Slope. To accommodate the widest range of users, provide ramps with the least possible running slope and, wherever possible, accompany ramps with stairs for use by those individuals for whom distance presents a greater barrier than steps, e.g., people with heart disease or limited stamina.

405.3 Cross Slope. Cross slope of ramp runs shall not be steeper than 1:48.

Advisory

405.3 Cross Slope. Cross slope is the slope of the surface perpendicular to the direction of travel. Cross slope is measured the same way as slope is measured (i.e., the rise over the run).

405.4 Floor or Ground Surfaces. Floor or ground surfaces of ramp runs shall comply with 302. Changes in level other than the running slope and cross slope are not permitted on ramp runs.

405.5 Clear Width. The clear width of a ramp run and, where handrails are provided, the clear width between handrails shall be 36 inches (915 mm) minimum.

EXCEPTION: Within employee work areas, the required clear width of ramps that are a part of common use circulation paths shall be permitted to be decreased by work area equipment provided that the decrease is essential to the function of the work being performed.

405.6 Rise. The rise for any ramp run shall be 30 inches (760 mm) maximum.

405.7 Landings. Ramps shall have landings at the top and the bottom of each ramp run. Landings shall comply with 405.7.

Advisory

405.7 Landings. Ramps that do not have level landings at changes in direction can create a compound slope that will not meet the requirements of this document. Circular or curved ramps continually change direction. Curvilinear ramps with small radii also can create compound cross slopes and cannot, by their nature, meet the requirements for accessible routes. A level landing is needed at the accessible door to permit maneuvering and simultaneously door operation.

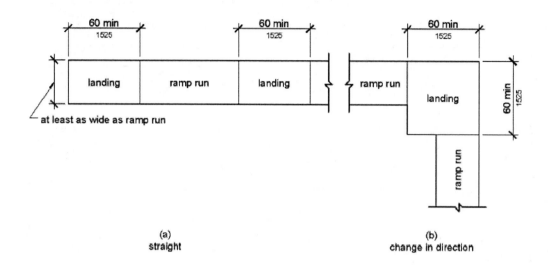

Figure 405.7 Ramp Landings

405.7.1 Slope. Landings shall comply with 302. Changes in level are not permitted.

EXCEPTION: Slopes not steeper than 1:48 shall be permitted.

405.7.2 Width. The landing clear width shall be at least as wide as the widest ramp run leading to the landing.

405.7.3 Length. The landing clear length shall be 60 inches (1525 mm) long minimum.

405.7.4 Change in Direction. Ramps that change direction between runs at landings shall have a clear landing 60 inches (1525 mm) minimum by 60 inches (1525 mm) minimum.

405.7.5 Doorways. Where doorways are located adjacent to a ramp landing, maneuvering clearances required by 404.2.4 and 404.3.2 shall be permitted to overlap the required landing area.

405.8 Handrails. Ramp runs with a rise greater than 6 inches (150 mm) shall have handrails complying with 505.

EXCEPTION: Within employee work areas, handrails shall not be required where ramps that are part of common use circulation paths are designed to permit the installation of handrails complying with 505. Ramps not subject to the exception to 405.5 shall be designed to maintain a 36 inch (915 mm) minimum clear width when handrails are installed.

405.9 Edge Protection. Edge protection complying with 405.9.1 or 405.9.2 shall be provided on each side of ramp runs and at each side of ramp landings.

EXCEPTIONS:

1. Edge protection shall not be required on ramps that are not required to have handrails and have sides complying with 406.3.

2. Edge protection shall not be required on the sides of ramp landings serving an adjoining ramp run or stairway.

3. Edge protection shall not be required on the sides of ramp landings having a vertical drop-off of 1/2 inch (13 mm) maximum within 10 inches (255 mm) horizontally of the minimum landing area specified in 405.7.

405.9.1 Extended Floor or Ground Surface. The floor or ground surface of the ramp run or landing shall extend 12 inches (305 mm) minimum beyond the inside face of a handrail complying with 505.

Advisory

405.9.1 Extended Floor or Ground Surface. The extended surface prevents wheelchair casters and crutch tips from slipping off the ramp surface.

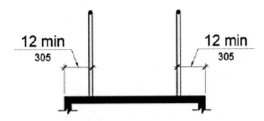

Figure 405.9.1 Extended Floor or Ground Surface Edge Protection

405.9.2 Curb or Barrier. A curb or barrier shall be provided that prevents the passage of a 4 inch (100 mm) diameter sphere, where any portion of the sphere is within 4 inches (100 mm) of the finish floor or ground surface.

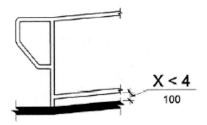

Figure 405.9.2 Curb or Barrier Edge Protection

405.10 Wet Conditions. Landings subject to wet conditions shall be designed to prevent the accumulation of water.

406 Curb Ramps

406.1 General. Curb ramps on accessible routes shall comply with 406, 405.2 through 405.5, and 405.10.

406.2 Counter Slope. Counter slopes of adjoining gutters and road surfaces immediately adjacent to the curb ramp shall not be steeper than 1:20. The adjacent surfaces at transitions at curb ramps to walks, gutters, and streets shall be at the same level.

Figure 406.2 Counter Slope of Surfaces Adjacent to Curb Ramps

406.3 Sides of Curb Ramps. Where provided, curb ramp flares shall not be steeper than 1:10.

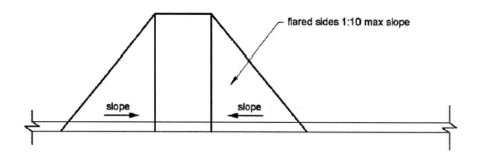

Figure 406.3 Sides of Curb Ramps

406.4 Landings. Landings shall be provided at the tops of curb ramps. The landing clear length shall be 36 inches (915 mm) minimum. The landing clear width shall be at least as wide as the curb ramp, excluding flared sides, leading to the landing.

> **EXCEPTION:** In alterations, where there is no landing at the top of curb ramps, curb ramp flares shall be provided and shall not be steeper than 1:12.

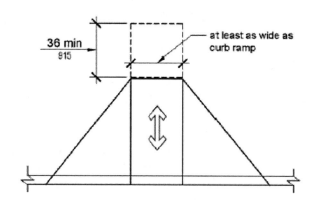

Figure 406.4 Landings at the Top of Curb Ramps

406.5 Location. Curb ramps and the flared sides of curb ramps shall be located so that they do not project into vehicular traffic lanes, parking spaces, or parking access aisles. Curb ramps at marked crossings shall be wholly contained within the markings, excluding any flared sides.

406.6 Diagonal Curb Ramps. Diagonal or corner type curb ramps with returned curbs or other well-defined edges shall have the edges parallel to the direction of pedestrian flow. The bottom of diagonal curb ramps shall have a clear space 48 inches (1220 mm) minimum outside active traffic lanes of the roadway. Diagonal curb ramps provided at marked crossings shall provide the 48 inches (1220 mm) minimum clear space within the markings. Diagonal curb ramps with flared sides shall have a segment of curb 24 inches (610 mm) long minimum located on each side of the curb ramp and within the marked crossing.

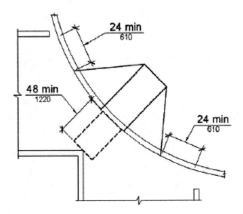

Figure 406.6 Diagonal or Corner Type Curb Ramps

406.7 Islands. Raised islands in crossings shall be cut through level with the street or have curb ramps at both sides. Each curb ramp shall have a level area 48 inches (1220 mm) long minimum by 36 inches (915 mm) wide minimum at the top of the curb ramp in the part of the island intersected by the crossings. Each 48 inch (1220 mm) minimum by 36 inch (915 mm) minimum area shall be oriented so that the 48 inch (1220 mm) minimum length is in the direction of the running slope of the curb ramp it serves. The 48 inch (1220 mm) minimum by 36 inch (915 mm) minimum areas and the accessible route shall be permitted to overlap.

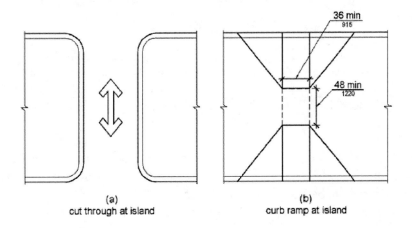

Figure 406.7 Islands in Crossings

407 Elevators

407.1 General. Elevators shall comply with 407 and with ASME A17.1 (incorporated by reference, see "Referenced Standards" in Chapter 1). They shall be passenger elevators as classified by ASME A17.1. Elevator operation shall be automatic.

Advisory

407.1 General. The ADA and other Federal civil rights laws require that accessible features be maintained in working order so that they are accessible to and usable by those people they are intended to benefit. Building owners should note that the ASME Safety Code for Elevators and Escalators requires routine maintenance and inspections. Isolated or temporary interruptions in service due to maintenance or repairs may be unavoidable; however, failure to take prompt action to effect repairs could constitute a violation of Federal laws and these requirements.

407.2 Elevator Landing Requirements. Elevator landings shall comply with 407.2.

407.2.1 Call Controls. Where elevator call buttons or keypads are provided, they shall comply with 407.2.1 and 309.4. Call buttons shall be raised or flush.

EXCEPTION: Existing elevators shall be permitted to have recessed call buttons.

407.2.1.1 Height. Call buttons and keypads shall be located within one of the reach ranges specified in 308, measured to the centerline of the highest operable part.

EXCEPTION: Existing call buttons and existing keypads shall be permitted to be located at 54 inches (1370 mm) maximum above the finish floor, measured to the centerline of the highest operable part.

407.2.1.2 Size. Call buttons shall be 3/4 inch (19 mm) minimum in the smallest dimension.

EXCEPTION: Existing elevator call buttons shall not be required to comply with 407.2.1.2.

407.2.1.3 Clear Floor or Ground Space. A clear floor or ground space complying with 305 shall be provided at call controls.

Advisory

407.2.1.3 Clear Floor or Ground Space. The clear floor or ground space required at elevator call buttons must remain free of obstructions including ashtrays, plants, and other decorative elements that prevent wheelchair users and others from reaching the call buttons. The height of the clear floor or ground space is considered to be a volume from the floor to 80 inches (2030 mm) above the floor. Recessed ashtrays should not be placed near elevator call buttons so that persons who are blind or visually impaired do not inadvertently contact them or their contents as they reach for the call buttons.

407.2.1.4 Location. The call button that designates the up direction shall be located above the call button that designates the down direction.

EXCEPTION: Destination-oriented elevators shall not be required to comply with 407.2.1.4.

Advisory

407.2.1.4 Location Exception. A destination-oriented elevator system provides lobby controls enabling passengers to select floor stops, lobby indicators designating which elevator to use, and a car indicator designating the floors at which the car will stop. Responding cars are programmed for maximum efficiency by reducing the number of stops any passenger experiences.

407.2.1.5 Signals. Call buttons shall have visible signals to indicate when each call is registered and when each call is answered.

EXCEPTIONS:

1. Destination-oriented elevators shall not be required to comply with 407.2.1.5 provided that visible and audible signals complying with 407.2.2 indicating which elevator car to enter are provided.

2. Existing elevators shall not be required to comply with 407.2.1.5.

407.2.1.6 Keypads. Where keypads are provided, keypads shall be in a standard telephone keypad arrangement and shall comply with 407.4.7.2.

407.2.2 Hall Signals. Hall signals, including in-car signals, shall comply with 407.2.2.

407.2.2.1 Visible and Audible Signals. A visible and audible signal shall be provided at each hoistway entrance to indicate which car is answering a call and the car's direction of travel. Where in-car signals are provided, they shall be visible from the floor area adjacent to the hall call buttons.

EXCEPTIONS:

1. Visible and audible signals shall not be required at each destination-oriented elevator where a visible and audible signal complying with 407.2.2 is provided indicating the elevator car designation information.

2. In existing elevators, a signal indicating the direction of car travel shall not be required.

407.2.2.2 Visible Signals. Visible signal fixtures shall be centered at 72 inches (1830 mm) minimum above the finish floor or ground. The visible signal elements shall be 2 1/2 inches (64 mm) minimum measured along the vertical centerline of the element. Signals shall be visible from the floor area adjacent to the hall call button.

EXCEPTIONS:

1. Destination-oriented elevators shall be permitted to have signals visible from the floor area adjacent to the hoistway entrance.

2. Existing elevators shall not be required to comply with 407.2.2.2.

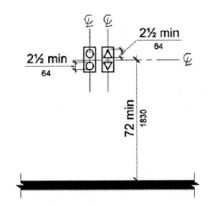

Figure 407.2.2.2 Visible Hall Signals

407.2.2.3 Audible Signals. Audible signals shall sound once for the up direction and twice for the down direction, or shall have verbal annunciators that indicate the direction of elevator car travel. Audible signals shall have a frequency of 1500 Hz maximum. Verbal annunciators shall have a frequency of 300 Hz minimum and 3000 Hz maximum. The audible signal and verbal annunciator shall be 10 dB minimum above ambient, but shall not exceed 80 dB, measured at the hall call button.

EXCEPTIONS:

1. Destination-oriented elevators shall not be required to comply with 407.2.2.3 provided that the audible tone and verbal announcement is the same as those given at the call button or call button keypad.

2. Existing elevators shall not be required to comply with the requirements for frequency and dB range of audible signals.

407.2.2.4 Differentiation. Each destination-oriented elevator in a bank of elevators shall have audible and visible means for differentiation.

407.2.3 Hoistway Signs. Signs at elevator hoistways shall comply with 407.2.3.

407.2.3.1 Floor Designation. Floor designations complying with 703.2 and 703.4.1 shall be provided on both jambs of elevator hoistway entrances. Floor designations shall be provided in both tactile characters and braille. Tactile characters shall be 2 inches (51 mm) high minimum. A tactile star shall be provided on both jambs at the main entry level.

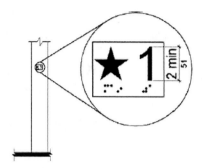

Figure 407.2.3.1 Floor Designations on Jambs of Elevator Hoistway Entrances

407.2.3.2 Car Designations. Destination-oriented elevators shall provide tactile car identification complying with 703.2 on both jambs of the hoistway immediately below the floor designation. Car designations shall be provided in both tactile characters and braille. Tactile characters shall be 2 inches (51 mm) high minimum.

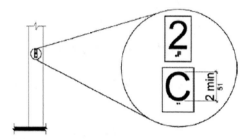

Figure 407.2.3.2 Car Designations on Jambs of Destination-Oriented Elevator Hoistway Entrances

407.3 Elevator Door Requirements. Hoistway and car doors shall comply with 407.3.

407.3.1 Type. Elevator doors shall be the horizontal sliding type. Car gates shall be prohibited.

407.3.2 Operation. Elevator hoistway and car doors shall open and close automatically.

> **EXCEPTION:** Existing manually operated hoistway swing doors shall be permitted provided that they comply with 404.2.3 and 404.2.9. Car door closing shall not be initiated until the hoistway door is closed.

407.3.3 Reopening Device. Elevator doors shall be provided with a reopening device complying with 407.3.3 that shall stop and reopen a car door and hoistway door automatically if the door becomes obstructed by an object or person.

> **EXCEPTION:** Existing elevators with manually operated doors shall not be required to comply with 407.3.3.

407.3.3.1 Height. The device shall be activated by sensing an obstruction passing through the opening at 5 inches (125 mm) nominal and 29 inches (735 mm) nominal above the finish floor.

407.3.3.2 Contact. The device shall not require physical contact to be activated, although contact is permitted to occur before the door reverses.

407.3.3.3 Duration. Door reopening devices shall remain effective for 20 seconds minimum.

407.3.4 Door and Signal Timing. The minimum acceptable time from notification that a car is answering a call or notification of the car assigned at the means for the entry of destination information until the doors of that car start to close shall be calculated from the following equation:

T = D/(1.5 ft/s) or T = D/(455 mm/s) = 5 seconds minimum where T equals the total time in seconds and D equals the distance (in feet or millimeters) from the point in the lobby or corridor 60 inches (1525 mm) directly in front of the farthest call button controlling that car to the centerline of its hoistway door.

EXCEPTIONS:

1. For cars with in-car lanterns, T shall be permitted to begin when the signal is visible from the point 60 inches (1525 mm) directly in front of the farthest hall call button and the audible signal is sounded.

2. Destination-oriented elevators shall not be required to comply with 407.3.4.

407.3.5 Door Delay. Elevator doors shall remain fully open in response to a car call for 3 seconds minimum.

407.3.6 Width. The width of elevator doors shall comply with Table 407.4.1.

EXCEPTION: In existing elevators, a power-operated car door complying with 404.2.3 shall be permitted.

407.4 Elevator Car Requirements. Elevator cars shall comply with 407.4.

407.4.1 Car Dimensions. Inside dimensions of elevator cars and clear width of elevator doors shall comply with Table 407.4.1.

EXCEPTION: Existing elevator car configurations that provide a clear floor area of 16 square feet (1.5 m^2) minimum and also provide an inside clear depth 54 inches (1370 mm) minimum and a clear width 36 inches (915 mm) minimum shall be permitted.

Table 407.4.1 Elevator Car Dimensions (text version)				
	Minimum Dimensions			
Door Location	**Door Clear Width**	**Inside Car, Side to Side**	**Inside Car, Back Wall to Front Return**	**Inside Car, Back Wall to Inside Face of Door**
Centered	42 inches (1065 mm)	80 inches (2030 mm)	51 inches (1295 mm)	54 inches (1370 mm)
Side (off-centered)	36 inches (915 mm)[1]	68 inches (1725 mm)	51 inches (1295 mm)	54 inches (1370 mm)
Any	36 inches (915 mm)[1]	54 inches (1370 mm)	80 inches (2030 mm)	80 inches (2030 mm)
Any	36 inches (915 mm)[1]	60 inches (1525 mm)[2]	60 inches (1525 mm)[2]	60 inches (1525 mm)[2]

[1.] A tolerance of minus 5/8 inch (16 mm) is permitted.

[2.] Other car configurations that provide a turning space complying with 304 with the door closed shall be permitted.

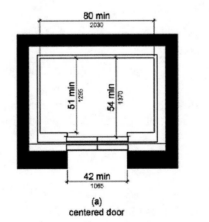

(a)
centered door

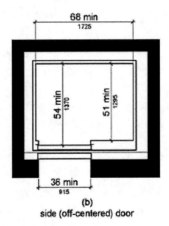

(b)
side (off-centered) door

Figure 407.4.1 Elevator Car Dimensions

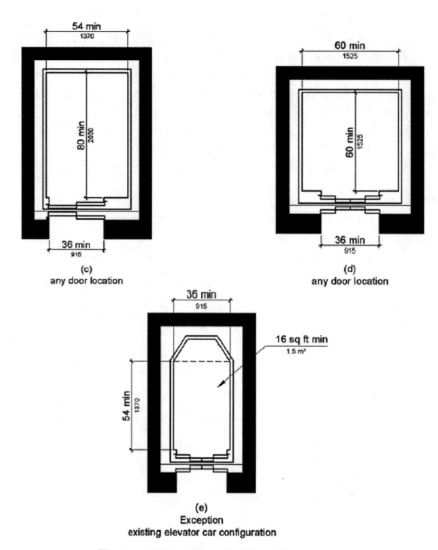

Figure 407.4.1 Elevator Car Dimensions

407.4.2 Floor Surfaces. Floor surfaces in elevator cars shall comply with 302 and 303.

407.4.3 Platform to Hoistway Clearance. The clearance between the car platform sill and the edge of any hoistway landing shall be 1 1/4 inch (32 mm) maximum.

407.4.4 Leveling. Each car shall be equipped with a self-leveling feature that will automatically bring and maintain the car at floor landings within a tolerance of 1/2 inch (13 mm) under rated loading to zero loading conditions.

407.4.5 Illumination. The level of illumination at the car controls, platform, car threshold and car landing sill shall be 5 foot candles (54 lux) minimum.

407.4.6 Elevator Car Controls. Where provided, elevator car controls shall comply with 407.4.6 and 309.4.

    EXCEPTION: In existing elevators, where a new car operating panel complying with 407.4.6 is provided, existing car operating panels shall not be required to comply with 407.4.6.

407.4.6.1 Location. Controls shall be located within one of the reach ranges specified in 308.

EXCEPTIONS:

1. Where the elevator panel serves more than 16 openings and a parallel approach is provided, buttons with floor designations shall be permitted to be 54 inches (1370 mm) maximum above the finish floor.

2. In existing elevators, car control buttons with floor designations shall be permitted to be located 54 inches (1370 mm) maximum above the finish floor where a parallel approach is provided.

407.4.6.2 Buttons. Car control buttons with floor designations shall comply with 407.4.6.2 and shall be raised or flush.

EXCEPTION: In existing elevators, buttons shall be permitted to be recessed.

407.4.6.2.1 Size. Buttons shall be 3/4 inch (19 mm) minimum in their smallest dimension.

407.4.6.2.2 Arrangement. Buttons shall be arranged with numbers in ascending order. When two or more columns of buttons are provided they shall read from left to right.

407.4.6.3 Keypads. Car control keypads shall be in a standard telephone keypad arrangement and shall comply with 407.4.7.2.

407.4.6.4 Emergency Controls. Emergency controls shall comply with 407.4.6.4.

407.4.6.4.1 Height. Emergency control buttons shall have their centerlines 35 inches (890 mm) minimum above the finish floor.

407.4.6.4.2 Location. Emergency controls, including the emergency alarm, shall be grouped at the bottom of the panel.

407.4.7 Designations and Indicators of Car Controls. Designations and indicators of car controls shall comply with 407.4.7.

EXCEPTION: In existing elevators, where a new car operating panel complying with 407.4.7 is provided, existing car operating panels shall not be required to comply with 407.4.7.

407.4.7.1 Buttons. Car control buttons shall comply with 407.4.7.1.

407.4.7.1.1 Type. Control buttons shall be identified by tactile characters complying with 703.2.

407.4.7.1.2 Location. Raised character and braille designations shall be placed immediately to the left of the control button to which the designations apply.

EXCEPTION: Where space on an existing car operating panel precludes tactile markings to the left of the controls, markings shall be placed as near to the control as possible.

407.4.7.1.3 Symbols. The control button for the emergency stop, alarm, door open, door close, main entry floor, and phone, shall be identified with tactile symbols as shown in Table 407.4.7.1.3.

Table 407.4.7.1.3 Elevator Control Button Identification		
Control Button	**Tactile Symbol**	**Braille Message**
Emergency Stop	⊗	"ST"OP Three cells
Alarm	🔔	AL"AR"M Four cells
Door Open	◀❚▶	OP"EN" Three cells
Door Close	▶❚◀	CLOSE Five cells
Main Entry Floor	★	MA"IN" Three cells
Phone	☎	PH"ONE" Four cells

407.4.7.1.4 Visible Indicators. Buttons with floor designations shall be provided with visible indicators to show that a call has been registered. The visible indication shall extinguish when the car arrives at the designated floor.

407.4.7.2 Keypads. Keypads shall be identified by characters complying with 703.5 and shall be centered on the corresponding keypad button. The number five key shall have a single raised dot. The dot shall be 0.118 inch (3 mm) to 0.120 inch (3.05 mm) base diameter and in other aspects comply with Table 703.3.1.

407.4.8 Car Position Indicators. Audible and visible car position indicators shall be provided in elevator cars.

407.4.8.1 Visible Indicators. Visible indicators shall comply with 407.4.8.1.

407.4.8.1.1 Size. Characters shall be 1/2 inch (13 mm) high minimum.

407.4.8.1.2 Location. Indicators shall be located above the car control panel or above the door.

407.4.8.1.3 Floor Arrival. As the car passes a floor and when a car stops at a floor served by the elevator, the corresponding character shall illuminate.

> **EXCEPTION:** Destination-oriented elevators shall not be required to comply with 407.4.8.1.3 provided that the visible indicators extinguish when the call has been answered.

407.4.8.1.4 Destination Indicator. In destination-oriented elevators, a display shall be provided in the car with visible indicators to show car destinations.

407.4.8.2 Audible Indicators. Audible indicators shall comply with 407.4.8.2.

407.4.8.2.1 Signal Type. The signal shall be an automatic verbal annunciator which announces the floor at which the car is about to stop.

> **EXCEPTION:** For elevators other than destination-oriented elevators that have a rated speed of 200 feet per minute (1 m/s) or less, a non-verbal audible signal with a frequency of 1500 Hz maximum which sounds as the car passes or is about to stop at a floor served by the elevator shall be permitted.

407.4.8.2.2 Signal Level. The verbal annunciator shall be 10 dB minimum above ambient, but shall not exceed 80 dB, measured at the annunciator.

407.4.8.2.3 Frequency. The verbal annunciator shall have a frequency of 300 Hz minimum to 3000 Hz maximum.

407.4.9 Emergency Communication. Emergency two-way communication systems shall comply with 308. Tactile symbols and characters shall be provided adjacent to the device and shall comply with 703.2.

408 Limited-Use/Limited-Application Elevators

408.1 General. Limited-use/limited-application elevators shall comply with 408 and with ASME A17.1 (incorporated by reference, see "Referenced Standards" in Chapter 1). They shall be passenger elevators as classified by ASME A17.1. Elevator operation shall be automatic.

408.2 Elevator Landings. Landings serving limited-use/limited-application elevators shall comply with 408.2.

408.2.1 Call Buttons. Elevator call buttons and keypads shall comply with 407.2.1.

408.2.2 Hall Signals. Hall signals shall comply with 407.2.2.

408.2.3 Hoistway Signs. Signs at elevator hoistways shall comply with 407.2.3.1.

408.3 Elevator Doors. Elevator hoistway doors shall comply with 408.3.

408.3.1 Sliding Doors. Sliding hoistway and car doors shall comply with 407.3.1 through 407.3.3 and 408.4.1.

408.3.2 Swinging Doors. Swinging hoistway doors shall open and close automatically and shall comply with 404, 407.3.2 and 408.3.2.

408.3.2.1 Power Operation. Swinging doors shall be power-operated and shall comply with ANSI/BHMA A156.19 (1997 or 2002 edition) (incorporated by reference, see "Referenced Standards" in Chapter 1).

408.3.2.2 Duration. Power-operated swinging doors shall remain open for 20 seconds minimum when activated.

408.4 Elevator Cars. Elevator cars shall comply with 408.4.

408.4.1 Car Dimensions and Doors. Elevator cars shall provide a clear width 42 inches (1065 mm) minimum and a clear depth 54 inches (1370 mm) minimum. Car doors shall be positioned at the narrow ends of cars and shall provide 32 inches (815 mm) minimum clear width.

EXCEPTIONS:

1. Cars that provide a clear width 51 inches (1295 mm) minimum shall be permitted to provide a clear depth 51 inches (1295 mm) minimum provided that car doors provide a clear opening 36 inches (915 mm) wide minimum.

2. Existing elevator cars shall be permitted to provide a clear width 36 inches (915 mm) minimum, clear depth 54 inches (1370 mm) minimum, and a net clear platform area 15 square feet (1.4 m^2) minimum.

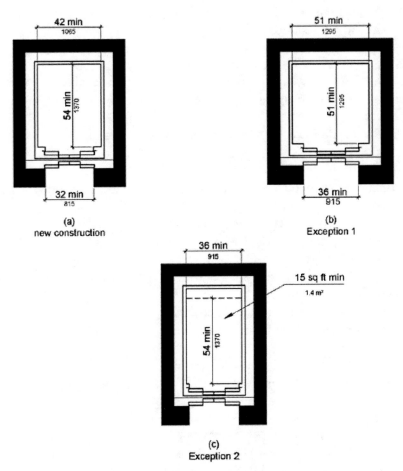

Figure 408.4.1 Limited-Use/Limited-Application (LULA) Elevator Car Dimensions

408.4.2 Floor Surfaces. Floor surfaces in elevator cars shall comply with 302 and 303.

408.4.3 Platform to Hoistway Clearance. The platform to hoistway clearance shall comply with 407.4.3.

408.4.4 Leveling. Elevator car leveling shall comply with 407.4.4.

408.4.5 Illumination. Elevator car illumination shall comply with 407.4.5.

408.4.6 Car Controls. Elevator car controls shall comply with 407.4.6. Control panels shall be centered on a side wall.

408.4.7 Designations and Indicators of Car Controls. Designations and indicators of car controls shall comply with 407.4.7.

408.4.8 Emergency Communications. Car emergency signaling devices complying with 407.4.9 shall be provided.

409 Private Residence Elevators

409.1 General. Private residence elevators that are provided within a residential dwelling unit required to provide mobility features complying with 809.2 through 809.4 shall comply with 409 and with ASME A17.1 (incorporated by reference, see "Referenced Standards" in Chapter 1). They shall be passenger elevators as classified by ASME A17.1. Elevator operation shall be automatic.

409.2 Call Buttons. Call buttons shall be 3/4 inch (19 mm) minimum in the smallest dimension and shall comply with 309.

409.3 Elevator Doors. Hoistway doors, car doors, and car gates shall comply with 409.3 and 404.

> **EXCEPTION:** Doors shall not be required to comply with the maneuvering clearance requirements in 404.2.4.1 for approaches to the push side of swinging doors.

409.3.1 Power Operation. Elevator car and hoistway doors and gates shall be power operated and shall comply with ANSI/BHMA A156.19 (1997 or 2002 edition) (incorporated by reference, see "Referenced Standards" in Chapter 1). Power operated doors and gates shall remain open for 20 seconds minimum when activated.

> **EXCEPTION:** In elevator cars with more than one opening, hoistway doors and gates shall be permitted to be of the manual-open, self-close type.

409.3.2 Location. Elevator car doors or gates shall be positioned at the narrow end of the clear floor spaces required by 409.4.1.

409.4 Elevator Cars. Private residence elevator cars shall comply with 409.4.

409.4.1 Inside Dimensions of Elevator Cars. Elevator cars shall provide a clear floor space of 36 inches (915 mm) minimum by 48 inches (1220 mm) minimum and shall comply with 305.

409.4.2 Floor Surfaces. Floor surfaces in elevator cars shall comply with 302 and 303.

409.4.3 Platform to Hoistway Clearance. The clearance between the car platform and the edge of any landing sill shall be 1 1/2 inch (38 mm) maximum.

409.4.4 Leveling. Each car shall automatically stop at a floor landing within a tolerance of 1/2 inch (13 mm) under rated loading to zero loading conditions.

409.4.5 Illumination Levels. Elevator car illumination shall comply with 407.4.5.

409.4.6 Car Controls. Elevator car control buttons shall comply with 409.4.6, 309.3, 309.4, and shall be raised or flush.

409.4.6.1 Size. Control buttons shall be 3/4 inch (19 mm) minimum in their smallest dimension.

409.4.6.2 Location. Control panels shall be on a side wall, 12 inches (305 mm) minimum from any adjacent wall.

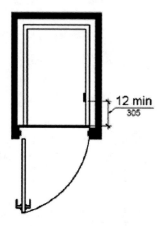

Figure 409.4.6.2 Location of Private Residence Elevator Control Panel

409.4.7 Emergency Communications. Emergency two-way communication systems shall comply with 409.4.7.

409.4.7.1 Type. A telephone and emergency signal device shall be provided in the car.

409.4.7.2 Operable Parts. The telephone and emergency signaling device shall comply with 309.3 and 309.4.

409.4.7.3 Compartment. If the telephone or device is in a closed compartment, the compartment door hardware shall comply with 309.

409.4.7.4 Cord. The telephone cord shall be 29 inches (735 mm) long minimum.

410 Platform Lifts

410.1 General. Platform lifts shall comply with ASME A18.1 (1999 edition or 2003 edition) (incorporated by reference, see "Referenced Standards" in Chapter 1). Platform lifts shall not be attendant-operated and shall provide unassisted entry and exit from the lift.

Advisory

410.1 General. Inclined stairway chairlifts and inclined and vertical platform lifts are available for short-distance vertical transportation. Because an accessible route requires an 80 inch (2030 mm) vertical clearance, care should be taken in selecting lifts as they may not be equally suitable for use by people using wheelchairs and people standing. If a lift does not provide 80 inch (2030 mm) vertical clearance, it cannot be considered part of an accessible route in new construction.

The ADA and other Federal civil rights laws require that accessible features be maintained in working order so that they are accessible to and usable by those people they are intended to benefit. Building owners are reminded that the ASME A18 Safety Standard for Platform Lifts and Stairway Chairlifts requires routine maintenance and inspections. Isolated or temporary interruptions in service due to maintenance or repairs may be unavoidable; however, failure to take prompt action to effect repairs could constitute a violation of Federal laws and these requirements.

410.2 Floor Surfaces. Floor surfaces in platform lifts shall comply with 302 and 303.

410.3 Clear Floor Space. Clear floor space in platform lifts shall comply with 305.

410.4 Platform to Runway Clearance. The clearance between the platform sill and the edge of any runway landing shall be 1 inch (32 mm) maximum.

410.5 Operable Parts. Controls for platform lifts shall comply with 309.

410.6 Doors and Gates. Platform lifts shall have low-energy power-operated doors or gates complying with 404.3. Doors shall remain open for 20 seconds minimum. End doors and gates shall provide a clear width 32 inches (815 mm) minimum. Side doors and gates shall provide a clear width 42 inches (1065 mm) minimum.

EXCEPTION: Platform lifts serving two landings maximum and having doors or gates on opposite sides shall be permitted to have self-closing manual doors or gates.

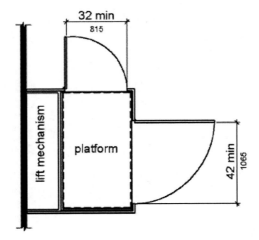

Figure 410.6 Platform Lift Doors and Gates

CHAPTER 5: GENERAL SITE AND BUILDING ELEMENTS

501 General

501.1 Scope. The provisions of Chapter 5 shall apply where required by Chapter 2 or where referenced by a requirement in this document.

502 Parking Spaces

502.1 General. Car and van parking spaces shall comply with 502. Where parking spaces are marked with lines, width measurements of parking spaces and access aisles shall be made from the centerline of the markings.

> **EXCEPTION:** Where parking spaces or access aisles are not adjacent to another parking space or access aisle, measurements shall be permitted to include the full width of the line defining the parking space or access aisle.

502.2 Vehicle Spaces. Car parking spaces shall be 96 inches (2440 mm) wide minimum and van parking spaces shall be 132 inches (3350 mm) wide minimum, shall be marked to define the width, and shall have an adjacent access aisle complying with 502.3.

> **EXCEPTION:** Van parking spaces shall be permitted to be 96 inches (2440 mm) wide minimum where the access aisle is 96 inches (2440 mm) wide minimum.

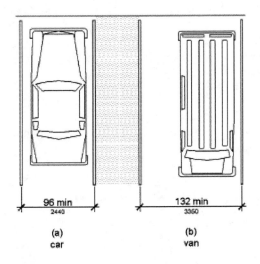

96 min
2440

132 min
3350

(a)
car

(b)
van

Figure 502.2 Vehicle Parking Spaces

502.3 Access Aisle. Access aisles serving parking spaces shall comply with 502.3. Access aisles shall adjoin an accessible route. Two parking spaces shall be permitted to share a common access aisle.

Advisory

502.3 Access Aisle. Accessible routes must connect parking spaces to accessible entrances. In parking facilities where the accessible route must cross vehicular traffic lanes, marked crossings enhance pedestrian safety, particularly for people using wheelchairs and other mobility aids. Where possible, it is preferable that the accessible route not pass behind parked vehicles.

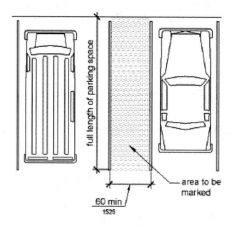

Figure 502.3 Parking Space Access Aisle

502.3.1 Width. Access aisles serving car and van parking spaces shall be 60 inches (1525 mm) wide minimum.

502.3.2 Length. Access aisles shall extend the full length of the parking spaces they serve.

502.3.3 Marking. Access aisles shall be marked so as to discourage parking in them.

> *Advisory*
>
> *502.3.3 Marking. The method and color of marking are not specified by these requirements but may be addressed by State or local laws or regulations. Because these requirements permit the van access aisle to be as wide as a parking space, it is important that the aisle be clearly marked.*

502.3.4 Location. Access aisles shall not overlap the vehicular way. Access aisles shall be permitted to be placed on either side of the parking space except for angled van parking spaces which shall have access aisles located on the passenger side of the parking spaces.

> *Advisory*
>
> *502.3.4 Location. Wheelchair lifts typically are installed on the passenger side of vans. Many drivers, especially those who operate vans, find it more difficult to back into parking spaces than to back out into comparatively unrestricted vehicular lanes. For this reason, where a van and car share an access aisle, consider locating the van space so that the access aisle is on the passenger side of the van space.*

502.4 Floor or Ground Surfaces. Parking spaces and access aisles serving them shall comply with 302. Access aisles shall be at the same level as the parking spaces they serve. Changes in level are not permitted.

    EXCEPTION: Slopes not steeper than 1:48 shall be permitted.

> *Advisory*
>
> *502.4 Floor or Ground Surfaces. Access aisles are required to be nearly level in all directions to provide a surface for wheelchair transfer to and from vehicles. The exception allows sufficient slope for drainage. Built-up curb ramps are not permitted to project into access aisles and parking spaces because they would create slopes greater than 1:48.*

502.5 Vertical Clearance. Parking spaces for vans and access aisles and vehicular routes serving them shall provide a vertical clearance of 98 inches (2490 mm) minimum.

> *Advisory*
>
> *502.5 Vertical Clearance. Signs provided at entrances to parking facilities informing drivers of clearances and the location of van accessible parking spaces can provide useful customer assistance.*

502.6 Identification. Parking space identification signs shall include the International Symbol of Accessibility complying with 703.7.2.1. Signs identifying van parking spaces shall contain the designation "van accessible." Signs shall be 60 inches (1525 mm) minimum above the finish floor or ground surface measured to the bottom of the sign.

Advisory

502.6 Identification. The required "van accessible" designation is intended to be informative, not restrictive, in identifying those spaces that are better suited for van use. Enforcement of motor vehicle laws, including parking privileges, is a local matter.

502.7 Relationship to Accessible Routes. Parking spaces and access aisles shall be designed so that cars and vans, when parked, cannot obstruct the required clear width of adjacent accessible routes.

Advisory

502.7 Relationship to Accessible Routes. Wheel stops are an effective way to prevent vehicle overhangs from reducing the clear width of accessible routes.

Guidance

General. Where parking spaces are provided, the 1991 Standards, at sections 4.1.2 (5)(a) and (7) and 7(a), and the 2010 Standards, at section 208.1, require a specified number of the parking spaces to be accessible. The 2010 Standards, at section 208, include an exception that exempts parking spaces used exclusively for buses, trucks, delivery vehicles, law enforcement vehicles, or for purposes of vehicular impound, from the scoping requirement for parking spaces, provided that when these lots are accessed by the public the lot has an accessible passenger loading zone.

The 2010 Standards require accessible parking spaces to be identified by signs that display the International Symbol of Accessibility. Section 216.5, Exceptions 1 and 2, of the 2010 Standards exempt certain accessible parking spaces from this signage requirement. The first exception exempts sites that have four or fewer parking spaces from the signage requirement. Residential facilities where parking spaces are assigned to specific dwelling units are also exempted from the signage requirement.

Commenters stated that the first exception, by allowing a small parking lot with four or fewer spaces not to post a sign at its one accessible space, is problematic because it could allow all drivers to park in accessible parking spaces. The Department believes that this exception provides necessary relief for small business entities that may otherwise face the prospect of having between twenty-five percent (25%) and one hundred percent (100%) of their limited parking area unavailable to their customers because they are reserved for the exclusive use of persons whose vehicles display accessible tags or parking placards. The 2010 Standards still require these businesses to ensure that at least one of their available parking spaces is designed to be accessible.

A commenter stated that accessible parking spaces must be clearly marked. The Department notes that section 502.6 of the 2010 Standards provides that accessible parking spaces must be identified by signs that include the International Symbol of Accessibility. Also, section 502.3.3 of the 2010 Standards requires that access aisles be marked so as to discourage parking in them.

Access Aisle. Section 502.3 of the 2010 Standards requires that an accessible route adjoin each access aisle serving accessible parking spaces. The accessible route connects each access aisle to accessible entrances.

Commenters questioned why the 2010 Standards would permit an accessible route used by individuals with disabilities to coincide with the path of moving vehicles. The Department believes that the 2010 Standards appropriately recognize that not all parking facilities provide separate pedestrian routes. Section 502.3 of the 2010 Standards provides the flexibility necessary to permit designers and others to determine the most appropriate location of the accessible route to the accessible entrances. If all pedestrians using the parking facility are expected to share the vehicular lanes, then the ADA permits covered entities to use the vehicular lanes as part of the accessible route. The advisory note in section 502.3 of the 2010 Standards, however, calls attention to the fact that this practice, while permitted, is not ideal. Accessible parking spaces must be located on the shortest accessible route of travel to an accessible entrance. Accessible parking spaces and the required accessible route should be located where individuals with disabilities do not have to cross vehicular lanes or pass behind parked vehicles to have access to an accessible entrance. If it is necessary to cross a vehicular lane because, for example, local fire engine access requirements prohibit parking immediately adjacent to a building, then a marked crossing running perpendicular to the vehicular route should be included as part of the accessible route to an accessible entrance.

Van Accessible Parking Spaces. The 1991 Standards, at sections 4.1.2 (5)(b), 4.6.3, 4.6.4, and 4.6.5, require one in every eight accessible parking spaces to be van accessible. Section 208.2.4 of the 2010 Standards requires one in every six accessible parking spaces to be van accessible.

A commenter asked whether automobiles other than vans may park in van accessible parking spaces. The 2010 Standards do not prohibit automobiles other than vans from using van accessible parking spaces. The Department does not distinguish between vehicles that are actual "vans" versus other vehicles such as trucks, station wagons, sport utility vehicles, etc. since many vehicles other than vans may be used by individuals with disabilities to transport mobility devices.

Commenters' opinions were divided on this point. Facility operators and others asked for a reduction in the number of required accessible parking spaces, especially the number of van accessible parking spaces, because they claimed these spaces often are not used. Individuals with disabilities, however, requested an increase in the scoping requirements for these parking spaces.

The Department is aware that a strong difference of opinion exists between those who use such spaces and those who must provide or maintain them. Therefore, the Department did not increase the total number of accessible spaces required. The only change was to increase the proportion of spaces that must be accessible to vans and other vehicles equipped to transport mobility devices.

Direct Access Entrances from Parking Structures. Where levels in a parking garage have direct connections for pedestrians to another facility, the 1991 Standards, at section 4.1.3(8)(b)(i), require at least one of the direct connections to be accessible. The 2010 Standards, at section 206.4.2, require all of these direct connections to be accessible.

503 Passenger Loading Zones

503.1 General. Passenger loading zones shall comply with 503.

503.2 Vehicle Pull-Up Space. Passenger loading zones shall provide a vehicular pull-up space 96 inches (2440 mm) wide minimum and 20 feet (6100 mm) long minimum.

503.3 Access Aisle. Passenger loading zones shall provide access aisles complying with 503 adjacent to the vehicle pull-up space. Access aisles shall adjoin an accessible route and shall not overlap the vehicular way.

503.3.1 Width. Access aisles serving vehicle pull-up spaces shall be 60 inches (1525 mm) wide minimum.

503.3.2 Length. Access aisles shall extend the full length of the vehicle pull-up spaces they serve.

503.3.3 Marking. Access aisles shall be marked so as to discourage parking in them.

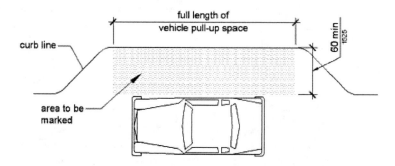

Figure 503.3 Passenger Loading Zone Access Aisle

503.4 Floor and Ground Surfaces. Vehicle pull-up spaces and access aisles serving them shall comply with 302. Access aisles shall be at the same level as the vehicle pull-up space they serve. Changes in level are not permitted.

EXCEPTION: Slopes not steeper than 1:48 shall be permitted.

503.5 Vertical Clearance. Vehicle pull-up spaces, access aisles serving them, and a vehicular route from an entrance to the passenger loading zone, and from the passenger loading zone to a vehicular exit shall provide a vertical clearance of 114 inches (2895 mm) minimum.

Guidance

Passenger Loading Zones at Medical Care and Long-Term Care Facilities. Sections 6.1 and 6.2 of the 1991 Standards and section 209.3 of the 2010 Standards require medical care and long-term care facilities, where the period of stay exceeds 24 hours, to provide at least one accessible passenger loading zone at an accessible entrance. The 1991 Standards also require a canopy or roof overhang at this passenger loading zone. The 2010 Standards do not require a canopy or roof overhang.

Commenters urged the Department to reinstate the requirement for a canopy or roof overhang at accessible passenger loading zones at medical care and long-term care facilities. While the Department recognizes that a canopy or roof overhang may afford useful protection from inclement weather conditions to everyone using a facility, it is not clear that the absence of such protection would impede access by individuals with disabilities. Therefore, the Department declined to reinstate that requirement.

Passenger Loading Zones. Where passenger loading zones are provided, the 1991 Standards, at sections 4.1.2(5) and 4.6.6, require at least one passenger loading zone to be accessible. Sections 209.2.1 and 503 of the 2010 Standards, require facilities such as airport passenger terminals that have long, continuous passenger loading zones to provide one accessible passenger loading zone in every continuous 100 linear feet of loading zone space. The 1991 Standards and the 2010 Standards both include technical requirements for the vehicle pull-up space (96 inches wide minimum and 20 feet long minimum). Accessible passenger loading zones must have an access aisle that is 60 inches wide minimum and extends the full length of the vehicle pull-up space. The 1991 Standards permit the access aisle to be on the same level as the vehicle pull-up space, or on the sidewalk. The 2010 Standards require the access aisle to be on the same level as the vehicle pull-up space and to be marked so as to discourage parking in the access aisle.

Commenters expressed concern that certain covered entities, particularly airports, cannot accommodate the requirements of the 2010 Standards to provide passenger loading zones, and urged a revision that would require one accessible passenger loading zone located in reasonable proximity to each building entrance served by the curb.

Commenters raised a variety of issues about the requirements at section 503 of the 2010 Standards stating that the requirements for an access aisle, width, length, and marking of passenger loading zones are not clear, do not fully meet the needs of individuals with disabilities, may run afoul of state or local requirements, or may not be needed because many passenger loading zones are typically staffed by doormen or valet parkers. The wide range of opinions expressed in these comments indicates that this provision is controversial. However, none of these comments provided sufficient data to enable the Department to determine that the requirement is not appropriate.

Valet Parking and Mechanical Access Parking Garages. The 1991 Standards, at sections 4.1.2(5)(a) and (e), and sections 208.2, 209.4, and 209.5 of the 2010 Standards require parking facilities that provide valet parking services to have an accessible passenger loading zone. The 2010 Standards extend this requirement to mechanical access parking garages. The 1991 Standards contained an exception that exempted valet parking facilities from providing accessible parking spaces. The 2010 Standards eliminate this exception. The reason for not retaining the provision is that valet parking is a service, not a facility type.

Commenters questioned why the exception for valet parking facilities from providing accessible parking spaces was eliminated. The provision was eliminated because valet parkers may not have the skills necessary to drive a vehicle that is equipped to be accessible, including use of hand controls, or when a seat is not present to accommodate a driver using a wheelchair. In that case, permitting the individual with a disability to self-park may be a required reasonable modification of policy by a covered entity.

504 Stairways

504.1 General. Stairs shall comply with 504.

504.2 Treads and Risers. All steps on a flight of stairs shall have uniform riser heights and uniform tread depths. Risers shall be 4 inches (100 mm) high minimum and 7 inches (180 mm) high maximum. Treads shall be 11 inches (280 mm) deep minimum.

504.3 Open Risers. Open risers are not permitted.

504.4 Tread Surface. Stair treads shall comply with 302. Changes in level are not permitted.

 EXCEPTION: Treads shall be permitted to have a slope not steeper than 1:48.

Advisory
504.4 Tread Surface. Consider providing visual contrast on tread nosings, or at the leading edges of treads without nosings, so that stair treads are more visible for people with low vision.

504.5 Nosings. The radius of curvature at the leading edge of the tread shall be 1/2 inch (13 mm) maximum. Nosings that project beyond risers shall have the underside of the leading edge curved or beveled. Risers shall be permitted to slope under the tread at an angle of 30 degrees maximum from vertical. The permitted projection of the nosing shall extend 1 1/2 inches (38 mm) maximum over the tread below.

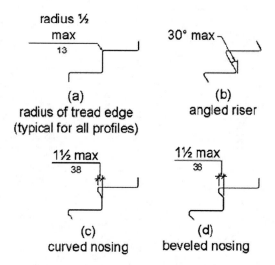

Figure 504.5 Stair Nosings

504.6 Handrails. Stairs shall have handrails complying with 505.

504.7 Wet Conditions. Stair treads and landings subject to wet conditions shall be designed to prevent the accumulation of water.

> ### Guidance
>
> The 1991 Standards require stairs to be accessible only when they provide access to floor levels not otherwise connected by an accessible route (e.g., where the accessible route is provided by an elevator, lift, or ramp). The 2010 Standards, at sections 210.1 and 504, require all *newly constructed stairs* that are part of a *means of egress* to comply with the requirements for accessible stairs, which include requirements for accessible treads, risers, and handrails. In existing facilities, where floor levels are connected by an accessible route, only the handrail requirement will apply when the stairs are altered. Exception 2 to section 210.1 of the 2010 Standards permits altered stairs to not comply with the requirements for accessible treads and risers where there is an accessible route between floors served by the stairs.
>
> Most commenters were in favor of this requirement for handrails in alterations and stated that adding handrails to stairs during alterations would be feasible and not costly while providing important safety benefits. The Department believes that it strikes an appropriate balance by focusing the expanded requirements on new construction. The 2010 Standards apply to stairs which are part of a required means of egress. Few stairways are not part of a means of egress. The 2010 Standards are consistent with most building codes which do not exempt stairways when the route is also served by a ramp or elevator.

505 Handrails

505.1 General. Handrails provided along walking surfaces complying with 403, required at ramps complying with 405, and required at stairs complying with 504 shall comply with 505.

> *Advisory*
>
> ***505.1 General.*** *Handrails are required on ramp runs with a rise greater than 6 inches (150 mm) (see 405.8) and on certain stairways (see 504). Handrails are not required on walking surfaces with running slopes less than 1:20. However, handrails are required to comply with 505 when they are provided on walking surfaces with running slopes less than 1:20 (see 403.6). Sections 505.2, 505.3, and 505.10 do not apply to handrails provided on walking surfaces with running slopes less than 1:20 as these sections only reference requirements for ramps and stairs.*

505.2 Where Required. Handrails shall be provided on both sides of stairs and ramps.

EXCEPTION: In assembly areas, handrails shall not be required on both sides of aisle ramps where a handrail is provided at either side or within the aisle width.

505.3 Continuity. Handrails shall be continuous within the full length of each stair flight or ramp run. Inside handrails on switchback or dogleg stairs and ramps shall be continuous between flights or runs.

EXCEPTION: In assembly areas, handrails on ramps shall not be required to be continuous in aisles serving seating.

505.4 Height. Top of gripping surfaces of handrails shall be 34 inches (865 mm) minimum and 38 inches (965 mm) maximum vertically above walking surfaces, stair nosings, and ramp surfaces. Handrails shall be at a consistent height above walking surfaces, stair nosings, and ramp surfaces.

> *Advisory*
>
> ***505.4 Height.*** *The requirements for stair and ramp handrails in this document are for adults. When children are the principal users in a building or facility (e.g., elementary schools), a second set of handrails at an appropriate height can assist them and aid in preventing accidents. A maximum height of 28 inches (710 mm) measured to the top of the gripping surface from the ramp surface or stair nosing is recommended for handrails designed for children. Sufficient vertical clearance between upper and lower handrails, 9 inches (230 mm) minimum, should be provided to help prevent entrapment.*

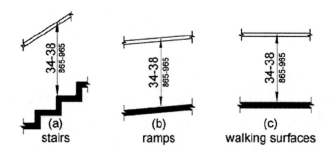

Figure 505.4 Handrail Height

505.5 Clearance. Clearance between handrail gripping surfaces and adjacent surfaces shall be 1 1/2 inches (38 mm) minimum.

Figure 505.5 Handrail Clearance

505.6 Gripping Surface. Handrail gripping surfaces shall be continuous along their length and shall not be obstructed along their tops or sides. The bottoms of handrail gripping surfaces shall not be obstructed for more than 20 percent of their length. Where provided, horizontal projections shall occur 1 1/2 inches (38 mm) minimum below the bottom of the handrail gripping surface.

EXCEPTIONS:

1. Where handrails are provided along walking surfaces with slopes not steeper than 1:20, the bottoms of handrail gripping surfaces shall be permitted to be obstructed along their entire length where they are integral to crash rails or bumper guards.

2. The distance between horizontal projections and the bottom of the gripping surface shall be permitted to be reduced by 1/8 inch (3.2 mm) for each 1/2 inch (13 mm) of additional handrail perimeter dimension that exceeds 4 inches (100 mm).

Figure 505.6 Horizontal Projections Below Gripping Surface

505.7 Cross Section. Handrail gripping surfaces shall have a cross section complying with 505.7.1 or 505.7.2.

505.7.1 Circular Cross Section. Handrail gripping surfaces with a circular cross section shall have an outside diameter of 1 1/4 inches (32 mm) minimum and 2 inches (51 mm) maximum.

505.7.2 Non-Circular Cross Sections. Handrail gripping surfaces with a non-circular cross section shall have a perimeter dimension of 4 inches (100 mm) minimum and 6 1/4 inches (160 mm) maximum, and a cross-section dimension of 2 1/4 inches (57 mm) maximum.

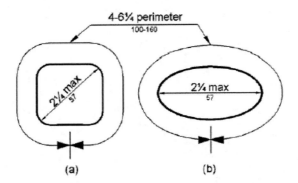

Figure 505.7.2 Handrail Non-Circular Cross Section

505.8 Surfaces. Handrail gripping surfaces and any surfaces adjacent to them shall be free of sharp or abrasive elements and shall have rounded edges.

505.9 Fittings. Handrails shall not rotate within their fittings.

505.10 Handrail Extensions. Handrail gripping surfaces shall extend beyond and in the same direction of stair flights and ramp runs in accordance with 505.10.

EXCEPTIONS:

1. Extensions shall not be required for continuous handrails at the inside turn of switchback or dogleg stairs and ramps.

2. In assembly areas, extensions shall not be required for ramp handrails in aisles serving seating where the handrails are discontinuous to provide access to seating and to permit crossovers within aisles.

3. In alterations, full extensions of handrails shall not be required where such extensions would be hazardous due to plan configuration.

505.10.1 Top and Bottom Extension at Ramps. Ramp handrails shall extend horizontally above the landing for 12 inches (305 mm) minimum beyond the top and bottom of ramp runs. Extensions shall return to a wall, guard, or the landing surface, or shall be continuous to the handrail of an adjacent ramp run.

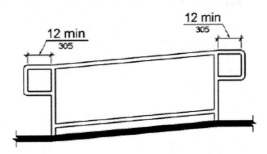

Figure 505.10.1 Top and Bottom Handrail Extension at Ramps

505.10.2 Top Extension at Stairs. At the top of a stair flight, handrails shall extend horizontally above the landing for 12 inches (305 mm) minimum beginning directly above the first riser nosing. Extensions shall return to a wall, guard, or the landing surface, or shall be continuous to the handrail of an adjacent stair flight.

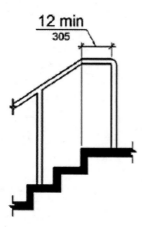

Figure 505.10.2 Top Handrail Extension at Stairs

505.10.3 Bottom Extension at Stairs. At the bottom of a stair flight, handrails shall extend at the slope of the stair flight for a horizontal distance at least equal to one tread depth beyond the last riser nosing. Extension shall return to a wall, guard, or the landing surface, or shall be continuous to the handrail of an adjacent stair flight.

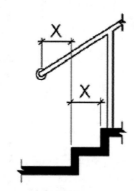

Note: X = tread depth

Figure 505.10.3 Bottom Handrail Extension at Stairs

Guidance

The 2010 Standards add a new technical requirement at section 406.3 for handrails along walking surfaces.

The 1991 Standards, at sections 4.8.5, 4.9.4, and 4.26, and the 2010 Standards, at section 505, contain technical requirements for handrails. The 2010 Standards provide more flexibility than the 1991 Standards as follows:

• Section 4.26.4 of the 1991 Standards requires handrail gripping surfaces to have edges with a minimum radius of 1/8 inch. Section 505.8 of the 2010 Standards requires handrail gripping surfaces to have rounded edges.

• Section 4.26.2 of the 1991 Standards requires handrail gripping surfaces to have a diameter of 1 ¼ inches to 1 1/2 inches, or to provide an equivalent gripping surface. Section 505.7 of the 2010 Standards requires handrail gripping surfaces with a circular cross section to have an outside diameter of 1 ¼ inches to 2 inches. Handrail gripping surfaces with a non-circular cross section must have a perimeter dimension of 4 inches to 6 ¼ inches, and a cross section dimension of 2 ¼ inches maximum.

• Sections 4.8.5 and 4.9.4 of the 1991 Standards require handrail gripping surfaces to be continuous, and to be uninterrupted by newel posts, other construction elements, or obstructions. Section 505.3 of the 2010 Standards sets technical requirements for continuity of gripping surfaces. Section 505.6 requires handrail gripping surfaces to be continuous along their length and not to be obstructed along their tops or sides. The bottoms of handrail gripping surfaces must not be obstructed for more than twenty percent (20%) of their length. Where provided, horizontal projections must occur at least 1 1/2 inches below the bottom of the handrail gripping surface. An exception permits the distance between the horizontal projections and the bottom of the gripping surface to be reduced by 1/8 inch for each 1/2 inch of additional handrail perimeter dimension that exceeds 4 inches.

• Section 4.9.4 of the 1991 Standards requires handrails at the bottom of stairs to continue to slope for a distance of the width of one tread beyond the bottom riser nosing and to further extend horizontally at least 12 inches. Section 505.10 of the 2010 Standards requires handrails at the bottom of stairs to extend at the slope of the stair flight for a horizontal distance at least equal to one tread depth beyond the last riser nosing. Section 4.1.6(3) of the 1991 Standards has a special technical provision for alterations to existing facilities that exempts handrails at the top and bottom of ramps and stairs from providing full extensions where it will be hazardous due to plan configuration. Section 505.10 of the 2010 Standards has a similar exception that applies in alterations.

A commenter noted that handrail extensions are currently required at the top and bottom of stairs, but the proposed regulations do not include this requirement, and urged the Department to retain the current requirement. Other commenters questioned the need for the extension at the bottom of stairs.

Sections 505.10.2 and 505.10.3 of the 2010 Standards require handrail extensions at both the top and bottom of a flight of stairs. The requirement in the 1991 Standards that handrails extend horizontally at least 12 inches beyond the width of one tread at the bottom of a stair was changed in the 2004 ADAAG by the Access Board in response to public comments. Existing horizontal handrail extensions that comply with 4.9.4(2) of the 1991 Standards should meet or exceed the requirements of the 2010 Standards.

Commenters noted that the 2010 Standards will require handrail gripping surfaces with a circular cross section to have an outside diameter of 2 inches, and that this requirement would impose a physical barrier to individuals with disabilities who need the handrail for stability and support while accessing stairs.

The requirement permits an outside diameter of 1 ¼ inches to 2 inches. This range allows flexibility in meeting the needs of individuals with disabilities and designers and architects. The Department is not aware of any data indicating that an outside diameter of 2 inches would pose any adverse impairment to use by individuals with disabilities.

Handrails Along Walkways. The 1991 Standards do not contain any technical requirement for handrails provided along walkways that are not ramps. Section 403.6 of the 2010 Standards specifies that where handrails are provided along walkways that are not ramps, they shall comply with certain technical requirements. The change is expected to have minimal impact.

CHAPTER 6: PLUMBING ELEMENTS AND FACILITIES

601 General

601.1 Scope. The provisions of Chapter 6 shall apply where required by Chapter 2 or where referenced by a requirement in this document.

602 Drinking Fountains

602.1 General. Drinking fountains shall comply with 307 and 602.

602.2 Clear Floor Space. Units shall have a clear floor or ground space complying with 305 positioned for a forward approach and centered on the unit. Knee and toe clearance complying with 306 shall be provided.

EXCEPTION: A parallel approach complying with 305 shall be permitted at units for children's use where the spout is 30 inches (760 mm) maximum above the finish floor or ground and is 3 1/2 inches (90 mm) maximum from the front edge of the unit, including bumpers.

602.3 Operable Parts. Operable parts shall comply with 309.

602.4 Spout Height. Spout outlets shall be 36 inches (915 mm) maximum above the finish floor or ground.

602.5 Spout Location. The spout shall be located 15 inches (380 mm) minimum from the vertical support and 5 inches (125 mm) maximum from the front edge of the unit, including bumpers.

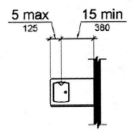

Figure 602.5 Drinking Fountain Spout Location

602.6 Water Flow. The spout shall provide a flow of water 4 inches (100 mm) high minimum and shall be located 5 inches (125 mm) maximum from the front of the unit. The angle of the water stream shall be measured horizontally relative to the front face of the unit. Where spouts are located less than 3 inches (75 mm) of the front of the unit, the angle of the water stream shall be 30 degrees maximum. Where spouts are located between 3 inches (75 mm) and 5 inches (125 mm) maximum from the front of the unit, the angle of the water stream shall be 15 degrees maximum.

Advisory

602.6 Water Flow. The purpose of requiring the drinking fountain spout to produce a flow of water 4 inches (100 mm) high minimum is so that a cup can be inserted under the flow of water to provide a drink of water for an individual who, because of a disability, would otherwise be incapable of using the drinking fountain.

602.7 Drinking Fountains for Standing Persons. Spout outlets of drinking fountains for standing persons shall be 38 inches (965 mm) minimum and 43 inches (1090 mm) maximum above the finish floor or ground.

Guidance

Sections 4.1.3(10) and 4.15 of the 1991 Standards and sections 211 and 602 of the 2010 Standards require drinking fountains to be provided for persons who use wheelchairs and for others who stand. The 1991 Standards require wall and post-mounted cantilevered drinking fountains mounted at a height for wheelchair users to provide clear floor space for a forward approach with knee and toe clearance and free standing or built-in drinking fountains to provide clear floor space for a parallel approach. The 2010 Standards require drinking fountains mounted at a height for wheelchair users to provide clear floor space for a forward approach with knee and toe clearance, and include an exception for a parallel approach for drinking fountains installed at a height to accommodate very small children. The 2010 Standards also include a technical requirement for drinking fountains for standing persons.

---

603 Toilet and Bathing Rooms

603.1 General. Toilet and bathing rooms shall comply with 603.

603.2 Clearances. Clearances shall comply with 603.2.

603.2.1 Turning Space. Turning space complying with 304 shall be provided within the room.

603.2.2 Overlap. Required clear floor spaces, clearance at fixtures, and turning space shall be permitted to overlap.

603.2.3 Door Swing. Doors shall not swing into the clear floor space or clearance required for any fixture. Doors shall be permitted to swing into the required turning space.

EXCEPTIONS:

1. Doors to a toilet room or bathing room for a single occupant accessed only through a private office and not for common use or public use shall be permitted to swing into the clear floor space or clearance provided the swing of the door can be reversed to comply with 603.2.3.

2. Where the toilet room or bathing room is for individual use and a clear floor space complying with 305.3 is provided within the room beyond the arc of the door swing, doors shall be permitted to swing into the clear floor space or clearance required for any fixture.

Advisory

603.2.3 Door Swing Exception 1. At the time the door is installed, and if the door swing is reversed in the future, the door must meet all the requirements specified in 404. Additionally, the door swing cannot reduce the required width of an accessible route. Also, avoid violating other building or life safety codes when the door swing is reversed.

603.3 Mirrors. Mirrors located above lavatories or countertops shall be installed with the bottom edge of the reflecting surface 40 inches (1015 mm) maximum above the finish floor or ground. Mirrors not located above lavatories or countertops shall be installed with the bottom edge of the reflecting surface 35 inches (890 mm) maximum above the finish floor or ground.

Advisory

603.3 Mirrors. A single full-length mirror can accommodate a greater number of people, including children. In order for mirrors to be usable by people who are ambulatory and people who use wheelchairs, the top edge of mirrors should be 74 inches (1880 mm) minimum from the floor or ground.

603.4 Coat Hooks and Shelves. Coat hooks shall be located within one of the reach ranges specified in 308. Shelves shall be located 40 inches (1015 mm) minimum and 48 inches (1220 mm) maximum above the finish floor.

Guidance

General. Where toilet facilities and bathing facilities are provided, they must comply with section 213 of the 2010 Standards.

A commenter recommended that all accessible toilet facilities, toilet rooms, and compartments should be required to have signage indicating that such spaces are restricted solely for the use of individuals with disabilities. The Department believes that it is neither necessary nor appropriate to restrict the use of accessible toilet facilities. Like many other facilities designed to be accessible, accessible toilet facilities can and do serve a wide range of individuals with and without disabilities.

A commenter recommended that more than one wheelchair accessible compartment be provided in toilet rooms serving airports and train stations because these compartments are likely to be occupied by individuals with luggage and persons with disabilities often take longer to use them. The Access Board is examining airport terminal accessibility as part of an ongoing effort to facilitate accessibility and promote effective design. As part of these efforts, the Access Board will examine requirements for accessible toilet compartments in larger airport restrooms. The Department declines to change the scoping for accessible toilet compartments at this time.

Ambulatory Accessible Toilet Compartments. Section 213.3.1 of the 2010 Standards requires multi-user men's toilet rooms, where the total of toilet compartments and urinals is six or more, to contain at least one ambulatory accessible compartment. The 1991 Standards count only toilet stalls (compartments) for this purpose. The 2010 Standards establish parity between multi-user women's toilet rooms and multi-user men's toilet rooms with respect to ambulatory accessible toilet compartments.

Urinals. Men's toilet rooms with only one urinal will no longer be required to provide an accessible urinal under the 2010 Standards. Such toilet rooms will still be required to provide an accessible toilet compartment. Commenters urged that the exception be eliminated. The Department believes that this change will provide flexibility to many small businesses and it does not alter the requirement that all common use restrooms must be accessible.

Multiple Single-User Toilet Rooms. Where multiple single-user toilet rooms are clustered in a single location, fifty percent (50%), rather than the one hundred percent (100%) required by the 1991 Standards, are required to be accessible by section 213.2, Exception 4 of the 2010 Standards. Section 216.8 of the 2010 Standards requires that accessible single-user toilet rooms must be identified by the International Symbol of Accessibility where all single-user toilet rooms are not accessible.

Hospital Patient Toilet Rooms. An exception was added in section 223.1 of the 2010 Standards to allow toilet rooms that are part of critical or intensive care patient sleeping rooms to no longer be required to provide mobility features.

Water Closet Location and Rear Grab Bar. Section 604.2 of the 2010 Standards allows greater flexibility for the placement of the centerline of wheelchair accessible and ambulatory accessible water closets. Section 604.5.2, Exception 1 permits a shorter grab bar on the rear wall where there is not enough wall space due to special circumstances (e.g., when a lavatory or other recessed fixture is located next to the water closet and the wall behind the lavatory is recessed so that the lavatory does not overlap the required clear floor space at the water closet). The 1991 Standards contain no exception for grab bar length, and require the water closet centerline to be exactly 18 inches from the side wall, while the 2010 Standards requirement allows the centerline to be between 16 and 18 inches from the side wall in wheelchair accessible toilet compartments and 17 to 19 inches in ambulatory accessible toilet compartments.

Water Closet Clearance. Section 604.3 of the 2010 Standards represents a change in the accessibility requirements where a lavatory is installed adjacent to the water closet. The 1991 Standards allow the nearest side of a lavatory to be placed 18 inches minimum from the water closet centerline and 36 inches minimum from the side wall adjacent to the water closet. However, locating the lavatory so close to the water closet prohibits many individuals with disabilities from using a side transfer. To allow greater transfer options, including side transfers, the 2010 Standards prohibit lavatories from overlapping the clear floor space at water closets, except in covered residential dwelling units.

A majority of commenters, including persons who use wheelchairs, strongly agreed with the requirement to provide enough space for a side transfer. These commenters believed that the requirement will increase the usability of accessible single-user toilet rooms by making side transfers possible for many individuals who use wheelchairs and would have been unable to transfer to a water closet using a side transfer even if the water closet complied with the 1991 Standards. In addition, many commenters noted that the additional clear floor space at the side of the water closet is also critical for those providing assistance with transfers and personal care for persons with disabilities. Numerous comments noted that this requirement is already included in other model accessibility standards and many state and local building codes and its adoption in the 2010 Standards is a important part of harmonization efforts. The Department agrees that the provision of enough clear floor space to permit side transfers at water closets is an important feature that must be provided to ensure access for persons with disabilities in toilet and bathing facilities. Furthermore, the adoption of this requirement closely harmonizes with the model codes and many state and local building codes.

Other commenters urged the Department not to adopt section 604.3 of the 2010 Standards claiming that it will require single-user toilet rooms to be two feet wider than the 1991 Standards require, and this additional requirement will be difficult to meet. Multiple commentators also expressed concern that the size of single-user toilet rooms would be increased but they did not specify how much larger such toilet rooms would have to be in their estimation. In response to these concerns, the Department developed a series of single-user toilet room floor plans demonstrating that the total square footage between representative layouts complying with the 1991 Standards and the 2010 Standards are comparable. The Department believes the floor plan comparisons clearly show that size differences between the two Standards are not substantial and several of the 2010 Standards-compliant plans do not require additional square footage compared to the 1991 Standards plans. These single-user toilet room floor plans are shown below.

Several commenters concluded that alterations of single-user toilet rooms should be exempt from the requirements of section 604.3 of the 2010 Standards because of the significant reconfiguration and reconstruction that would be required, such as moving plumbing fixtures, walls, and/or doors at significant additional expense. The Department disagrees with this conclusion since it fails to take into account several key points. The 2010 Standards contain provisions for in-swinging doors, 603.2.3, Exception 2, and recessed fixtures adjacent to water closets, 604.5.2, Exception 1. These provisions give flexibility to create more compact room designs and maintain required clearances around fixtures. As with the 1991 Standards, any alterations must comply to the extent that it is technically feasible to do so.

The requirements at section 604.3.2 of the 2010 Standards specify how required clearance around the water closet can overlap with specific elements and spaces. An exception that applies only to covered residential dwelling units permits a lavatory to be located no closer than 18 inches from the centerline of the water closet. The requirements at section 604.3.2 of the 2010 Standards increase accessibility for individuals with disabilities. One commenter expressed concern about other items that might overlap the clear floor space, such as dispensers, shelves, and coat hooks on the side of the water closet where a wheelchair would be positioned for a transfer. Section 604.3.2 of the 2010 Standards allows items such as associated grab bars, dispensers, sanitary napkin disposal units, coat hooks, and shelves to overlap the clear floor space. These are items that typically do not affect the usability of the clear floor space.

Toilet Room Doors. Sections 4.22.2 and 4.22.3 of the 1991 Standards and Section 603.2.3 of the 2010 Standards permit the doors of all toilet or bathing rooms with in-swinging doors to swing into the required turning space, but not into the clear floor space required at any fixture. In single-user toilet rooms or bathing rooms, Section 603.2.3 Exception 2 of the 2010 Standards permits the door to swing into the clear floor space of an accessible fixture if a clear floor space that measures at least 30 inches by 48 inches is provided outside of the door swing.

Several commenters expressed reservations about Exception 2 of Section 603.2.3. Concerns were raised that permitting doors of single-user toilet or bathing rooms with in-swinging doors to swing into the clearance around any fixture will result in inaccessibility to individuals using larger wheelchairs and scooters. Additionally, a commenter stated that the exception would require an unacceptable amount of precision maneuvering by individuals who use standard size wheelchairs. The Department believes that this provision achieves necessary flexibility while providing a minimum standard for maneuvering space. The standard does permit additional maneuvering space to be provided, if needed.

In the NPRM, the Department provided a series of plan drawings illustrating comparisons of the minimum size single-user toilet rooms. These floor plans showed typical examples that met the minimum requirements of the proposed ADA Standards. A commenter was of the opinion that the single-user toilet plans shown in the NPRM demonstrated that the new requirements will not result in a substantial increase in room size. Several other commenters representing industry offered criticisms of the single-user toilet floor plans to support their assertion that a 2010 Standards-compliant single-user toilet room will never be smaller and will likely be larger than such a toilet room required under the 1991 Standards. Commenters also asserted that the floor plans prepared by the Department were of a very basic design which could be accommodated in a minimal sized space whereas the types of facilities their customers demand would require additional space to be added to the rooms shown in the floor plans. The Department recognizes that there are many design choices that can affect the size of a room or space. Choices to install additional features may result in more space being needed to provide sufficient clear floor space for that additional feature to comply. However, many facilities that have these extra features also tend to have ample space to meet accessibility requirements. Other commenters asserted that public single-user toilet rooms always include a closer and a latch on the entry door, requiring a larger clear floor space than shown on the push side of the door shown in Plan 1B. The Department acknowledges that in instances where a latch is provided and a closer is required by other regulations or codes, the minimum size of a room with an out-swinging door may be slightly larger than as shown in Plan 1C.

Additional floor plans of single-user toilet rooms are now included in further response to the commentary received.

Comparison of Single-User Toilet Room Layouts

1991 Standards	2010 Standards

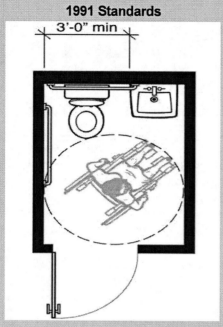

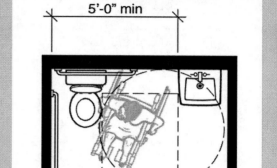

Plan-1B: 2010 Standards Minimum with Out-Swinging Door

Plan-1A: 1991 Standards Minimum with Out-Swinging Door

5'-0" x 7'-3" • 36.25 Square Feet

This plan shows a typical example of a single-user toilet room that meets the minimum requirements of the 1991 Standards. The size of this space is determined by the minimum width required for the water closet and lavatory between the side walls, the minimum wheelchair turning space, and the space required for the out-swinging door. A lavatory with knee space can overlap the clear floor space required for the water closet provided that at least 36 inches of clearance is maintained between the side wall next to the water closet and the lavatory (see section 4.16.2 and Fig. 28 of the 1991 Standards). A wheelchair turning space meeting section 4.2.3 of the 1991 Standards must be provided. The size of this room requires that the entry door swing out. The room would be larger if the door were in-swinging.

7'-0" x 5'-0" • 35.00 Square Feet

This plan shows a typical example of a single-user toilet room that meets the minimum requirements of the 2010 Standards. Features include: five-foot minimum width between the side wall of the water closet and the lavatory; 60-inch minimum circular wheelchair turning space; and 36-inch by 48-inch clear maneuvering space for the out-swinging entry door. Section 604.3.1 of the 2010 Standards requires a floor clearance at a water closet that is a minimum of 60 inches wide by 56 inches deep regardless of approach. Section 604.3.2 prohibits any other plumbing fixtures from being located in this clear space, except in residential dwelling units. The 2010 Standards, at section 304.3, allows the turning space to extend into toe and knee space provided beneath fixtures and other elements. Required maneuvering space for the entry door (inside the room) must be clear of all fixtures. If the door had both a closer and latch, section 404.2.4.1 and Figure 404.2.4.1(c) require additional space on the latch side.

This layout is three point five percent (3.5%) smaller than the accompanying Plan-1A: 1991 Standards Minimum with Out-Swinging Door example.

Comparison of Single-User Toilet Room Layouts

1991 Standards N/A   **2010 Standards**

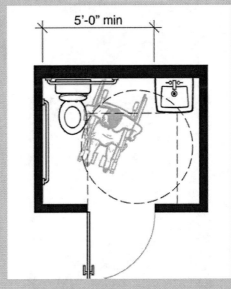

Plan-1C: 2010 Standards Minimum with Out-Swinging Door

(entry door has both closer and latch)

7'-0" x 5'-6" 38.50 Square Feet

This plan shows the same typical features of a single-user toilet room that meets the minimum requirements of the 2010 Standards as Plan-1B does except the entry door has both a closer and latch. Because the door has both a closer and latch, a minimum additional foot of maneuvering space is required on the latch side (see section 404.2.4.1 and Figure 404.2.4.1(c) of the 2010 Standards).

This layout is six point two percent (6.2%) larger than the accompanying Plan-1A: 1991 Standards Minimum with Out-Swinging Door example.

Comparison of Single-User Toilet Room Layouts

1991 Standards

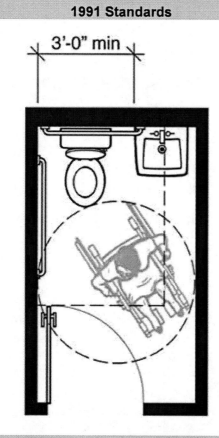

3'-0" min

2010 Standards

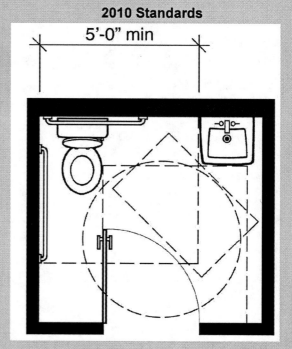

5'-0" min

Plan-2A: 1991 Standards Minimum with In-Swinging Door

5'-0" x 8'-6" 42.50 Square Feet

This plan shows a typical example of a single-user toilet room that meets the minimum requirements of the 1991 Standards. Depending on the width of the hallway and other circulation issues, it can be preferable to swing the entry door into the toilet room. Businesses and public entities typically prefer to have an in-swinging door. The in-swinging door increases overall room size because it cannot swing over the required clear floor space at any accessible fixture, (see section 4.22.2 of the 1991 Standards). This increases the room depth from Plan-1A. The door is permitted to swing over the required turning space shown as a 60-inch circle.

Plan-2B: 2010 Standards Minimum with In-Swinging Door

7'-0" x 6'-6" 45.50 Square Feet

This plan shows a typical example of a single-user toilet room that meets the minimum requirements of the 2010 Standards when the entry door swings into the room. In the 2010 Standards an exception allows the entry door to swing over the clear floor spaces and clearances required at the fixtures if a clear floor space complying with section 305.3 (minimum 30 inches by 48 inches) is provided outside the arc of the door swing, section 603.3.3 exception 2. The required maneuvering space for the door, section 404.2.4.1 and Figure 404.2.4.1(a), also is a factor in room size. This clear space cannot be obstructed by the plumbing fixtures. Note that this layout provides more space for turning when the door is closed than Plan-1B.

This layout is seven percent (7%) larger than the accompanying Plan-2A: 1991 Standards Minimum with In-Swinging Door example.

Comparison of Single-User Toilet Room Layouts

1991 Standards N/A   **2010 Standards**

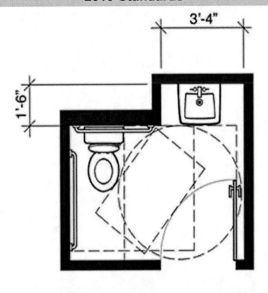

**Plan-2C: 2010 Standards Minimum
with In-Swinging Door**

7'-0" x 6'-6" 40.00 Square Feet
(plumbing chase not included)

This plan shows the same typical features of a single-user toilet room that meets the minimum requirements of the 2010 Standards as Plan-2B when the entry door swings into the room. Note that this layout also provides more space for turning when the door is closed than Plan-1B.

This layout is six point two five percent (6.25%) smaller than the accompanying Plan-2A: 1991 Standards Minimum with In-Swinging Door example.

Comparison of Single-User Toilet Room Layouts

1991 Standards N/A	1991 Standards and 2010 Standards

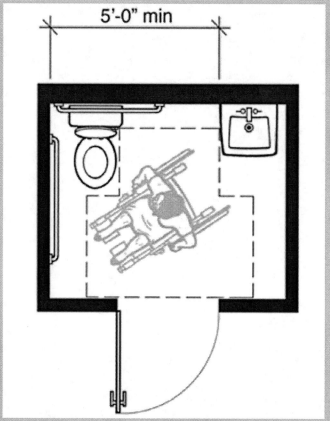

5'-0" min

Plan-3: Meets Both 1991 Standards and 2010 Standards

7'-0" x 5'-9" 40.25 Square Feet

This plan shows an example of a single-user toilet room that meets the minimum requirements of both the 1991 Standards and 2010 Standards. A T-shaped turning space has been used (see Fig. 3(a) of the 1991 Standards and Figure 304.3.2 of the 2010 Standards) to maintain a compact room size. An out-swinging door also minimizes the overall layout depth and cannot swing over the required clear floor space or clearance at any accessible plumbing fixture.

This layout is eleven percent (11%) larger than the Plan-1A: 1991 Standards Minimum with Out-Swinging Door example shown at the beginning of these plan comparisons.

Comparison of Single-User Toilet Room "Pairs" With Fixtures Side-by-Side

1991 Standards   2010 Standards

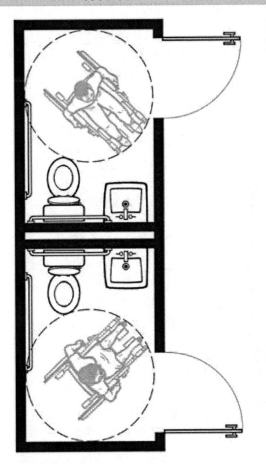

Plan-1B Pair: 2010 Standards with Out-Swinging Doors

Two 7'-0" x 5'-0" Rooms–70.00 Square Feet Total

Plan-1A Pair: 1991 Standards with Out-Swinging Doors

Two 5'-0" x 7'-3" Rooms–72.50 Square Feet Total

These plans show men's/women's room configurations using Plans 1A and 1B.

Comparison of Single-User Toilet Room "Pairs" With Fixtures Side-by-Side

1991 Standards N/A   2010 Standards

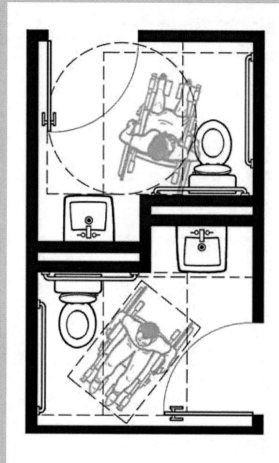

**Plan-2C Pair: 2010 Standards with
In-Swinging Doors**

**Two 7'-2" x 6'-6" Rooms -
82.00 Square Feet Total**

This plan shows a men's/women's room
configuration using Plan 2C.

Toilet Paper Dispensers. The provisions for toilet paper dispensers at section 604.7 of the 2010 Standards require the dispenser to be located seven inches minimum and nine inches maximum in front of the water closet measured to the centerline of the dispenser. The paper outlet of the dispenser must be located 15 inches minimum and 48 inches maximum above the finish floor. In the 1991 Standards the location of the toilet paper dispenser is determined by the centerline and forward edge of the dispenser. In the 2010 Standards the mounting location of the toilet paper dispenser is determined by the centerline of the dispenser and the location of the outlet for the toilet paper.

One commenter discussed the difficulty of using large roll toilet paper dispensers and dispensers with two standard size rolls stacked on top of each other. The size of the large dispensers can block access to the grab bar and the outlet for the toilet paper can be too low or too high to be usable. Some dispensers also control the delivery of the toilet paper which can make it impossible to get the toilet paper. Toilet paper dispensers that control delivery or do not allow continuous paper flow are not permitted by the 1991 Standards or the 2010 Standards. Also, many of the large roll toilet paper dispensers do not comply with the 2010 Standards since their large size does not allow them to be mounted 12 inches above or 1 1/2 inches below the side grab bar as required by section 609.3.

Shower Spray Controls. In accessible bathtubs and shower compartments, sections 607.6 and 608.6 of the 2010 Standards require shower spray controls to have an on/off control and to deliver water that is 120¡F (49¡C) maximum. Neither feature was required by the 1991 Standards, but may be required by plumbing codes. Delivering water that is no hotter than 120¡F (49¡C) will require controlling the maximum temperature at each accessible shower spray unit.

Shower Compartments. The 1991 Standards at sections 4.21 and 9.1.2 and the 2010 Standards at section 608 contain technical requirements for transfer-type and roll-in shower compartments. The 2010 Standards provide more flexibility than the 1991 Standards as follows:

• Transfer-type showers are exactly 36 inches wide by 36 inches long.

• The 1991 Standards and the 2010 Standards permit a 1/2-inch maximum curb in transfer-type showers. The 2010 Standards add a new exception that permits a 2-inch maximum curb in transfer-type showers in alterations to existing facilities, where recessing the compartment to achieve a 1/2-inch curb will disturb the structural reinforcement of the floor slab.

• Roll-in showers are 30 inches wide minimum by 60 inches long minimum. Alternate roll-in showers are 36 inches wide by 60 inches long minimum, and have a 36-inch minimum wide opening on the long side of the compartment. The 1991 Standards require alternate roll-in showers in a portion of accessible transient lodging guest rooms, but provision of this shower type in other facilities is generally permitted as an equivalent facilitation. The 1991 Standards require a seat to be provided adjacent to the opening; and require the controls to be located on the side adjacent to the seat. The 2010 Standards permit alternate roll-in showers to be used in any facility, only require a seat in transient lodging guest rooms, and allow location of controls on the back wall opposite the seat as an alternative.

Commenters raised concerns that adding a new exception that permits a 2-inch maximum curb in transfer-type showers in alterations to existing facilities, where recessing the compartment to achieve a 1/2-inch curb will disturb the structural reinforcement of the floor slab, will impair the ability of individuals with disabilities to use transfer-type showers.

The exception in section 608.7 of the 2010 Standards permitting a 2-inch maximum curb in transfer-type showers is allowed only in existing facilities where provision of a 1/2-inch high threshold would disturb the structural reinforcement of the floor slab. Whenever this exception is used the least high threshold that can be used should be provided, up to a maximum height of 2 inches. This exception is intended to provide some flexibility where the existing structure precludes full compliance.

Toilet and Bathing Rooms. Section 213 of the 2010 Standards sets out the scoping requirements for toilet and bathing rooms.

Commenters recommended that section 213, Toilet Facilities and Bathing Facilities, of the 2010

Standards include requirements that unisex toilet and bathing rooms be provided in certain facilities. These commenters suggested that unisex toilet and bathing rooms are most useful as companion care facilities.

Model plumbing and building codes require single-user (unisex or family) toilet facilities in certain occupancies, primarily assembly facilities, covered malls, and transportation facilities. These types of toilet rooms provide flexibility for persons needing privacy so that they can obtain assistance from family members or persons of the opposite sex. When these facilities are provided, both the 1991 Standards and 2010 Standards require that they be accessible. The 2010 Standards do not scope unisex toilet facilities because plumbing codes generally determine the number and type of plumbing fixtures to be provided in a particular occupancy and often determine whether an occupancy must provide separate sex facilities in addition to single-user facilities. However, the scoping at section 213.2.1 of the 2010 Standards coordinates with model plumbing and building code requirements which will permit a small toilet room with two water closets or one water closet and one urinal to be considered a single-user toilet room provided that the room has a privacy latch. In this way, a person needing assistance from a person of the opposite sex can lock the door to use the facility while temporarily inconveniencing only one other potential user. These provisions strike a reasonable balance and impose less impact on covered entities.

A commenter recommended that in shower compartments rectangular seats as provided in section 610.3.1 of the 2010 Standards should not be permitted as a substitute for L-shaped seats as provided in 610.3.2.

The 2010 Standards do not indicate a preference for either rectangular or L-shaped seats in shower compartments. L-shaped seats in transfer and certain roll-in showers have been used for many years to provide users with poor balance additional support because they can position themselves in the corner while showering.

604 Water Closets and Toilet Compartments

604.1 General. Water closets and toilet compartments shall comply with 604.2 through 604.8.

EXCEPTION: Water closets and toilet compartments for children's use shall be permitted to comply with 604.9.

604.2 Location. The water closet shall be positioned with a wall or partition to the rear and to one side. The centerline of the water closet shall be 16 inches (405 mm) minimum to 18 inches (455 mm) maximum from the side wall or partition, except that the water closet shall be 17 inches (430 mm) minimum and 19 inches (485 mm) maximum from the side wall or partition in the ambulatory accessible toilet compartment specified in 604.8.2. Water closets shall be arranged for a left-hand or right-hand approach.

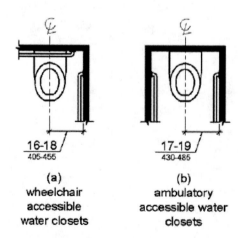

Figure 604.2 Water Closet Location

604.3 Clearance. Clearances around water closets and in toilet compartments shall comply with 604.3.

604.3.1 Size. Clearance around a water closet shall be 60 inches (1525 mm) minimum measured perpendicular from the side wall and 56 inches (1420 mm) minimum measured perpendicular from the rear wall.

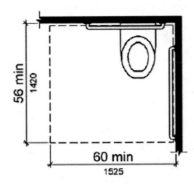

Figure 604.3.1 Size of Clearance at Water Closets

604.3.2 Overlap. The required clearance around the water closet shall be permitted to overlap the water closet, associated grab bars, dispensers, sanitary napkin disposal units, coat hooks, shelves, accessible routes, clear floor space and clearances required at other fixtures, and the turning space. No other fixtures or obstructions shall be located within the required water closet clearance.

EXCEPTION: In residential dwelling units, a lavatory complying with 606 shall be permitted on the rear wall 18 inches (455 mm) minimum from the water closet centerline where the clearance at the water closet is 66 inches (1675 mm) minimum measured perpendicular from the rear wall.

Advisory

604.3.2 Overlap. When the door to the toilet room is placed directly in front of the water closet, the water closet cannot overlap the required maneuvering clearance for the door inside the room.

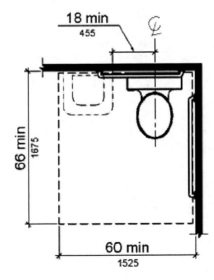

Figure 604.3.2 (Exception) Overlap of Water Closet Clearance in Residential Dwelling Units

604.4 Seats. The seat height of a water closet above the finish floor shall be 17 inches (430 mm) minimum and 19 inches (485 mm) maximum measured to the top of the seat. Seats shall not be sprung to return to a lifted position.

EXCEPTIONS:

1. A water closet in a toilet room for a single occupant accessed only through a private office and not for common use or public use shall not be required to comply with 604.4.

2. In residential dwelling units, the height of water closets shall be permitted to be 15 inches (380 mm) minimum and 19 inches (485 mm) maximum above the finish floor measured to the top of the seat.

604.5 Grab Bars. Grab bars for water closets shall comply with 609. Grab bars shall be provided on the side wall closest to the water closet and on the rear wall.

EXCEPTIONS:

1. Grab bars shall not be required to be installed in a toilet room for a single occupant accessed only through a private office and not for common use or public use provided that reinforcement has been installed in walls and located so as to permit the installation of grab bars complying with 604.5.

2. In residential dwelling units, grab bars shall not be required to be installed in toilet or bathrooms provided that reinforcement has been installed in walls and located so as to permit the installation of grab bars complying with 604.5.

3. In detention or correction facilities, grab bars shall not be required to be installed in housing or holding cells that are specially designed without protrusions for purposes of suicide prevention.

Advisory

604.5 Grab Bars Exception 2. Reinforcement must be sufficient to permit the installation of rear and side wall grab bars that fully meet all accessibility requirements including, but not limited to, required length, installation height, and structural strength.

604.5.1 Side Wall. The side wall grab bar shall be 42 inches (1065 mm) long minimum, located 12 inches (305 mm) maximum from the rear wall and extending 54 inches (1370 mm) minimum from the rear wall.

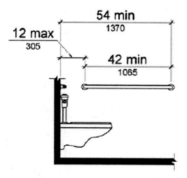

Figure 604.5.1 Side Wall Grab Bar at Water Closets

604.5.2 Rear Wall. The rear wall grab bar shall be 36 inches (915 mm) long minimum and extend from the centerline of the water closet 12 inches (305 mm) minimum on one side and 24 inches (610 mm) minimum on the other side.

EXCEPTIONS:

1. The rear grab bar shall be permitted to be 24 inches (610 mm) long minimum, centered on the water closet, where wall space does not permit a length of 36 inches (915 mm) minimum due to the location of a recessed fixture adjacent to the water closet.

2. Where an administrative authority requires flush controls for flush valves to be located in a position that conflicts with the location of the rear grab bar, then the rear grab bar shall be permitted to be split or shifted to the open side of the toilet area.

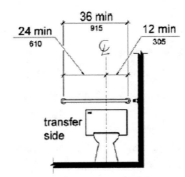

Figure 604.5.2 Rear Wall Grab Bar at Water Closets

604.6 Flush Controls. Flush controls shall be hand operated or automatic. Hand operated flush controls shall comply with 309. Flush controls shall be located on the open side of the water closet except in ambulatory accessible compartments complying with 604.8.2.

Advisory

604.6 Flush Controls. If plumbing valves are located directly behind the toilet seat, flush valves and related plumbing can cause injury or imbalance when a person leans back against them. To prevent causing injury or imbalance, the plumbing can be located behind walls or to the side of the toilet; or if approved by the local authority having jurisdiction, provide a toilet seat lid.

604.7 Dispensers. Toilet paper dispensers shall comply with 309.4 and shall be 7 inches (180 mm) minimum and 9 inches (230 mm) maximum in front of the water closet measured to the centerline of the dispenser. The outlet of the dispenser shall be 15 inches (380 mm) minimum and 48 inches (1220 mm) maximum above the finish floor and shall not be located behind grab bars. Dispensers shall not be of a type that controls delivery or that does not allow continuous paper flow.

Advisory

604.7 Dispensers. If toilet paper dispensers are installed above the side wall grab bar, the outlet of the toilet paper dispenser must be 48 inches (1220 mm) maximum above the finish floor and the top of the gripping surface of the grab bar must be 33 inches (840 mm) minimum and 36 inches (915 mm) maximum above the finish floor.

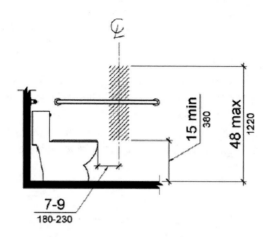

Figure 604.7 Dispenser Outlet Location

604.8 Toilet Compartments. Wheelchair accessible toilet compartments shall meet the requirements of 604.8.1 and 604.8.3. Compartments containing more than one plumbing fixture shall comply with 603. Ambulatory accessible compartments shall comply with 604.8.2 and 604.8.3.

604.8.1 Wheelchair Accessible Compartments. Wheelchair accessible compartments shall comply with 604.8.1.

604.8.1.1 Size. Wheelchair accessible compartments shall be 60 inches (1525 mm) wide minimum measured perpendicular to the side wall, and 56 inches (1420 mm) deep minimum for wall hung water closets and 59 inches (1500 mm) deep minimum for floor mounted water closets measured perpendicular to the rear wall. Wheelchair accessible compartments for children's use shall be 60 inches (1525 mm) wide minimum measured perpendicular to the side wall, and 59 inches (1500 mm) deep minimum for wall hung and floor mounted water closets measured perpendicular to the rear wall.

Advisory

604.8.1.1 Size. The minimum space required in toilet compartments is provided so that a person using a wheelchair can maneuver into position at the water closet. This space cannot be obstructed by baby changing tables or other fixtures or conveniences, except as specified at 604.3.2 (Overlap). If toilet compartments are to be used to house fixtures other than those associated with the water closet, they must be designed to exceed the minimum space requirements. Convenience fixtures such as baby changing tables must also be accessible to people with disabilities as well as to other users. Toilet compartments that are designed to meet, and not exceed, the minimum space requirements may not provide adequate space for maneuvering into position at a baby changing table.

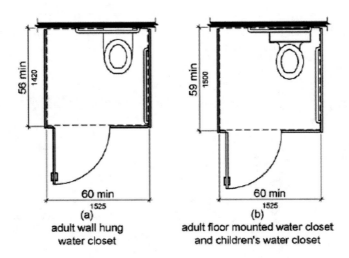

Figure 604.8.1.1 Size of Wheelchair Accessible Toilet Compartment

604.8.1.2 Doors. Toilet compartment doors, including door hardware, shall comply with 404 except that if the approach is to the latch side of the compartment door, clearance between the door side of the compartment and any obstruction shall be 42 inches (1065 mm) minimum. Doors shall be located in the front partition or in the side wall or partition farthest from the water closet. Where located in the front partition, the door opening shall be 4 inches (100 mm) maximum from the side wall or partition farthest from the water closet. Where located in the side wall or partition, the door opening shall be 4 inches (100 mm) maximum from the front partition. The door shall be self-closing. A door pull complying with 404.2.7 shall be placed on both sides of the door near the latch. Toilet compartment doors shall not swing into the minimum required compartment area.

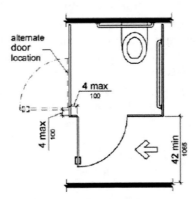

Figure 604.8.1.2 Wheelchair Accessible Toilet Compartment Doors

604.8.1.3 Approach. Compartments shall be arranged for left-hand or right-hand approach to the water closet.

604.8.1.4 Toe Clearance. The front partition and at least one side partition shall provide a toe clearance of 9 inches (230 mm) minimum above the finish floor and 6 inches (150 mm) deep minimum beyond the compartment-side face of the partition, exclusive of partition support members. Compartments for children's use shall provide a toe clearance of 12 inches (305 mm) minimum above the finish floor.

> **EXCEPTION:** Toe clearance at the front partition is not required in a compartment greater than 62 inches (1575 mm) deep with a wall-hung water closet or 65 inches (1650 mm) deep with a floor-mounted

water closet. Toe clearance at the side partition is not required in a compartment greater than 66 inches (1675 mm) wide. Toe clearance at the front partition is not required in a compartment for children's use that is greater than 65 inches (1650 mm) deep.

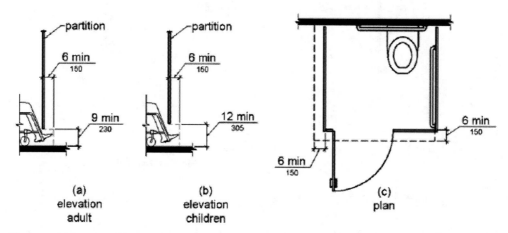

Figure 604.8.1.4 Wheelchair Accessible Toilet Compartment Toe Clearance

604.8.1.5 Grab Bars. Grab bars shall comply with 609. A side-wall grab bar complying with 604.5.1 shall be provided and shall be located on the wall closest to the water closet. In addition, a rear-wall grab bar complying with 604.5.2 shall be provided.

604.8.2 Ambulatory Accessible Compartments. Ambulatory accessible compartments shall comply with 604.8.2.

604.8.2.1 Size. Ambulatory accessible compartments shall have a depth of 60 inches (1525 mm) minimum and a width of 35 inches (890 mm) minimum and 37 inches (940 mm) maximum.

604.8.2.2 Doors. Toilet compartment doors, including door hardware, shall comply with 404, except that if the approach is to the latch side of the compartment door, clearance between the door side of the compartment and any obstruction shall be 42 inches (1065 mm) minimum. The door shall be self-closing. A door pull complying with 404.2.7 shall be placed on both sides of the door near the latch. Toilet compartment doors shall not swing into the minimum required compartment area.

604.8.2.3 Grab Bars. Grab bars shall comply with 609. A side-wall grab bar complying with 604.5.1 shall be provided on both sides of the compartment.

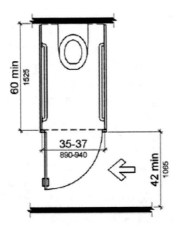

Figure 604.8.2 Ambulatory Accessible Toilet Compartment

604.8.3 Coat Hooks and Shelves. Coat hooks shall be located within one of the reach ranges specified in 308. Shelves shall be located 40 inches (1015 mm) minimum and 48 inches (1220 mm) maximum above the finish floor.

604.9 Water Closets and Toilet Compartments for Children's Use. Water closets and toilet compartments for children's use shall comply with 604.9.

Advisory

604.9 Water Closets and Toilet Compartments for Children's Use. The requirements in 604.9 are to be followed where the exception for children's water closets in 604.1 is used. The following table provides additional guidance in applying the specifications for water closets for children according to the age group served and reflects the differences in the size, stature, and reach ranges of children ages 3 through 12. The specifications chosen should correspond to the age of the primary user group. The specifications of one age group should be applied consistently in the installation of a water closet and related elements.

Advisory Specifications for Water Closets Serving Children Ages 3 through 12			
	Ages 3 and 4	**Ages 5 through 8**	**Ages 9 through 12**
Water Closet Centerline	12 inches (305 mm)	12 to 15 inches (305 to 380 mm)	15 to 18 inches (380 to 455 mm)
Toilet Seat Height	11 to 12 inches (280 to 305 mm)	12 to 15 inches (305 to 380 mm)	15 to 17 inches (380 to 430 mm)
Grab Bar Height	18 to 20 inches (455 to 510 mm)	20 to 25 inches (510 to 635 mm)	25 to 27 inches (635 to 685 mm)
Dispenser Height	14 inches (355 mm)	14 to 17 inches (355 to 430 mm)	17 to 19 inches (430 to 485 mm)

604.9.1 Location. The water closet shall be located with a wall or partition to the rear and to one side. The centerline of the water closet shall be 12 inches (305 mm) minimum and 18 inches (455 mm) maximum from the side wall or partition, except that the water closet shall be 17 inches (430 mm) minimum and 19 inches (485 mm) maximum from the side wall or partition in the ambulatory accessible toilet compartment specified in 604.8.2. Compartments shall be arranged for left-hand or right-hand approach to the water closet.

604.9.2 Clearance. Clearance around a water closet shall comply with 604.3.

604.9.3 Height. The height of water closets shall be 11 inches (280 mm) minimum and 17 inches (430 mm) maximum measured to the top of the seat. Seats shall not be sprung to return to a lifted position.

604.9.4 Grab Bars. Grab bars for water closets shall comply with 604.5.

604.9.5 Flush Controls. Flush controls shall be hand operated or automatic. Hand operated flush controls shall comply with 309.2 and 309.4 and shall be installed 36 inches (915 mm) maximum above the finish floor. Flush controls shall be located on the open side of the water closet except in ambulatory accessible compartments complying with 604.8.2.

604.9.6 Dispensers. Toilet paper dispensers shall comply with 309.4 and shall be 7 inches (180 mm) minimum and 9 inches (230 mm) maximum in front of the water closet measured to the centerline of the dispenser. The outlet of the dispenser shall be 14 inches (355 mm) minimum and 19 inches (485 mm) maximum above the finish floor. There shall be a clearance of 1 1/2 inches (38 mm) minimum below the grab bar. Dispensers shall not be of a type that controls delivery or that does not allow continuous paper flow.

604.9.7 Toilet Compartments. Toilet compartments shall comply with 604.8.

Guidance

General. Where toilet facilities and bathing facilities are provided, they must comply with section 213 of the 2010 Standards.

A commenter recommended that all accessible toilet facilities, toilet rooms, and compartments should be required to have signage indicating that such spaces are restricted solely for the use of individuals with disabilities. The Department believes that it is neither necessary nor appropriate to restrict the use of accessible toilet facilities. Like many other facilities designed to be accessible, accessible toilet facilities can and do serve a wide range of individuals with and without disabilities.

A commenter recommended that more than one wheelchair accessible compartment be provided in toilet rooms serving airports and train stations because these compartments are likely to be occupied by individuals with luggage and persons with disabilities often take longer to use them. The Access Board is examining airport terminal accessibility as part of an ongoing effort to facilitate accessibility and promote effective design. As part of these efforts, the Access Board will examine requirements for accessible toilet compartments in larger airport restrooms. The Department declines to change the scoping for accessible toilet compartments at this time.

Ambulatory Accessible Toilet Compartments. Section 213.3.1 of the 2010 Standards requires multi-user men´s toilet rooms, where the total of toilet compartments and urinals is six or more, to contain at least one ambulatory accessible compartment. The 1991 Standards count only toilet stalls (compartments) for this purpose. The 2010 Standards establish parity between multi-user women´s toilet rooms and multi-user men´s toilet rooms with respect to ambulatory accessible toilet compartments.

Urinals. Men´s toilet rooms with only one urinal will no longer be required to provide an accessible urinal under the 2010 Standards. Such toilet rooms will still be required to provide an accessible toilet compartment. Commenters urged that the exception be eliminated. The Department believes that this change will provide flexibility to many small businesses and it does not alter the requirement that all common use restrooms must be accessible.

Multiple Single-User Toilet Rooms. Where multiple single-user toilet rooms are clustered in a single location, fifty percent (50%), rather than the one hundred percent (100%) required by the 1991 Standards, are required to be accessible by section 213.2, Exception 4 of the 2010 Standards. Section 216.8 of the 2010 Standards requires that accessible single-user toilet rooms must be identified by the International Symbol of Accessibility where all single-user toilet rooms are not accessible.

Hospital Patient Toilet Rooms. An exception was added in section 223.1 of the 2010 Standards to allow toilet rooms that are part of critical or intensive care patient sleeping rooms to no longer be required to provide mobility features.

Water Closet Location and Rear Grab Bar. Section 604.2 of the 2010 Standards allows greater flexibility for the placement of the centerline of wheelchair accessible and ambulatory accessible water closets. Section 604.5.2, Exception 1 permits a shorter grab bar on the rear wall where there is not enough wall space due to special circumstances (e.g., when a lavatory or other recessed fixture is located next to the water closet and the wall behind the lavatory is recessed so that the lavatory does not overlap the required clear floor space at the water closet). The 1991 Standards contain no exception for grab bar length, and require the water closet centerline to be exactly 18 inches from the side wall, while the 2010 Standards requirement allows the centerline to be between 16 and 18 inches from the side wall in wheelchair accessible toilet compartments and 17 to 19 inches in ambulatory accessible toilet compartments.

Water Closet Clearance. Section 604.3 of the 2010 Standards represents a change in the accessibility requirements where a lavatory is installed adjacent to the water closet. The 1991 Standards allow the nearest side of a lavatory to be placed 18 inches minimum from the water closet centerline and 36 inches minimum from the side wall adjacent to the water closet. However, locating the lavatory so close to the water closet prohibits many individuals with disabilities from using a side transfer. To allow greater transfer options, including side transfers, the 2010 Standards prohibit lavatories from overlapping the clear floor space at water closets, except in covered residential dwelling units.

A majority of commenters, including persons who use wheelchairs, strongly agreed with the requirement to provide enough space for a side transfer. These commenters believed that the requirement will increase the usability of accessible single-user toilet rooms by making side transfers possible for many individuals who use wheelchairs and would have been unable to transfer to a water closet using a side transfer even if the water closet complied with the 1991 Standards. In addition, many commenters noted that the additional clear floor space at the side of the water closet is also critical for those providing assistance with transfers and personal care for persons with disabilities. Numerous comments noted that this requirement is already included in other model accessibility standards and many state and local building codes and its adoption in the 2010 Standards is a important part of harmonization efforts. The Department agrees that the provision of enough clear floor space to permit side transfers at water closets is an important feature that must be provided to ensure access for persons with disabilities in toilet and bathing facilities. Furthermore, the adoption of this requirement closely harmonizes with the model codes and many state and local building codes.

Other commenters urged the Department not to adopt section 604.3 of the 2010 Standards claiming that it will require single-user toilet rooms to be two feet wider than the 1991 Standards require, and this additional requirement will be difficult to meet. Multiple commentators also expressed concern that the size of single-user toilet rooms would be increased but they did not specify how much larger such toilet rooms would have to be in their estimation. In response to these concerns, the Department developed a series of single-user toilet room floor plans demonstrating that the total square footage between representative layouts complying with the 1991 Standards and the 2010 Standards are comparable. The Department believes the floor plan comparisons clearly show that size differences between the two Standards are not substantial and several of the 2010 Standards-compliant plans do not require additional square footage compared to the 1991 Standards plans. These single-user toilet room floor plans are shown below.

Several commenters concluded that alterations of single-user toilet rooms should be exempt from the requirements of section 604.3 of the 2010 Standards because of the significant reconfiguration and reconstruction that would be required, such as moving plumbing fixtures, walls, and/or doors at significant additional expense. The Department disagrees with this conclusion since it fails to take into account several key points. The 2010 Standards contain provisions for in-swinging doors, 603.2.3, Exception 2, and recessed fixtures adjacent to water closets, 604.5.2, Exception 1. These provisions give flexibility to create more compact room designs and maintain required clearances around fixtures. As with the 1991 Standards, any alterations must comply to the extent that it is technically feasible to do so.

The requirements at section 604.3.2 of the 2010 Standards specify how required clearance around the water closet can overlap with specific elements and spaces. An exception that applies only to covered residential dwelling units permits a lavatory to be located no closer than 18 inches from the centerline of the water closet. The requirements at section 604.3.2 of the 2010 Standards increase accessibility for individuals with disabilities. One commenter expressed concern about other items that might overlap the clear floor space, such as dispensers, shelves, and coat hooks on the side of the water closet where a wheelchair would be positioned for a transfer. Section 604.3.2 of the 2010 Standards allows items such as associated grab bars, dispensers, sanitary napkin disposal units, coat hooks, and shelves to overlap the clear floor space. These are items that typically do not affect the usability of the clear floor space.

Toilet Room Doors. Sections 4.22.2 and 4.22.3 of the 1991 Standards and Section 603.2.3 of the 2010 Standards permit the doors of all toilet or bathing rooms with in-swinging doors to swing into the required turning space, but not into the clear floor space required at any fixture. In single-user toilet rooms or bathing rooms, Section 603.2.3 Exception 2 of the 2010 Standards permits the door to swing into the clear floor space of an accessible fixture if a clear floor space that measures at least 30 inches by 48 inches is provided outside of the door swing.

Several commenters expressed reservations about Exception 2 of Section 603.2.3. Concerns were raised that permitting doors of single-user toilet or bathing rooms with in-swinging doors to swing into the clearance around any fixture will result in inaccessibility to individuals using larger wheelchairs and scooters. Additionally, a commenter stated that the exception would require an unacceptable amount of precision maneuvering by individuals who use standard size wheelchairs. The Department believes that this provision achieves necessary flexibility while providing a minimum standard for maneuvering space. The standard does permit additional maneuvering space to be provided, if needed.

In the NPRM, the Department provided a series of plan drawings illustrating comparisons of the minimum size single-user toilet rooms. These floor plans showed typical examples that met the minimum requirements of the proposed ADA Standards. A commenter was of the opinion that the single-user toilet plans shown in the NPRM demonstrated that the new requirements will not result in a substantial increase in room size. Several other commenters representing industry offered criticisms of the single-user toilet floor plans to support their assertion that a 2010 Standards-compliant single-user toilet room will never be smaller and will likely be larger than such a toilet room required under the 1991 Standards. Commenters also asserted that the floor plans prepared by the Department were of a very basic design which could be accommodated in a minimal sized space whereas the types of facilities their customers demand would require additional space to be added to the rooms shown in the floor plans. The Department recognizes that there are many design choices that can affect the size of a room or space. Choices to install additional features may result in more space being needed to provide sufficient clear floor space for that additional feature to comply. However, many facilities that have these extra features also tend to have ample space to meet accessibility requirements. Other commenters asserted that public single-user toilet rooms always include a closer and a latch on the entry door, requiring a larger clear floor space than shown on the push side of the door shown in Plan 1B. The Department acknowledges that in instances where a latch is provided and a closer is required by other regulations or codes, the minimum size of a room with an out-swinging door may be slightly larger than as shown in Plan 1C.

Additional floor plans of single-user toilet rooms are now included in further response to the commentary received.

Comparison of Single-User Toilet Room Layouts

1991 Standards

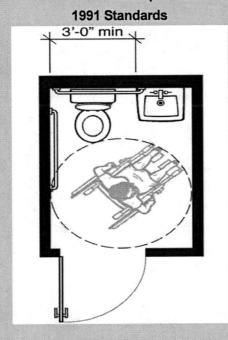

2010 Standards

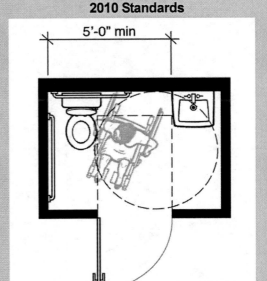

Plan-1A: 1991 Standards Minimum with Out-Swinging Door

Plan-1B: 2010 Standards Minimum with Out-Swinging Door

5'-0" x 7'-3" • 36.25 Square Feet

This plan shows a typical example of a single-user toilet room that meets the minimum requirements of the 1991 Standards. The size of this space is determined by the minimum width required for the water closet and lavatory between the side walls, the minimum wheelchair turning space, and the space required for the out-swinging door. A lavatory with knee space can overlap the clear floor space required for the water closet provided that at least 36 inches of clearance is maintained between the side wall next to the water closet and the lavatory (see section 4.16.2 and Fig. 28 of the 1991 Standards). A wheelchair turning space meeting section 4.2.3 of the 1991 Standards must be provided. The size of this room requires that the entry door swing out. The room would be larger if the door were in-swinging.

7'-0" x 5'-0" • 35.00 Square Feet

This plan shows a typical example of a single-user toilet room that meets the minimum requirements of the 2010 Standards. Features include: five-foot minimum width between the side wall of the water closet and the lavatory; 60-inch minimum circular wheelchair turning space; and 36-inch by 48-inch clear maneuvering space for the out-swinging entry door. Section 604.3.1 of the 2010 Standards requires a floor clearance at a water closet that is a minimum of 60 inches wide by 56 inches deep regardless of approach. Section 604.3.2 prohibits any other plumbing fixtures from being located in this clear space, except in residential dwelling units. The 2010 Standards, at section 304.3, allows the turning space to extend into toe and knee space provided beneath fixtures and other elements. Required maneuvering space for the entry door (inside the room) must be clear of all fixtures. If the door had both a closer and latch, section 404.2.4.1 and Figure 404.2.4.1(c) require additional space on the latch side.

This layout is three point five percent (3.5%) smaller than the accompanying Plan-1A: 1991 Standards Minimum with Out-Swinging Door example.

Comparison of Single-User Toilet Room Layouts

1991 Standards N/A

2010 Standards

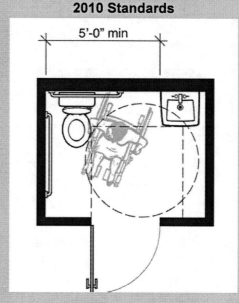

5'-0" min

Plan-1C: 2010 Standards Minimum with Out-Swinging Door

(entry door has both closer and latch)

7'-0" x 5'-6" 38.50 Square Feet

This plan shows the same typical features of a single-user toilet room that meets the minimum requirements of the 2010 Standards as Plan-1B does except the entry door has both a closer and latch. Because the door has both a closer and latch, a minimum additional foot of maneuvering space is required on the latch side (see section 404.2.4.1 and Figure 404.2.4.1(c) of the 2010 Standards).

This layout is six point two percent (6.2%) larger than the accompanying Plan-1A: 1991 Standards Minimum with Out-Swinging Door example.

Comparison of Single-User Toilet Room Layouts

1991 Standards	2010 Standards

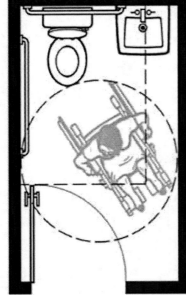

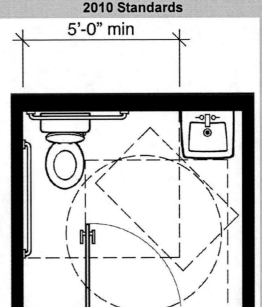

Plan-2B: 2010 Standards Minimum with In-Swinging Door

7'-0" x 6'-6" 45.50 Square Feet

This plan shows a typical example of a single-user toilet room that meets the minimum requirements of the 2010 Standards when the entry door swings into the room. In the 2010 Standards an exception allows the entry door to swing over the clear floor spaces and clearances required at the fixtures if a clear floor space complying with section 305.3 (minimum 30 inches by 48 inches) is provided outside the arc of the door swing, section 603.3.3 exception 2. The required maneuvering space for the door, section 404.2.4.1 and Figure 404.2.4.1(a), also is a factor in room size. This clear space cannot be obstructed by the plumbing fixtures. Note that this layout provides more space for turning when the door is closed than Plan-1B.

This layout is seven percent (7%) larger than the accompanying Plan-2A: 1991 Standards Minimum with In-Swinging Door example.

Plan-2A: 1991 Standards Minimum with In-Swinging Door

5'-0" x 8'-6" 42.50 Square Feet

This plan shows a typical example of a single-user toilet room that meets the minimum requirements of the 1991 Standards. Depending on the width of the hallway and other circulation issues, it can be preferable to swing the entry door into the toilet room. Businesses and public entities typically prefer to have an in-swinging door. The in-swinging door increases overall room size because it cannot swing over the required clear floor space at any accessible fixture, (see section 4.22.2 of the 1991 Standards). This increases the room depth from Plan-1A. The door is permitted to swing over the required turning space shown as a 60-inch circle.

Comparison of Single-User Toilet Room Layouts

1991 Standards N/A   **2010 Standards**

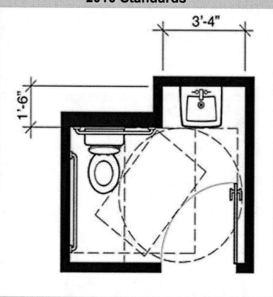

**Plan-2C: 2010 Standards Minimum
with In-Swinging Door**

7'-0" x 6'-6" 40.00 Square Feet
(plumbing chase not included)

This plan shows the same typical features of a single-user toilet room that meets the minimum requirements of the 2010 Standards as Plan-2B when the entry door swings into the room. Note that this layout also provides more space for turning when the door is closed than Plan-1B.

This layout is six point two five percent (6.25%) smaller than the accompanying Plan-2A: 1991 Standards Minimum with In-Swinging Door example.

Comparison of Single-User Toilet Room Layouts

1991 Standards N/A   **1991 Standards and 2010 Standards**

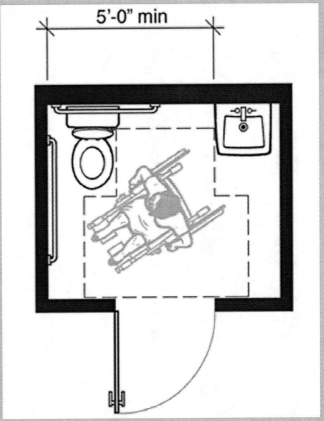

Plan-3: Meets Both 1991 Standards and 2010 Standards

7'-0" x 5'-9" 40.25 Square Feet

This plan shows an example of a single-user toilet room that meets the minimum requirements of both the 1991 Standards and 2010 Standards. A T-shaped turning space has been used (see Fig. 3(a) of the 1991 Standards and Figure 304.3.2 of the 2010 Standards) to maintain a compact room size. An out-swinging door also minimizes the overall layout depth and cannot swing over the required clear floor space or clearance at any accessible plumbing fixture.

This layout is eleven percent (11%) larger than the Plan-1A: 1991 Standards Minimum with Out-Swinging Door example shown at the beginning of these plan comparisons.

Comparison of Single-User Toilet Room "Pairs" With Fixtures Side-by-Side
1991 Standards   **2010 Standards**

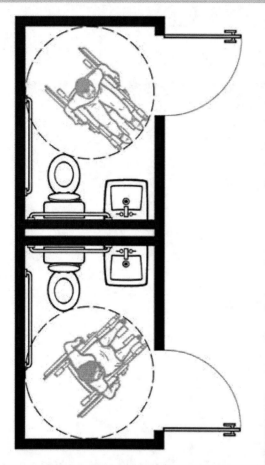

Plan-1B Pair: 2010 Standards with
Out-Swinging Doors

Two 7'-0" x 5'-0" Rooms-
70.00 Square Feet Total

Plan-1A Pair: 1991 Standards with
Out-Swinging Doors

Two 5'-0" x 7'-3" Rooms–
72.50 Square Feet Total

These plans show men's/women's room configurations using Plans 1A and 1B.

Comparison of Single-User Toilet Room "Pairs" With Fixtures Side-by-Side

1991 Standards N/A   2010 Standards

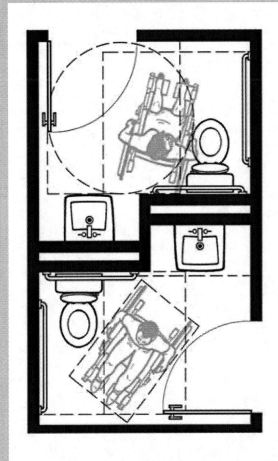

Plan-2C Pair: 2010 Standards with In-Swinging Doors

Two 7'-2" x 6'-6" Rooms - 82.00 Square Feet Total

This plan shows a men's/women's room configuration using Plan 2C.

Toilet Paper Dispensers. The provisions for toilet paper dispensers at section 604.7 of the 2010 Standards require the dispenser to be located seven inches minimum and nine inches maximum in front of the water closet measured to the centerline of the dispenser. The paper outlet of the dispenser must be located 15 inches minimum and 48 inches maximum above the finish floor. In the 1991 Standards the location of the toilet paper dispenser is determined by the centerline and forward edge of the dispenser. In the 2010 Standards the mounting location of the toilet paper dispenser is determined by the centerline of the dispenser and the location of the outlet for the toilet paper.

One commenter discussed the difficulty of using large roll toilet paper dispensers and dispensers with two standard size rolls stacked on top of each other. The size of the large dispensers can block access to the grab bar and the outlet for the toilet paper can be too low or too high to be usable. Some dispensers also control the delivery of the toilet paper which can make it impossible to get the toilet paper. Toilet paper dispensers that control delivery or do not allow continuous paper flow are not permitted by the 1991 Standards or the 2010 Standards. Also, many of the large roll toilet paper dispensers do not comply with the 2010 Standards since their large size does not allow them to be mounted 12 inches above or 1 1/2 inches below the side grab bar as required by section 609.3.

Shower Spray Controls. In accessible bathtubs and shower compartments, sections 607.6 and 608.6 of the 2010 Standards require shower spray controls to have an on/off control and to deliver water that is 120¡F (49¡C) maximum. Neither feature was required by the 1991 Standards, but may be required by plumbing codes. Delivering water that is no hotter than 120¡F (49¡C) will require controlling the maximum temperature at each accessible shower spray unit.

Shower Compartments. The 1991 Standards at sections 4.21 and 9.1.2 and the 2010 Standards at section 608 contain technical requirements for transfer-type and roll-in shower compartments. The 2010 Standards provide more flexibility than the 1991 Standards as follows:

- Transfer-type showers are exactly 36 inches wide by 36 inches long.
- The 1991 Standards and the 2010 Standards permit a 1/2-inch maximum curb in transfer-type showers. The 2010 Standards add a new exception that permits a 2-inch maximum curb in transfer-type showers in alterations to existing facilities, where recessing the compartment to achieve a 1/2-inch curb will disturb the structural reinforcement of the floor slab.
- Roll-in showers are 30 inches wide minimum by 60 inches long minimum. Alternate roll-in showers are 36 inches wide by 60 inches long minimum, and have a 36-inch minimum wide opening on the long side of the compartment. The 1991 Standards require alternate roll-in showers in a portion of accessible transient lodging guest rooms, but provision of this shower type in other facilities is generally permitted as an equivalent facilitation. The 1991 Standards require a seat to be provided adjacent to the opening; and require the controls to be located on the side adjacent to the seat. The 2010 Standards permit alternate roll-in showers to be used in any facility, only require a seat in transient lodging guest rooms, and allow location of controls on the back wall opposite the seat as an alternative.

Commenters raised concerns that adding a new exception that permits a 2-inch maximum curb in transfer-type showers in alterations to existing facilities, where recessing the compartment to achieve a 1/2-inch curb will disturb the structural reinforcement of the floor slab, will impair the ability of individuals with disabilities to use transfer-type showers.

The exception in section 608.7 of the 2010 Standards permitting a 2-inch maximum curb in transfer-type showers is allowed only in existing facilities where provision of a 1/2-inch high threshold would disturb the structural reinforcement of the floor slab. Whenever this exception is used the least high threshold that can be used should be provided, up to a maximum height of 2 inches. This exception is intended to provide some flexibility where the existing structure precludes full compliance.

Toilet and Bathing Rooms. Section 213 of the 2010 Standards sets out the scoping requirements for toilet and bathing rooms.

Commenters recommended that section 213, Toilet Facilities and Bathing Facilities, of the 2010 Standards include requirements that unisex toilet and bathing rooms be provided in certain facilities. These commenters suggested that unisex toilet and bathing rooms are most useful as companion care facilities.

Model plumbing and building codes require single-user (unisex or family) toilet facilities in certain occupancies, primarily assembly facilities, covered malls, and transportation facilities. These types of toilet rooms provide flexibility for persons needing privacy so that they can obtain assistance from family members or persons of the opposite sex. When these facilities are provided, both the 1991 Standards and 2010 Standards require that they be accessible. The 2010 Standards do not scope unisex toilet facilities because plumbing codes generally determine the number and type of plumbing fixtures to be provided in a particular occupancy and often determine whether an occupancy must provide separate sex facilities in addition to single-user facilities. However, the scoping at section 213.2.1 of the 2010 Standards coordinates with model plumbing and building code requirements which will permit a small toilet room with two water closets or one water closet and one urinal to be considered a single-user toilet room provided that the room has a privacy latch. In this way, a person needing assistance from a person of the opposite sex can lock the door to use the facility while temporarily inconveniencing only one other potential user. These provisions strike a reasonable balance and impose less impact on covered entities.

A commenter recommended that in shower compartments rectangular seats as provided in section 610.3.1 of the 2010 Standards should not be permitted as a substitute for L-shaped seats as provided in 610.3.2.

The 2010 Standards do not indicate a preference for either rectangular or L-shaped seats in shower compartments. L-shaped seats in transfer and certain roll-in showers have been used for many years to provide users with poor balance additional support because they can position themselves in the corner while showering.

605 Urinals

605.1 General. Urinals shall comply with 605.

Advisory

605.1 General. Stall-type urinals provide greater accessibility for a broader range of persons, including people of short stature.

605.2 Height and Depth. Urinals shall be the stall-type or the wall-hung type with the rim 17 inches (430 mm) maximum above the finish floor or ground. Urinals shall be 13 1/2 inches (345 mm) deep minimum measured from the outer face of the urinal rim to the back of the fixture.

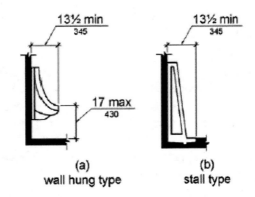

Figure 605.2 Height and Depth of Urinals

605.3 Clear Floor Space. A clear floor or ground space complying with 305 positioned for forward approach shall be provided.

605.4 Flush Controls. Flush controls shall be hand operated or automatic. Hand operated flush controls shall comply with 309.

606 Lavatories and Sinks

606.1 General. Lavatories and sinks shall comply with 606.

Advisory

606.1 General. If soap and towel dispensers are provided, they must be located within the reach ranges specified in 308. Locate soap and towel dispensers so that they are conveniently usable by a person at the accessible lavatory.

606.2 Clear Floor Space. A clear floor space complying with 305, positioned for a forward approach, and knee and toe clearance complying with 306 shall be provided.

EXCEPTIONS:

1. A parallel approach complying with 305 shall be permitted to a kitchen sink in a space where a cook top or conventional range is not provided and to wet bars.

2. A lavatory in a toilet room or bathing facility for a single occupant accessed only through a private office and not for common use or public use shall not be required to provide knee and toe clearance complying with 306.

3. In residential dwelling units, cabinetry shall be permitted under lavatories and kitchen sinks provided that all of the following conditions are met:

(a) the cabinetry can be removed without removal or replacement of the fixture;

(b) the finish floor extends under the cabinetry; and

(c) the walls behind and surrounding the cabinetry are finished.

4. A knee clearance of 24 inches (610 mm) minimum above the finish floor or ground shall be permitted at lavatories and sinks used primarily by children 6 through 12 years where the rim or counter surface is 31 inches (785 mm) maximum above the finish floor or ground.

5. A parallel approach complying with 305 shall be permitted to lavatories and sinks used primarily by children 5 years and younger.

6. The dip of the overflow shall not be considered in determining knee and toe clearances.

7. No more than one bowl of a multi-bowl sink shall be required to provide knee and toe clearance complying with 306.

606.3 Height. Lavatories and sinks shall be installed with the front of the higher of the rim or counter surface 34 inches (865 mm) maximum above the finish floor or ground.

EXCEPTIONS:

1. A lavatory in a toilet or bathing facility for a single occupant accessed only through a private office and not for common use or public use shall not be required to comply with 606.3.

2. In residential dwelling unit kitchens, sinks that are adjustable to variable heights, 29 inches (735 mm) minimum and 36 inches (915 mm) maximum, shall be permitted where rough-in plumbing permits connections of supply and drain pipes for sinks mounted at the height of 29 inches (735 mm).

606.4 Faucets. Controls for faucets shall comply with 309. Hand-operated metering faucets shall remain open for 10 seconds minimum.

606.5 Exposed Pipes and Surfaces. Water supply and drain pipes under lavatories and sinks shall be insulated or otherwise configured to protect against contact. There shall be no sharp or abrasive surfaces under lavatories and sinks.

Guidance

The 1991 Standards, at sections 4.24, and 9.2.2(7), contain technical requirements for sinks and only have specific scoping requirements for sinks in transient lodging. Section 212.3 of the 2010 Standards requires at least five percent (5%) of sinks in each accessible space to comply with the technical requirements for sinks. The technical requirements address clear floor space, height, faucets, and exposed pipes and surfaces. The 1991 Standards, at section 4.24, and the 2010 Standards, at section 606, both require the clear floor space at sinks to be positioned for a forward approach and knee and toe clearance to be provided under the sink. The 1991 Standards, at section 9.2.2(7), allow the clear floor space at kitchen sinks and wet bars in transient lodging guest rooms with mobility features to be positioned for either a forward approach with knee and toe clearance or for a parallel approach.

The 2010 Standards include an exception that permits the clear floor space to be positioned for a parallel approach at kitchen sinks in any space where a cook top or conventional range is not provided, and at a wet bar.

A commenter stated that it is unclear what the difference is between a sink and a lavatory, and that this is complicated by requirements that apply to sinks (five percent (5%) accessible) and lavatories (at least one accessible). The term "lavatory" generally refers to the specific type of plumbing fixture required for hand washing in toilet and bathing facilities. The more generic term "sink" applies to all other types of sinks located in covered facilities.

A commenter recommended that the mounting height of sinks and lavatories should take into consideration the increased use of three-wheeled scooters and some larger wheelchairs. The Department is aware that the use of three-wheeled scooters and larger wheelchairs may be increasing and that some of these devices may require changes in space requirements in the future. The Access Board is funding research to obtain data that may be used to develop design guidelines that provide access to individuals using these mobility devices.

---

607 Bathtubs

607.1 General. Bathtubs shall comply with 607.

607.2 Clearance. Clearance in front of bathtubs shall extend the length of the bathtub and shall be 30 inches (760 mm) wide minimum. A lavatory complying with 606 shall be permitted at the control end of the clearance. Where a permanent seat is provided at the head end of the bathtub, the clearance shall extend 12 inches (305 mm) minimum beyond the wall at the head end of the bathtub.

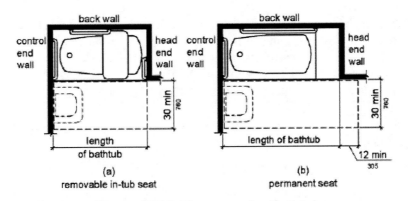

Figure 607.2 Clearance for Bathtubs

607.3 Seat. A permanent seat at the head end of the bathtub or a removable in-tub seat shall be provided. Seats shall comply with 610.

607.4 Grab Bars. Grab bars for bathtubs shall comply with 609 and shall be provided in accordance with 607.4.1 or 607.4.2.

EXCEPTIONS:

1. Grab bars shall not be required to be installed in a bathtub located in a bathing facility for a single occupant accessed only through a private office and not for common use or public use provided that reinforcement has been installed in walls and located so as to permit the installation of grab bars complying with 607.4.

2. In residential dwelling units, grab bars shall not be required to be installed in bathtubs located in bathing facilities provided that reinforcement has been installed in walls and located so as to permit the installation of grab bars complying with 607.4.

607.4.1 Bathtubs With Permanent Seats. For bathtubs with permanent seats, grab bars shall be provided in accordance with 607.4.1.

607.4.1.1 Back Wall. Two grab bars shall be installed on the back wall, one located in accordance with 609.4 and the other located 8 inches (205 mm) minimum and 10 inches (255 mm) maximum above the rim of the bathtub. Each grab bar shall be installed 15 inches (380 mm) maximum from the head end wall and 12 inches (305 mm) maximum from the control end wall.

607.4.1.2 Control End Wall. A grab bar 24 inches (610 mm) long minimum shall be installed on the control end wall at the front edge of the bathtub.

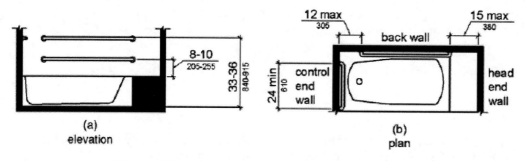

Figure 607.4.1 Grab Bars for Bathtubs with Permanent Seats

607.4.2 Bathtubs Without Permanent Seats. For bathtubs without permanent seats, grab bars shall comply with 607.4.2.

607.4.2.1 Back Wall. Two grab bars shall be installed on the back wall, one located in accordance with 609.4 and other located 8 inches (205 mm) minimum and 10 inches (255 mm) maximum above the rim of the bathtub. Each grab bar shall be 24 inches (610 mm) long minimum and shall be installed 24 inches (610 mm) maximum from the head end wall and 12 inches (305 mm) maximum from the control end wall.

607.4.2.2 Control End Wall. A grab bar 24 inches (610 mm) long minimum shall be installed on the control end wall at the front edge of the bathtub.

607.4.2.3 Head End Wall. A grab bar 12 inches (305 mm) long minimum shall be installed on the head end wall at the front edge of the bathtub.

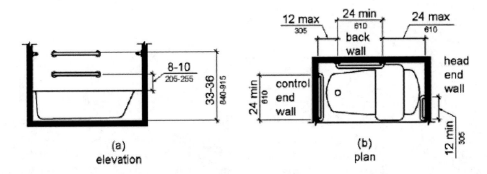

Figure 607.4.2 Grab Bars for Bathtubs with Removable In-Tub Seats

607.5 Controls. Controls, other than drain stoppers, shall be located on an end wall. Controls shall be between the bathtub rim and grab bar, and between the open side of the bathtub and the centerline of the width of the bathtub. Controls shall comply with 309.4.

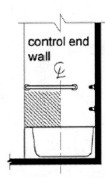

Figure 607.5 Bathtub Control Location

607.6 Shower Spray Unit and Water. A shower spray unit with a hose 59 inches (1500 mm) long minimum that can be used both as a fixed-position shower head and as a hand-held shower shall be provided. The shower spray unit shall have an on/off control with a non-positive shut-off. If an adjustable-height shower head on a vertical bar is used, the bar shall be installed so as not to obstruct the use of grab bars. Bathtub shower spray units shall deliver water that is 120°F (49°C) maximum.

Advisory
607.6 Shower Spray Unit and Water. Ensure that hand-held shower spray units are capable of delivering water pressure substantially equivalent to fixed shower heads.

607.7 Bathtub Enclosures. Enclosures for bathtubs shall not obstruct controls, faucets, shower and spray units or obstruct transfer from wheelchairs onto bathtub seats or into bathtubs. Enclosures on bathtubs shall not have tracks installed on the rim of the open face of the bathtub.

608 Shower Compartments

608.1 General. Shower compartments shall comply with 608.

Advisory

608.1 General. Shower stalls that are 60 inches (1525 mm) wide and have no curb may increase the usability of a bathroom because the shower area provides additional maneuvering space.

608.2 Size and Clearances for Shower Compartments. Shower compartments shall have sizes and clearances complying with 608.2.

608.2.1 Transfer Type Shower Compartments. Transfer type shower compartments shall be 36 inches (915 mm) by 36 inches (915 mm) clear inside dimensions measured at the center points of opposing sides and shall have a 36 inch (915 mm) wide minimum entry on the face of the shower compartment. Clearance of 36 inches (915 mm) wide minimum by 48 inches (1220 mm) long minimum measured from the control wall shall be provided.

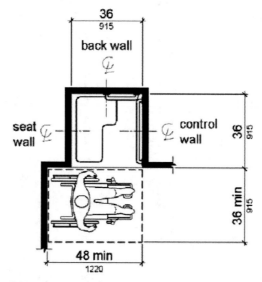

Note: inside finished dimensions measured at the center points of opposing sides

Figure 608.2.1 Transfer Type Shower Compartment Size and Clearance

608.2.2 Standard Roll-In Type Shower Compartments. Standard roll-in type shower compartments shall be 30 inches (760 mm) wide minimum by 60 inches (1525 mm) deep minimum clear inside dimensions measured at center points of opposing sides and shall have a 60 inches (1525 mm) wide minimum entry on the face of the shower compartment.

608.2.2.1 Clearance. A 30 inch (760 mm) wide minimum by 60 inch (1525 mm) long minimum clearance shall be provided adjacent to the open face of the shower compartment.

EXCEPTION: A lavatory complying with 606 shall be permitted on one 30 inch (760 mm) wide minimum side of the clearance provided that it is not on the side of the clearance adjacent to the controls or, where provided, not on the side of the clearance adjacent to the shower seat.

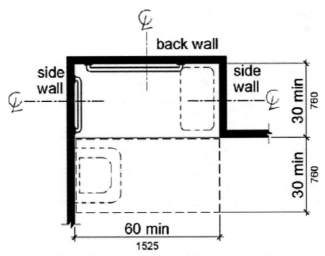

Note: inside finished dimensions measured at the center
points of opposing sides

Figure 608.2.2 Standard Roll-In Type Shower Compartment Size and Clearance

608.2.3 Alternate Roll-In Type Shower Compartments. Alternate roll-in type shower compartments shall be 36 inches (915 mm) wide and 60 inches (1525 mm) deep minimum clear inside dimensions measured at center points of opposing sides. A 36 inch (915 mm) wide minimum entry shall be provided at one end of the long side of the compartment.

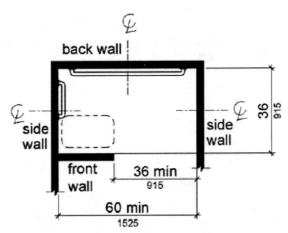

Note: inside finished dimensions measured at the center
points of opposing sides

Figure 608.2.3 Alternate Roll-In Type Shower Compartment Size and Clearance

608.3 Grab Bars. Grab bars shall comply with 609 and shall be provided in accordance with 608.3. Where multiple grab bars are used, required horizontal grab bars shall be installed at the same height above the finish floor.

EXCEPTIONS:

1. Grab bars shall not be required to be installed in a shower located in a bathing facility for a single occupant accessed only through a private office, and not for common use or public use provided that reinforcement has been installed in walls and located so as to permit the installation of grab bars complying with 608.3.

2. In residential dwelling units, grab bars shall not be required to be installed in showers located in bathing facilities provided that reinforcement has been installed in walls and located so as to permit the installation of grab bars complying with 608.3.

608.3.1 Transfer Type Shower Compartments. In transfer type compartments, grab bars shall be provided across the control wall and back wall to a point 18 inches (455 mm) from the control wall.

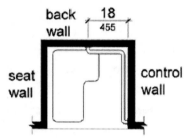

Figure 608.3.1 Grab Bars for Transfer Type Showers

608.3.2 Standard Roll-In Type Shower Compartments. Where a seat is provided in standard roll-in type shower compartments, grab bars shall be provided on the back wall and the side wall opposite the seat. Grab bars shall not be provided above the seat. Where a seat is not provided in standard roll-in type shower compartments, grab bars shall be provided on three walls. Grab bars shall be installed 6 inches (150 mm) maximum from adjacent walls.

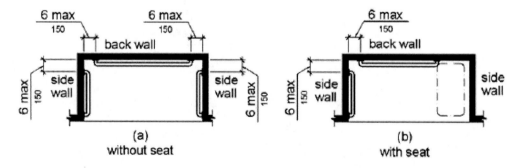

Figure 608.3.2 Grab Bars for Standard Roll-In Type Showers

608.3.3 Alternate Roll-In Type Shower Compartments. In alternate roll-in type shower compartments, grab bars shall be provided on the back wall and the side wall farthest from the compartment entry. Grab bars shall not be provided above the seat. Grab bars shall be installed 6 inches (150 mm) maximum from adjacent walls.

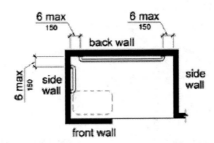

Figure 608.3.3 Grab Bars for Alternate Roll-In Type Showers

608.4 Seats. A folding or non-folding seat shall be provided in transfer type shower compartments. A folding seat shall be provided in roll-in type showers required in transient lodging guest rooms with mobility features complying with 806.2. Seats shall comply with 610.

EXCEPTION: In residential dwelling units, seats shall not be required in transfer type shower compartments provided that reinforcement has been installed in walls so as to permit the installation of seats complying with 608.4.

608.5 Controls. Controls, faucets, and shower spray units shall comply with 309.4.

608.5.1 Transfer Type Shower Compartments. In transfer type shower compartments, the controls, faucets, and shower spray unit shall be installed on the side wall opposite the seat 38 inches (965 mm) minimum and 48 inches (1220 mm) maximum above the shower floor and shall be located on the control wall 15 inches (380 mm) maximum from the centerline of the seat toward the shower opening.

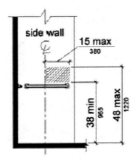

Figure 608.5.1 Transfer Type Shower Compartment Control Location

608.5.2 Standard Roll-In Type Shower Compartments. In standard roll-in type shower compartments, the controls, faucets, and shower spray unit shall be located above the grab bar, but no higher than 48 inches (1220 mm) above the shower floor. Where a seat is provided, the controls, faucets, and shower spray unit shall be installed on the back wall adjacent to the seat wall and shall be located 27 inches (685 mm) maximum from the seat wall.

Advisory

608.5.2 Standard Roll-in Type Shower Compartments. In standard roll-in type showers without seats, the shower head and operable parts can be located on any of the three walls of the shower without adversely affecting accessibility.

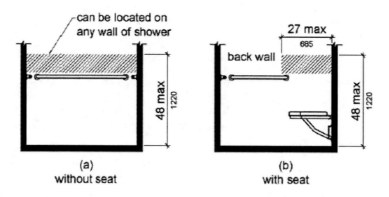

Figure 608.5.2 Standard Roll-In Type Shower Compartment Control Location

608.5.3 Alternate Roll-In Type Shower Compartments. In alternate roll-in type shower compartments, the controls, faucets, and shower spray unit shall be located above the grab bar, but no higher than 48 inches (1220 mm) above the shower floor. Where a seat is provided, the controls, faucets, and shower spray unit shall be located on the side wall adjacent to the seat 27 inches (685 mm) maximum from the side wall behind the seat or shall be located on the back wall opposite the seat 15 inches (380 mm) maximum, left or right, of the centerline of the seat. Where a seat is not provided, the controls, faucets, and shower spray unit shall be installed on the side wall farthest from the compartment entry.

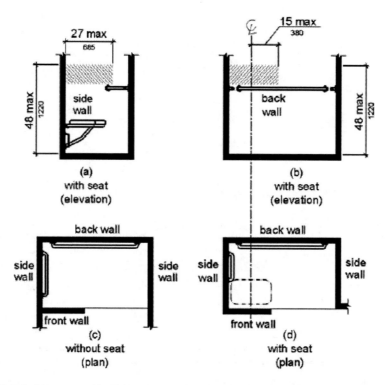

Figure 608.5.3 Alternate Roll-In Type Shower Compartment Control Location

608.6 Shower Spray Unit and Water. A shower spray unit with a hose 59 inches (1500 mm) long minimum that can be used both as a fixed-position shower head and as a hand-held shower shall be provided. The shower spray unit shall have an on/off control with a non-positive shut-off. If an adjustable-height shower head on a vertical bar is used, the bar shall be installed so as not to obstruct the use of grab bars. Shower spray units shall deliver water that is 120°F (49°C) maximum.

> **EXCEPTION:** A fixed shower head located at 48 inches (1220 mm) maximum above the shower finish floor shall be permitted instead of a hand-held spray unit in facilities that are not medical care facilities, long-term care facilities, transient lodging guest rooms, or residential dwelling units.

Advisory

608.6 Shower Spray Unit and Water. Ensure that hand-held shower spray units are capable of delivering water pressure substantially equivalent to fixed shower heads.

608.7 Thresholds. Thresholds in roll-in type shower compartments shall be 1/2 inch (13 mm) high maximum in accordance with 303. In transfer type shower compartments, thresholds 1/2 inch (13 mm) high maximum shall be beveled, rounded, or vertical.

> **EXCEPTION:** A threshold 2 inches (51 mm) high maximum shall be permitted in transfer type shower compartments in existing facilities where provision of a 1/2 inch (13 mm) high threshold would disturb the structural reinforcement of the floor slab.

608.8 Shower Enclosures. Enclosures for shower compartments shall not obstruct controls, faucets, and shower spray units or obstruct transfer from wheelchairs onto shower seats.

Guidance

General. Where toilet facilities and bathing facilities are provided, they must comply with section 213 of the 2010 Standards.

A commenter recommended that all accessible toilet facilities, toilet rooms, and compartments should be required to have signage indicating that such spaces are restricted solely for the use of individuals with disabilities. The Department believes that it is neither necessary nor appropriate to restrict the use of accessible toilet facilities. Like many other facilities designed to be accessible, accessible toilet facilities can and do serve a wide range of individuals with and without disabilities.

A commenter recommended that more than one wheelchair accessible compartment be provided in toilet rooms serving airports and train stations because these compartments are likely to be occupied by individuals with luggage and persons with disabilities often take longer to use them. The Access Board is examining airport terminal accessibility as part of an ongoing effort to facilitate accessibility and promote effective design. As part of these efforts, the Access Board will examine requirements for accessible toilet compartments in larger airport restrooms. The Department declines to change the scoping for accessible toilet compartments at this time.

Ambulatory Accessible Toilet Compartments. Section 213.3.1 of the 2010 Standards requires multi-user men's toilet rooms, where the total of toilet compartments and urinals is six or more, to contain at least one ambulatory accessible compartment. The 1991 Standards count only toilet stalls (compartments) for this purpose. The 2010 Standards establish parity between multi-user women's toilet rooms and multi-user men's toilet rooms with respect to ambulatory accessible toilet compartments.

Urinals. Men's toilet rooms with only one urinal will no longer be required to provide an accessible urinal under the 2010 Standards. Such toilet rooms will still be required to provide an accessible toilet compartment. Commenters urged that the exception be eliminated. The Department believes that this change will provide flexibility to many small businesses and it does not alter the requirement that all common use restrooms must be accessible.

Multiple Single-User Toilet Rooms. Where multiple single-user toilet rooms are clustered in a single location, fifty percent (50%), rather than the one hundred percent (100%) required by the 1991 Standards, are required to be accessible by section 213.2, Exception 4 of the 2010 Standards. Section 216.8 of the 2010 Standards requires that accessible single-user toilet rooms must be identified by the International Symbol of Accessibility where all single-user toilet rooms are not accessible.

Hospital Patient Toilet Rooms. An exception was added in section 223.1 of the 2010 Standards to allow toilet rooms that are part of critical or intensive care patient sleeping rooms to no longer be required to provide mobility features.

Water Closet Location and Rear Grab Bar. Section 604.2 of the 2010 Standards allows greater flexibility for the placement of the centerline of wheelchair accessible and ambulatory accessible water closets. Section 604.5.2, Exception 1 permits a shorter grab bar on the rear wall where there is not enough wall space due to special circumstances (e.g., when a lavatory or other recessed fixture is located next to the water closet and the wall behind the lavatory is recessed so that the lavatory does not overlap the required clear floor space at the water closet). The 1991 Standards contain no exception for grab bar length, and require the water closet centerline to be exactly 18 inches from the side wall, while the 2010 Standards requirement allows the centerline to be between 16 and 18 inches from the side wall in wheelchair accessible toilet compartments and 17 to 19 inches in ambulatory accessible toilet compartments.

Water Closet Clearance. Section 604.3 of the 2010 Standards represents a change in the accessibility requirements where a lavatory is installed adjacent to the water closet. The 1991 Standards allow the nearest side of a lavatory to be placed 18 inches minimum from the water closet centerline and 36 inches minimum from the side wall adjacent to the water closet. However, locating the lavatory so close to the water closet prohibits many individuals with disabilities from using a side transfer. To allow greater transfer options, including side transfers, the 2010 Standards prohibit lavatories from overlapping the clear floor space at water closets, except in covered residential dwelling units.

A majority of commenters, including persons who use wheelchairs, strongly agreed with the requirement to provide enough space for a side transfer. These commenters believed that the requirement will increase the usability of accessible single-user toilet rooms by making side transfers possible for many individuals who use wheelchairs and would have been unable to transfer to a water closet using a side transfer even if the water closet complied with the 1991 Standards. In addition, many commenters noted that the additional clear floor space at the side of the water closet is also critical for those providing assistance with transfers and personal care for persons with disabilities. Numerous comments noted that this requirement is already included in other model accessibility standards and many state and local building codes and its adoption in the 2010 Standards is a important part of harmonization efforts. The Department agrees that the provision of enough clear floor space to permit side transfers at water closets is an important feature that must be provided to ensure access for persons with disabilities in toilet and bathing facilities. Furthermore, the adoption of this requirement closely harmonizes with the model codes and many state and local building codes.

Other commenters urged the Department not to adopt section 604.3 of the 2010 Standards claiming that it will require single-user toilet rooms to be two feet wider than the 1991 Standards require, and this additional requirement will be difficult to meet. Multiple commentators also expressed concern that the size of single-user toilet rooms would be increased but they did not specify how much larger such toilet rooms would have to be in their estimation. In response to these concerns, the Department developed a series of single-user toilet room floor plans demonstrating that the total square footage between representative layouts complying with the 1991 Standards and the 2010 Standards are comparable. The Department believes the floor plan comparisons clearly show that size differences between the two Standards are not substantial and several of the 2010 Standards-compliant plans do not require additional square footage compared to the 1991 Standards plans. These single-user toilet room floor plans are shown below.

Several commenters concluded that alterations of single-user toilet rooms should be exempt from the requirements of section 604.3 of the 2010 Standards because of the significant reconfiguration and reconstruction that would be required, such as moving plumbing fixtures, walls, and/or doors at significant additional expense. The Department disagrees with this conclusion since it fails to take into account several key points. The 2010 Standards contain provisions for in-swinging doors, 603.2.3, Exception 2, and recessed fixtures adjacent to water closets, 604.5.2, Exception 1. These provisions give flexibility to create more compact room designs and maintain required clearances around fixtures. As with the 1991 Standards, any alterations must comply to the extent that it is technically feasible to do so.

The requirements at section 604.3.2 of the 2010 Standards specify how required clearance around the water closet can overlap with specific elements and spaces. An exception that applies only to covered residential dwelling units permits a lavatory to be located no closer than 18 inches from the centerline of the water closet. The requirements at section 604.3.2 of the 2010 Standards increase accessibility for individuals with disabilities. One commenter expressed concern about other items that might overlap the clear floor space, such as dispensers, shelves, and coat hooks on the side of the water closet where a wheelchair would be positioned for a transfer. Section 604.3.2 of the 2010 Standards allows items such as associated grab bars, dispensers, sanitary napkin disposal units, coat hooks, and shelves to overlap the clear floor space. These are items that typically do not affect the usability of the clear floor space.

Toilet Room Doors. Sections 4.22.2 and 4.22.3 of the 1991 Standards and Section 603.2.3 of the 2010 Standards permit the doors of all toilet or bathing rooms with in-swinging doors to swing into the required turning space, but not into the clear floor space required at any fixture. In single-user toilet rooms or bathing rooms, Section 603.2.3 Exception 2 of the 2010 Standards permits the door to swing into the clear floor space of an accessible fixture if a clear floor space that measures at least 30 inches by 48 inches is provided outside of the door swing.

Several commenters expressed reservations about Exception 2 of Section 603.2.3. Concerns were raised that permitting doors of single-user toilet or bathing rooms with in-swinging doors to swing into the clearance around any fixture will result in inaccessibility to individuals using larger wheelchairs and scooters. Additionally, a commenter stated that the exception would require an unacceptable amount of precision maneuvering by individuals who use standard size wheelchairs. The Department believes that this provision achieves necessary flexibility while providing a minimum standard for maneuvering space. The standard does permit additional maneuvering space to be provided, if needed.

In the NPRM, the Department provided a series of plan drawings illustrating comparisons of the minimum size single-user toilet rooms. These floor plans showed typical examples that met the minimum requirements of the proposed ADA Standards. A commenter was of the opinion that the single-user toilet plans shown in the NPRM demonstrated that the new requirements will not result in a substantial increase in room size. Several other commenters representing industry offered criticisms of the single-user toilet floor plans to support their assertion that a 2010 Standards-compliant single-user toilet room will never be smaller and will likely be larger than such a toilet room required under the 1991 Standards. Commenters also asserted that the floor plans prepared by the Department were of a very basic design which could be accommodated in a minimal sized space whereas the types of facilities their customers demand would require additional space to be added to the rooms shown in the floor plans. The Department recognizes that there are many design choices that can affect the size of a room or space. Choices to install additional features may result in more space being needed to provide sufficient clear floor space for that additional feature to comply. However, many facilities that have these extra features also tend to have ample space to meet accessibility requirements. Other commenters asserted that public single-user toilet rooms always include a closer and a latch on the entry door, requiring a larger clear floor space than shown on the push side of the door shown in Plan 1B. The Department acknowledges that in instances where a latch is provided and a closer is required by other regulations or codes, the minimum size of a room with an out-swinging door may be slightly larger than as shown in Plan 1C.

Additional floor plans of single-user toilet rooms are now included in further response to the commentary received.

Comparison of Single-User Toilet Room Layouts

1991 Standards

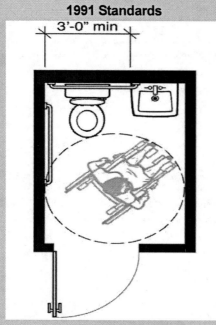

2010 Standards

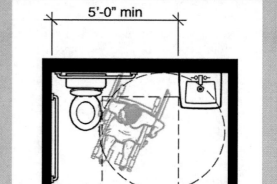

Plan-1A: 1991 Standards Minimum with Out-Swinging Door

Plan-1B: 2010 Standards Minimum with Out-Swinging Door

5'-0" x 7'-3" • 36.25 Square Feet

This plan shows a typical example of a single-user toilet room that meets the minimum requirements of the 1991 Standards. The size of this space is determined by the minimum width required for the water closet and lavatory between the side walls, the minimum wheelchair turning space, and the space required for the out-swinging door. A lavatory with knee space can overlap the clear floor space required for the water closet provided that at least 36 inches of clearance is maintained between the side wall next to the water closet and the lavatory (see section 4.16.2 and Fig. 28 of the 1991 Standards). A wheelchair turning space meeting section 4.2.3 of the 1991 Standards must be provided. The size of this room requires that the entry door swing out. The room would be larger if the door were in-swinging.

7'-0" x 5'-0" • 35.00 Square Feet

This plan shows a typical example of a single-user toilet room that meets the minimum requirements of the 2010 Standards. Features include: five-foot minimum width between the side wall of the water closet and the lavatory; 60-inch minimum circular wheelchair turning space; and 36-inch by 48-inch clear maneuvering space for the out-swinging entry door. Section 604.3.1 of the 2010 Standards requires a floor clearance at a water closet that is a minimum of 60 inches wide by 56 inches deep regardless of approach. Section 604.3.2 prohibits any other plumbing fixtures from being located in this clear space, except in residential dwelling units. The 2010 Standards, at section 304.3, allows the turning space to extend into toe and knee space provided beneath fixtures and other elements. Required maneuvering space for the entry door (inside the room) must be clear of all fixtures. If the door had both a closer and latch, section 404.2.4.1 and Figure 404.2.4.1(c) require additional space on the latch side.

This layout is three point five percent (3.5%) smaller than the accompanying Plan-1A: 1991 Standards Minimum with Out-Swinging Door example.

Comparison of Single-User Toilet Room Layouts

1991 Standards N/A   **2010 Standards**

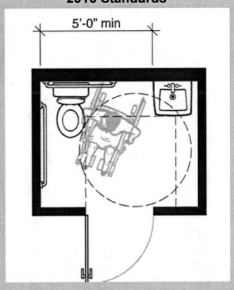

Plan-1C: 2010 Standards Minimum with Out-Swinging Door
(entry door has both closer and latch)

7'-0" x 5'-6" 38.50 Square Feet

This plan shows the same typical features of a single-user toilet room that meets the minimum requirements of the 2010 Standards as Plan-1B does except the entry door has both a closer and latch. Because the door has both a closer and latch, a minimum additional foot of maneuvering space is required on the latch side (see section 404.2.4.1 and Figure 404.2.4.1(c) of the 2010 Standards).

This layout is six point two percent (6.2%) larger than the accompanying Plan-1A: 1991 Standards Minimum with Out-Swinging Door example.

Comparison of Single-User Toilet Room Layouts

1991 Standards

2010 Standards

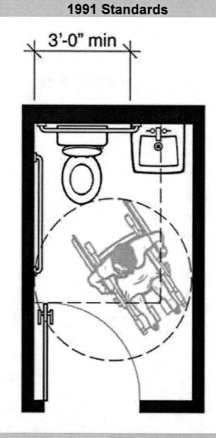

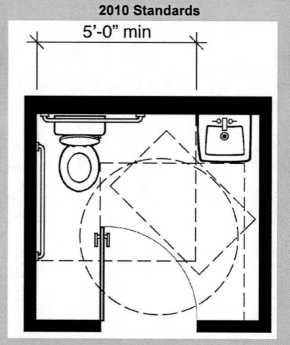

Plan-2A: 1991 Standards Minimum with In-Swinging Door

Plan-2B: 2010 Standards Minimum with In-Swinging Door

5'-0" x 8'-6" 42.50 Square Feet

This plan shows a typical example of a single-user toilet room that meets the minimum requirements of the 1991 Standards. Depending on the width of the hallway and other circulation issues, it can be preferable to swing the entry door into the toilet room. Businesses and public entities typically prefer to have an in-swinging door. The in-swinging door increases overall room size because it cannot swing over the required clear floor space at any accessible fixture, (see section 4.22.2 of the 1991 Standards). This increases the room depth from Plan-1A. The door is permitted to swing over the required turning space shown as a 60-inch circle.

7'-0" x 6'-6" 45.50 Square Feet

This plan shows a typical example of a single-user toilet room that meets the minimum requirements of the 2010 Standards when the entry door swings into the room. In the 2010 Standards an exception allows the entry door to swing over the clear floor spaces and clearances required at the fixtures if a clear floor space complying with section 305.3 (minimum 30 inches by 48 inches) is provided outside the arc of the door swing, section 603.3.3 exception 2. The required maneuvering space for the door, section 404.2.4.1 and Figure 404.2.4.1(a), also is a factor in room size. This clear space cannot be obstructed by the plumbing fixtures. Note that this layout provides more space for turning when the door is closed than Plan-1B.

This layout is seven percent (7%) larger than the accompanying Plan-2A: 1991 Standards Minimum with In-Swinging Door example.

Comparison of Single-User Toilet Room Layouts

1991 Standards N/A

2010 Standards

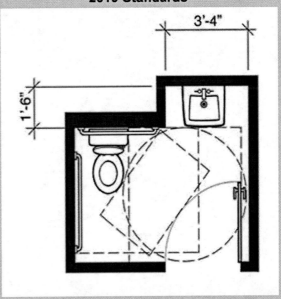

**Plan-2C: 2010 Standards Minimum
with In-Swinging Door**

7'-0" x 6'-6" 40.00 Square Feet
(plumbing chase not included)

This plan shows the same typical features of a single-user toilet room that meets the minimum requirements of the 2010 Standards as Plan-2B when the entry door swings into the room. Note that this layout also provides more space for turning when the door is closed than Plan-1B.

This layout is six point two five percent (6.25%) smaller than the accompanying Plan-2A: 1991 Standards Minimum with In-Swinging Door example.

Comparison of Single-User Toilet Room Layouts

1991 Standards N/A   **1991 Standards and 2010 Standards**

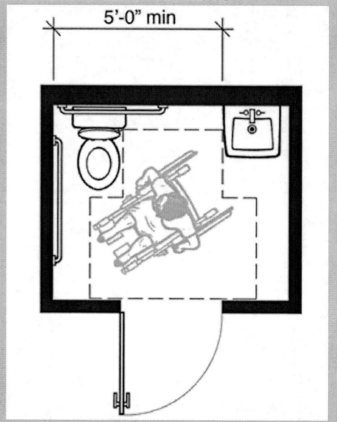

5'-0" min

Plan-3: Meets Both 1991 Standards and 2010 Standards

7'-0" x 5'-9" 40.25 Square Feet

This plan shows an example of a single-user toilet room that meets the minimum requirements of both the 1991 Standards and 2010 Standards. A T-shaped turning space has been used (see Fig. 3(a) of the 1991 Standards and Figure 304.3.2 of the 2010 Standards) to maintain a compact room size. An out-swinging door also minimizes the overall layout depth and cannot swing over the required clear floor space or clearance at any accessible plumbing fixture.

This layout is eleven percent (11%) larger than the Plan-1A: 1991 Standards Minimum with Out-Swinging Door example shown at the beginning of these plan comparisons.

Comparison of Single-User Toilet Room "Pairs" With Fixtures Side-by-Side

1991 Standards   **2010 Standards**

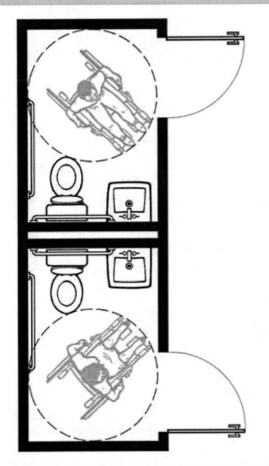

**Plan-1B Pair: 2010 Standards with
Out-Swinging Doors**

**Two 7'-0" x 5'-0" Rooms-
70.00 Square Feet Total**

**Plan-1A Pair: 1991 Standards with
Out-Swinging Doors**

**Two 5'-0" x 7'-3" Rooms–
72.50 Square Feet Total**

These plans show men's/women's room configurations using Plans 1A and 1B.

Comparison of Single-User Toilet Room "Pairs" With Fixtures Side-by-Side
1991 Standards N/A   **2010 Standards**

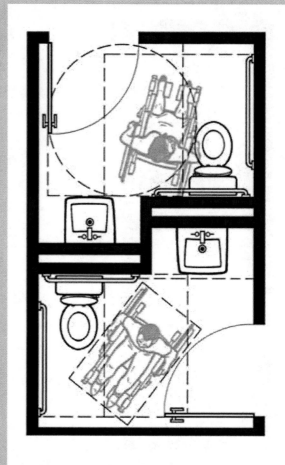

Plan-2C Pair: 2010 Standards with
In-Swinging Doors

Two 7'-2" x 6'-6" Rooms -
82.00 Square Feet Total

This plan shows a men's/women's room
configuration using Plan 2C.

Toilet Paper Dispensers. The provisions for toilet paper dispensers at section 604.7 of the 2010 Standards require the dispenser to be located seven inches minimum and nine inches maximum in front of the water closet measured to the centerline of the dispenser. The paper outlet of the dispenser must be located 15 inches minimum and 48 inches maximum above the finish floor. In the 1991 Standards the location of the toilet paper dispenser is determined by the centerline and forward edge of the dispenser. In the 2010 Standards the mounting location of the toilet paper dispenser is determined by the centerline of the dispenser and the location of the outlet for the toilet paper.

One commenter discussed the difficulty of using large roll toilet paper dispensers and dispensers with two standard size rolls stacked on top of each other. The size of the large dispensers can block access to the grab bar and the outlet for the toilet paper can be too low or too high to be usable. Some dispensers also control the delivery of the toilet paper which can make it impossible to get the toilet paper. Toilet paper dispensers that control delivery or do not allow continuous paper flow are not permitted by the 1991 Standards or the 2010 Standards. Also, many of the large roll toilet paper dispensers do not comply with the 2010 Standards since their large size does not allow them to be mounted 12 inches above or 1 1/2 inches below the side grab bar as required by section 609.3.

Shower Spray Controls. In accessible bathtubs and shower compartments, sections 607.6 and 608.6 of the 2010 Standards require shower spray controls to have an on/off control and to deliver water that is 120¡F (49¡C) maximum. Neither feature was required by the 1991 Standards, but may be required by plumbing codes. Delivering water that is no hotter than 120¡F (49¡C) will require controlling the maximum temperature at each accessible shower spray unit.

Shower Compartments. The 1991 Standards at sections 4.21 and 9.1.2 and the 2010 Standards at section 608 contain technical requirements for transfer-type and roll-in shower compartments. The 2010 Standards provide more flexibility than the 1991 Standards as follows:

• Transfer-type showers are exactly 36 inches wide by 36 inches long.

• The 1991 Standards and the 2010 Standards permit a 1/2-inch maximum curb in transfer-type showers. The 2010 Standards add a new exception that permits a 2-inch maximum curb in transfer-type showers in alterations to existing facilities, where recessing the compartment to achieve a 1/2-inch curb will disturb the structural reinforcement of the floor slab.

• Roll-in showers are 30 inches wide minimum by 60 inches long minimum. Alternate roll-in showers are 36 inches wide by 60 inches long minimum, and have a 36-inch minimum wide opening on the long side of the compartment. The 1991 Standards require alternate roll-in showers in a portion of accessible transient lodging guest rooms, but provision of this shower type in other facilities is generally permitted as an equivalent facilitation. The 1991 Standards require a seat to be provided adjacent to the opening; and require the controls to be located on the side adjacent to the seat. The 2010 Standards permit alternate roll-in showers to be used in any facility, only require a seat in transient lodging guest rooms, and allow location of controls on the back wall opposite the seat as an alternative.

Commenters raised concerns that adding a new exception that permits a 2-inch maximum curb in transfer-type showers in alterations to existing facilities, where recessing the compartment to achieve a 1/2-inch curb will disturb the structural reinforcement of the floor slab, will impair the ability of individuals with disabilities to use transfer-type showers.

The exception in section 608.7 of the 2010 Standards permitting a 2-inch maximum curb in transfer-type showers is allowed only in existing facilities where provision of a 1/2-inch high threshold would disturb the structural reinforcement of the floor slab. Whenever this exception is used the least high threshold that can be used should be provided, up to a maximum height of 2 inches. This exception is intended to provide some flexibility where the existing structure precludes full compliance.

Toilet and Bathing Rooms. Section 213 of the 2010 Standards sets out the scoping requirements for toilet and bathing rooms.

Commenters recommended that section 213, Toilet Facilities and Bathing Facilities, of the 2010

Standards include requirements that unisex toilet and bathing rooms be provided in certain facilities. These commenters suggested that unisex toilet and bathing rooms are most useful as companion care facilities.

Model plumbing and building codes require single-user (unisex or family) toilet facilities in certain occupancies, primarily assembly facilities, covered malls, and transportation facilities. These types of toilet rooms provide flexibility for persons needing privacy so that they can obtain assistance from family members or persons of the opposite sex. When these facilities are provided, both the 1991 Standards and 2010 Standards require that they be accessible. The 2010 Standards do not scope unisex toilet facilities because plumbing codes generally determine the number and type of plumbing fixtures to be provided in a particular occupancy and often determine whether an occupancy must provide separate sex facilities in addition to single-user facilities. However, the scoping at section 213.2.1 of the 2010 Standards coordinates with model plumbing and building code requirements which will permit a small toilet room with two water closets or one water closet and one urinal to be considered a single-user toilet room provided that the room has a privacy latch. In this way, a person needing assistance from a person of the opposite sex can lock the door to use the facility while temporarily inconveniencing only one other potential user. These provisions strike a reasonable balance and impose less impact on covered entities.

A commenter recommended that in shower compartments rectangular seats as provided in section 610.3.1 of the 2010 Standards should not be permitted as a substitute for L-shaped seats as provided in 610.3.2.

The 2010 Standards do not indicate a preference for either rectangular or L-shaped seats in shower compartments. L-shaped seats in transfer and certain roll-in showers have been used for many years to provide users with poor balance additional support because they can position themselves in the corner while showering.

609 Grab Bars

609.1 General. Grab bars in toilet facilities and bathing facilities shall comply with 609.

609.2 Cross Section. Grab bars shall have a cross section complying with 609.2.1 or 609.2.2.

609.2.1 Circular Cross Section. Grab bars with circular cross sections shall have an outside diameter of 1 1/4 inches (32 mm) minimum and 2 inches (51 mm) maximum.

609.2.2 Non-Circular Cross Section. Grab bars with non-circular cross sections shall have a cross-section dimension of 2 inches (51 mm) maximum and a perimeter dimension of 4 inches (100 mm) minimum and 4.8 inches (120 mm) maximum.

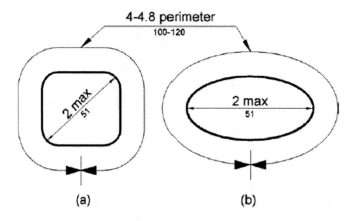

Figure 609.2.2 Grab Bar Non-Circular Cross Section

609.3 Spacing. The space between the wall and the grab bar shall be 1 1/2 inches (38 mm). The space between the grab bar and projecting objects below and at the ends shall be 1 1/2 inches (38 mm) minimum. The space between the grab bar and projecting objects above shall be 12 inches (305 mm) minimum.

EXCEPTION: The space between the grab bars and shower controls, shower fittings, and other grab bars above shall be permitted to be 1 1/2 inches (38 mm) minimum.

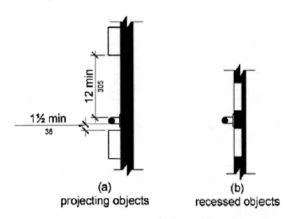

Figure 609.3 Spacing of Grab Bars

609.4 Position of Grab Bars. Grab bars shall be installed in a horizontal position, 33 inches (840 mm) minimum and 36 inches (915 mm) maximum above the finish floor measured to the top of the gripping surface, except that at water closets for children's use complying with 604.9, grab bars shall be installed in a horizontal position 18 inches (455 mm) minimum and 27 inches (685 mm) maximum above the finish floor measured to the top of the gripping surface. The height of the lower grab bar on the back wall of a bathtub shall comply with 607.4.1.1 or 607.4.2.1.

609.5 Surface Hazards. Grab bars and any wall or other surfaces adjacent to grab bars shall be free of sharp or abrasive elements and shall have rounded edges.

609.6 Fittings. Grab bars shall not rotate within their fittings.

609.7 Installation. Grab bars shall be installed in any manner that provides a gripping surface at the specified locations and that does not obstruct the required clear floor space.

609.8 Structural Strength. Allowable stresses shall not be exceeded for materials used when a vertical or horizontal force of 250 pounds (1112 N) is applied at any point on the grab bar, fastener, mounting device, or supporting structure.

610 Seats

610.1 General. Seats in bathtubs and shower compartments shall comply with 610.

610.2 Bathtub Seats. The top of bathtub seats shall be 17 inches (430 mm) minimum and 19 inches (485 mm) maximum above the bathroom finish floor. The depth of a removable in-tub seat shall be 15 inches (380 mm) minimum and 16 inches (405 mm) maximum. The seat shall be capable of secure placement. Permanent seats at the head end of the bathtub shall be 15 inches (380 mm) deep minimum and shall extend from the back wall to or beyond the outer edge of the bathtub.

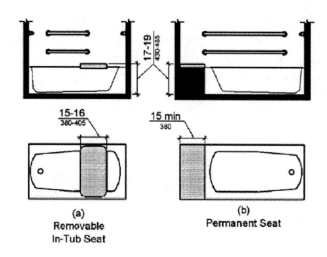

Figure 610.2 Bathtub Seats

610.3 Shower Compartment Seats. Where a seat is provided in a standard roll-in shower compartment, it shall be a folding type, shall be installed on the side wall adjacent to the controls, and shall extend from the back wall to a point within 3 inches (75 mm) of the compartment entry. Where a seat is provided in an alternate roll-in type shower compartment, it shall be a folding type, shall be installed on the front wall opposite the back wall, and shall extend from the adjacent side wall to a point within 3 inches (75 mm) of the compartment entry. In transfer-type showers, the seat shall extend from the back wall to a point within 3 inches (75 mm) of the compartment entry. The top of the seat shall be 17 inches (430 mm) minimum and 19 inches (485 mm) maximum above the bathroom finish floor. Seats shall comply with 610.3.1 or 610.3.2.

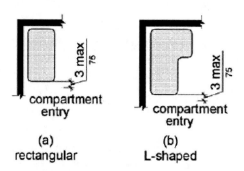

Figure 610.3 Extent of Seat

610.3.1 Rectangular Seats. The rear edge of a rectangular seat shall be 2 1/2 inches (64 mm) maximum and the front edge 15 inches (380 mm) minimum and 16 inches (405 mm) maximum from the seat wall. The side edge of the seat shall be 1 1/2 inches (38 mm) maximum from the adjacent wall.

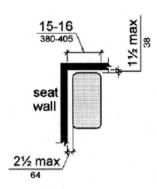

Figure 610.3.1 Rectangular Shower Seat

610.3.2 L-Shaped Seats. The rear edge of an L-shaped seat shall be 2 1/2 inches (64 mm) maximum and the front edge 15 inches (380 mm) minimum and 16 inches (405 mm) maximum from the seat wall. The rear edge of the "L" portion of the seat shall be 1 1/2 inches (38 mm) maximum from the wall and the front edge shall be 14 inches (355 mm) minimum and 15 inches (380 mm) maximum from the wall. The end of the "L" shall be 22 inches (560 mm) minimum and 23 inches maximum (585 mm) from the main seat wall.

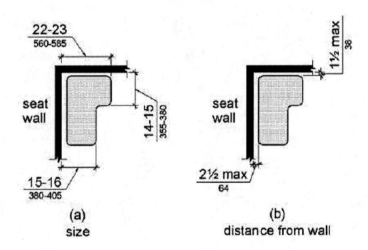

Figure 610.3.2 L-Shaped Shower Seat

610.4 Structural Strength. Allowable stresses shall not be exceeded for materials used when a vertical or horizontal force of 250 pounds (1112 N) is applied at any point on the seat, fastener, mounting device, or supporting structure.

611 Washing Machines and Clothes Dryers

611.1 General. Washing machines and clothes dryers shall comply with 611.

611.2 Clear Floor Space. A clear floor or ground space complying with 305 positioned for parallel approach shall be provided. The clear floor or ground space shall be centered on the appliance.

611.3 Operable Parts. Operable parts, including doors, lint screens, and detergent and bleach compartments shall comply with 309.

611.4 Height. Top loading machines shall have the door to the laundry compartment located 36 inches (915 mm) maximum above the finish floor. Front loading machines shall have the bottom of the opening to the laundry compartment located 15 inches (380 mm) minimum and 36 inches (915 mm) maximum above the finish floor.

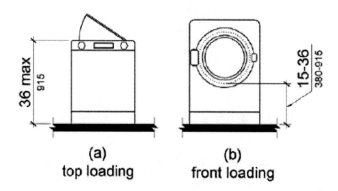

Figure 611.4 Height of Laundry Compartment Opening

Guidance
Sections 214.2 (washing machines) and 214.3 (clothes dryers) of the 2010 Standards specify the number of each type of these machines required to be accessible (one to two depending upon the total number of machines provided) and section 611 specifies the technical requirements. An exception will permit the maximum height for the tops of these machines to be 2 inches higher than the general requirement for maximum high reach over an obstruction.
A commenter objected to the scoping provision for accessible washing machines and clothes dryers stating that the probability is low that more than one accessible machine would be needed at the same time in the laundry facility of a place of transient lodging.
The scoping in this provision is based on the relative size of the facility. The Department assumes that the size of the facility (and, therefore, the number of accessible machines provided) will be determined by the covered entity's assessment of the demand for laundry facilities. The Department declines to assume that persons with disabilities will have less use for accessible facilities in transient lodging than in other public accommodations.

612 Saunas and Steam Rooms

612.1 General. Saunas and steam rooms shall comply with 612.

612.2 Bench. Where seating is provided in saunas and steam rooms, at least one bench shall comply with 903. Doors shall not swing into the clear floor space required by 903.2.

> **EXCEPTION:** A readily removable bench shall be permitted to obstruct the turning space required by 612.3 and the clear floor or ground space required by 903.2.

612.3 Turning Space. A turning space complying with 304 shall be provided within saunas and steam rooms.

Guidance

Section 241 of the 2010 Standards sets scoping for saunas and steam rooms and section 612 sets technical requirements including providing accessible turning space and an accessible bench. Doors are not permitted to swing into the clear floor or ground space for the accessible bench. The exception in section 612.2 of the 2010 Standards permits a readily removable bench to obstruct the required wheelchair turning space and the required clear floor or ground space. Where they are provided in clusters, five percent (5%) but at least one sauna or steam room in each cluster must be accessible.

Commenters raised concerns that the safety of individuals with disabilities outweighs the usefulness in providing accessible saunas and steam rooms. The Department believes that there is an element of risk in many activities available to the general public. One of the major tenets of the ADA is that individuals with disabilities should have the same opportunities as other persons to decide what risks to take. It is not appropriate for covered entities to prejudge the abilities of persons with disabilities.

CHAPTER 7: COMMUNICATION ELEMENTS AND FEATURES

701 General

701.1 Scope. The provisions of Chapter 7 shall apply where required by Chapter 2 or where referenced by a requirement in this document.

702 Fire Alarm Systems

702.1 General. Fire alarm systems shall have permanently installed audible and visible alarms complying with NFPA 72 (1999 or 2002 edition) (incorporated by reference, see "Referenced Standards" in Chapter 1), except that the maximum allowable sound level of audible notification appliances complying with section 4-3.2.1 of NFPA 72 (1999 edition) shall have a sound level no more than 110 dB at the minimum hearing distance from the audible appliance. In addition, alarms in guest rooms required to provide communication features shall comply with sections 4-3 and 4-4 of NFPA 72 (1999 edition) or sections 7.4 and 7.5 of NFPA 72 (2002 edition).

> **EXCEPTION:** Fire alarm systems in medical care facilities shall be permitted to be provided in accordance with industry practice.

703 Signs

703.1 General. Signs shall comply with 703. Where both visual and tactile characters are required, either one sign with both visual and tactile characters, or two separate signs, one with visual, and one with tactile characters, shall be provided.

703.2 Raised Characters. Raised characters shall comply with 703.2 and shall be duplicated in braille complying with 703.3. Raised characters shall be installed in accordance with 703.4.

Advisory

703.2 Raised Characters. Signs that are designed to be read by touch should not have sharp or abrasive edges.

703.2.1 Depth. Raised characters shall be 1/32 inch (0.8 mm) minimum above their background.

703.2.2 Case. Characters shall be uppercase.

703.2.3 Style. Characters shall be sans serif. Characters shall not be italic, oblique, script, highly decorative, or of other unusual forms.

703.2.4 Character Proportions. Characters shall be selected from fonts where the width of the uppercase letter "O" is 55 percent minimum and 110 percent maximum of the height of the uppercase letter "I".

703.2.5 Character Height. Character height measured vertically from the baseline of the character shall be 5/8 inch (16 mm) minimum and 2 inches (51 mm) maximum based on the height of the uppercase letter "I".

> **EXCEPTION:** Where separate raised and visual characters with the same information are provided, raised character height shall be permitted to be 1/2 inch (13 mm) minimum.

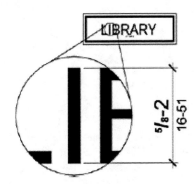

Figure 703.2.5 Height of Raised Characters

703.2.6 Stroke Thickness. Stroke thickness of the uppercase letter "I" shall be 15 percent maximum of the height of the character.

703.2.7 Character Spacing. Character spacing shall be measured between the two closest points of adjacent raised characters within a message, excluding word spaces. Where characters have rectangular cross sections, spacing between individual raised characters shall be 1/8 inch (3.2 mm) minimum and 4 times the raised character stroke width maximum. Where characters have other cross sections, spacing between individual raised characters shall be 1/16 inch (1.6 mm) minimum and 4 times the raised character stroke width maximum at the base of the cross sections, and 1/8 inch (3.2 mm) minimum and 4 times the raised character stroke width maximum at the top of the cross sections. Characters shall be separated from raised borders and decorative elements 3/8 inch (9.5 mm) minimum.

703.2.8 Line Spacing. Spacing between the baselines of separate lines of raised characters within a message shall be 135 percent minimum and 170 percent maximum of the raised character height.

703.3 Braille. Braille shall be contracted (Grade 2) and shall comply with 703.3 and 703.4.

703.3.1 Dimensions and Capitalization. Braille dots shall have a domed or rounded shape and shall comply with Table 703.3.1. The indication of an uppercase letter or letters shall only be used before the first word of sentences, proper nouns and names, individual letters of the alphabet, initials, and acronyms.

Table 703.3.1 Braille Dimensions

Measurement Range	Minimum in Inches Maximum in Inches
Dot base diameter	0.059 (1.5 mm) to 0.063 (1.6 mm)
Distance between two dots in the same cell[1]	0.090 (2.3 mm) to 0.100 (2.5 mm)
Distance between corresponding dots in adjacent cells[1]	0.241 (6.1 mm) to 0.300 (7.6 mm)
Dot height	0.025 (0.6 mm) to 0.037 (0.9 mm)
Distance between corresponding dots from one cell directly below[1]	0.395 (10 mm) to 0.400 (10.2 mm)

[1] Measured center to center.

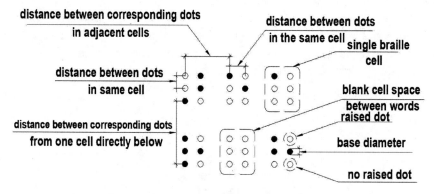

Figure 703.3.1 Braille Measurement

703.3.2 Position. Braille shall be positioned below the corresponding text. If text is multi-lined, braille shall be placed below the entire text. Braille shall be separated 3/8 inch (9.5 mm) minimum from any other tactile characters and 3/8 inch (9.5 mm) minimum from raised borders and decorative elements.

EXCEPTION: Braille provided on elevator car controls shall be separated 3/16 inch (4.8 mm) minimum and shall be located either directly below or adjacent to the corresponding raised characters or symbols.

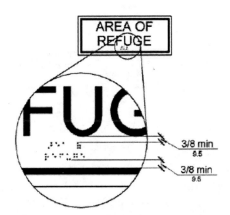

Figure 703.3.2 Position of Braille

703.4 Installation Height and Location. Signs with tactile characters shall comply with 703.4.

703.4.1 Height Above Finish Floor or Ground. Tactile characters on signs shall be located 48 inches (1220 mm) minimum above the finish floor or ground surface, measured from the baseline of the lowest tactile character and 60 inches (1525 mm) maximum above the finish floor or ground surface, measured from the baseline of the highest tactile character.

EXCEPTION: Tactile characters for elevator car controls shall not be required to comply with 703.4.1.

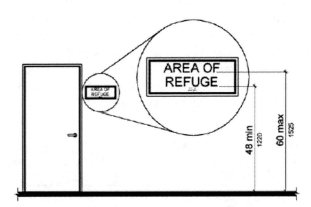

Figure 703.4.1 Height of Tactile Characters Above Finish Floor or Ground

703.4.2 Location. Where a tactile sign is provided at a door, the sign shall be located alongside the door at the latch side. Where a tactile sign is provided at double doors with one active leaf, the sign shall be located on the inactive leaf. Where a tactile sign is provided at double doors with two active leafs, the sign shall be located to the right of the right hand door. Where there is no wall space at the latch side of a single door or at the right side of double doors, signs shall be located on the nearest adjacent wall. Signs containing tactile characters shall be located so that a clear floor space of 18 inches (455 mm) minimum by 18 inches (455 mm) minimum, centered on the tactile characters, is provided beyond the arc of any door swing between the closed position and 45 degree open position.

EXCEPTION: Signs with tactile characters shall be permitted on the push side of doors with closers and without hold-open devices.

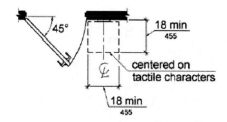

Figure 703.4.2 Location of Tactile Signs at Doors

703.5 Visual Characters. Visual characters shall comply with 703.5.

EXCEPTION: Where visual characters comply with 703.2 and are accompanied by braille complying with 703.3, they shall not be required to comply with 703.5.2 through 703.5.9.

703.5.1 Finish and Contrast. Characters and their background shall have a non-glare finish. Characters shall contrast with their background with either light characters on a dark background or dark characters on a light background.

Advisory

703.5.1 Finish and Contrast. Signs are more legible for persons with low vision when characters contrast as much as possible with their background. Additional factors affecting the ease with which the text can be distinguished from its background include shadows cast by lighting sources, surface glare, and the uniformity of the text and its background colors and textures.

703.5.2 Case. Characters shall be uppercase or lowercase or a combination of both.

703.5.3 Style. Characters shall be conventional in form. Characters shall not be italic, oblique, script, highly decorative, or of other unusual forms.

703.5.4 Character Proportions. Characters shall be selected from fonts where the width of the uppercase letter "O" is 55 percent minimum and 110 percent maximum of the height of the uppercase letter "I".

703.5.5 Character Height. Minimum character height shall comply with Table 703.5.5. Viewing distance shall be measured as the horizontal distance between the character and an obstruction preventing further approach towards the sign. Character height shall be based on the uppercase letter "I".

Table 703.5.5 Visual Character Height (text version)		
Height to Finish Floor or Ground From Baseline of Character	**Horizontal Viewing Distance**	**Minimum Character Height**
40 inches (1015 mm) to less than or equal to 70 inches (1780 mm)	less than 72 inches (1830 mm)	5/8 inch (16 mm)
	72 inches (1830 mm) and greater	5/8 inch (16 mm), plus 1/8 inch (3.2 mm) per foot (305 mm) of viewing distance above 72 inches (1830 mm)
Greater than 70 inches (1780 mm) to less than or equal to 120 inches (3050 mm)	less than 180 inches (4570 mm)	2 inches (51 mm)
	180 inches (4570 mm) and greater	2 inches (51 mm), plus 1/8 inch (3.2 mm) per foot (305 mm) of viewing distance above 180 inches (4570 mm)
greater than 120 inches (3050 mm)	less than 21 feet (6400 mm)	3 inches (75 mm)
	21 feet (6400 mm) and greater	3 inches (75 mm), plus 1/8 inch (3.2 mm) per foot (305 mm) of viewing distance above 21 feet (6400 mm)

703.5.6 Height From Finish Floor or Ground. Visual characters shall be 40 inches (1015 mm) minimum above the finish floor or ground.

EXCEPTION: Visual characters indicating elevator car controls shall not be required to comply with 703.5.6.

703.5.7 Stroke Thickness. Stroke thickness of the uppercase letter "I" shall be 10 percent minimum and 30 percent maximum of the height of the character.

703.5.8 Character Spacing. Character spacing shall be measured between the two closest points of adjacent characters, excluding word spaces. Spacing between individual characters shall be 10 percent minimum and 35 percent maximum of character height.

703.5.9 Line Spacing. Spacing between the baselines of separate lines of characters within a message shall be 135 percent minimum and 170 percent maximum of the character height.

703.6 Pictograms. Pictograms shall comply with 703.6.

703.6.1 Pictogram Field. Pictograms shall have a field height of 6 inches (150 mm) minimum. Characters and braille shall not be located in the pictogram field.

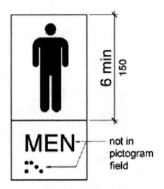

Figure 703.6.1 Pictogram Field

703.6.2 Finish and Contrast. Pictograms and their field shall have a non-glare finish. Pictograms shall contrast with their field with either a light pictogram on a dark field or a dark pictogram on a light field.

703.6.3 Text Descriptors. Pictograms shall have text descriptors located directly below the pictogram field. Text descriptors shall comply with 703.2, 703.3 and 703.4.

703.7 Symbols of Accessibility. Symbols of accessibility shall comply with 703.7.

703.7.1 Finish and Contrast. Symbols of accessibility and their background shall have a non-glare finish. Symbols of accessibility shall contrast with their background with either a light symbol on a dark background or a dark symbol on a light background.

703.7.2 Symbols.

703.7.2.1 International Symbol of Accessibility. The International Symbol of Accessibility shall comply with Figure 703.7.2.1.

Figure 703.7.2.1 International Symbol of Accessibility

703.7.2.2 International Symbol of TTY. The International Symbol of TTY shall comply with Figure 703.7.2.2.

Figure 703.7.2.2 International Symbol of TTY

703.7.2.3 Volume Control Telephones. Telephones with a volume control shall be identified by a pictogram of a telephone handset with radiating sound waves on a square field such as shown in Figure 703.7.2.3.

Figure 703.7.2.3 Volume Control Telephone

703.7.2.4 Assistive Listening Systems. Assistive listening systems shall be identified by the International Symbol of Access for Hearing Loss complying with Figure 703.7.2.4.

Figure 703.7.2.4 International Symbol of Access for Hearing Loss

Guidance
The following types of signs, though they are not specifically subject to the 1991 Standards requirement for signs, will now be explicitly exempted by sections 216 and 703 of the 2010 Standards. These types of signs include: seat and row designations in assembly areas; occupant names, building addresses; company names and logos; signs in parking facilities (except those identifying accessible parking spaces and means of egress); and exterior signs identifying permanent rooms and spaces that are not located at the door to the space they serve. This requirement also clarifies that the exception for temporary signs applies to signs used for seven days or less.
The 2010 Standards retain the option to provide one sign where both visual and tactile characters are provided or two signs, one with visual, and one with tactile characters.

704 Telephones

704.1 General. Public telephones shall comply with 704.

704.2 Wheelchair Accessible Telephones. Wheelchair accessible telephones shall comply with 704.2.

704.2.1 Clear Floor or Ground Space. A clear floor or ground space complying with 305 shall be provided. The clear floor or ground space shall not be obstructed by bases, enclosures, or seats.

Advisory

704.2.1 Clear Floor or Ground Space. Because clear floor and ground space is required to be unobstructed, telephones, enclosures and related telephone book storage cannot encroach on the required clear floor or ground space and must comply with the provisions for protruding objects. (See Section 307).

704.2.1.1 Parallel Approach. Where a parallel approach is provided, the distance from the edge of the telephone enclosure to the face of the telephone unit shall be 10 inches (255 mm) maximum.

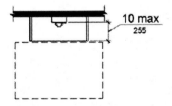

Figure 704.2.1.1 Parallel Approach to Telephone

704.2.1.2 Forward Approach. Where a forward approach is provided, the distance from the front edge of a counter within the telephone enclosure to the face of the telephone unit shall be 20 inches (510 mm) maximum.

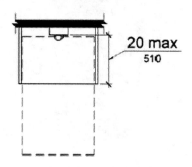

Figure 704.2.1.2 Forward Approach to Telephone

704.2.2 Operable Parts. Operable parts shall comply with 309. Telephones shall have push-button controls where such service is available.

704.2.3 Telephone Directories. Telephone directories, where provided, shall be located in accordance with 309.

704.2.4 Cord Length. The cord from the telephone to the handset shall be 29 inches (735 mm) long minimum.

704.3 Volume Control Telephones. Public telephones required to have volume controls shall be equipped with a receive volume control that provides a gain adjustable up to 20 dB minimum. For incremental volume control, provide at least one intermediate step of 12 dB of gain minimum. An automatic reset shall be provided.

Advisory

704.3 Volume Control Telephones. Amplifiers on pay phones are located in the base or the handset or are built into the telephone. Most are operated by pressing a button or key. If the microphone in the handset is not being used, a mute button that temporarily turns off the microphone can also reduce the amount of background noise which the person hears in the earpiece. If a volume adjustment is provided that allows the user to set the level anywhere from the base volume to the upper requirement of 20 dB, there is no need to specify a lower limit. If a stepped volume control is provided, one of the intermediate levels must provide 12 dB of gain. Consider compatibility issues when matching an amplified handset with a phone or phone system. Amplified handsets that can be switched with pay telephone handsets are available. Portable and in-line amplifiers can be used with some phones but are not practical at most public phones covered by these requirements.

704.4 TTYs. TTYs required at a public pay telephone shall be permanently affixed within, or adjacent to, the telephone enclosure. Where an acoustic coupler is used, the telephone cord shall be sufficiently long to allow connection of the TTY and the telephone receiver.

Advisory

704.4 TTYs. Ensure that sufficient electrical service is available where TTYs are to be installed.

704.4.1 Height. When in use, the touch surface of TTY keypads shall be 34 inches (865 mm) minimum above the finish floor.

EXCEPTION: Where seats are provided, TTYs shall not be required to comply with 704.4.1.

Advisory

704.4.1 Height. A telephone with a TTY installed underneath cannot also be a wheelchair accessible telephone because the required 34 inches (865 mm) minimum keypad height can causes the highest operable part of the telephone, usually the coin slot, to exceed the maximum permitted side and forward reach ranges. (See Section 308).

704.4.1 Height Exception. While seats are not required at TTYs, reading and typing at a TTY is more suited to sitting than standing. Facilities that often provide seats at TTY's include, but are not limited to, airports and other passenger terminals or stations, courts, art galleries, and convention centers.

704.5 TTY Shelf. Public pay telephones required to accommodate portable TTYs shall be equipped with a shelf and an electrical outlet within or adjacent to the telephone enclosure. The telephone handset shall be capable of being placed flush on the surface of the shelf. The shelf shall be capable of accommodating a TTY and shall have 6 inches (150 mm) minimum vertical clearance above the area where the TTY is to be placed.

Guidance

Drive-up Public Telephones. Where public telephones are provided, the 1991 Standards, at section 4.1.3(17)(a), and section 217.2 of the 2010 Standards, require a certain number of telephones to be wheelchair accessible. The 2010 Standards add a new exception that exempts drive-up public telephones.

Text Telephones (TTY). Section 4.1.3(17) of the 1991 Standards requires a public TTY to be provided if there are four or more public pay telephones at a site and at least one is in an interior location. Section 217.4.2 of the 2010 Standards requires that a building or facility provide a public TTY on each floor that has four or more public telephones, and in each telephone bank that has four or more telephones. Additionally, section 217.4.4 of the 2010 Standards requires that at least one public TTY be installed where four or more public pay telephones are provided on an exterior site. Section 217.4.5 of the 2010 Standards also requires that a public TTY be provided where at least one public pay telephone is provided at a public rest stop, emergency roadside stop, or service plaza. Section 217.4.6 of the 2010 Standards also requires that a public TTY be provided at each location where at least one public pay telephone is provided serving a hospital emergency room, a hospital recovery room, or a hospital waiting room. Section 217.4.7 of the 2010 Standards also requires that, in addition to the requirements for a public TTY to be provided at each location where at least four or more public pay telephones are provided at a bank of pay telephones and where at least one public pay telephone is provided on a floor or in a public building, where at least one public pay telephone serves a particular entrance to a bus or rail facility at least one public TTY must serve that entrance. In airports, in addition to the requirements for the provision of a public TTY at phone banks, on floors, and in public buildings with pay phones, where four or more public pay phones are located in a terminal outside the security areas, in a concourse within the security areas, or a baggage claim area in a terminal at least one public TTY must be provided. Section 217.4.8 of the 2010 Standards also requires that a TTY be provided in at least one secured area where at least one pay telephone is provided in a secured area used only by detainees or inmates and security personnel in detention and correctional facilities.

Wheelchair Accessible Telephones

Section 217.2 of the 2010 Standards requires that where public telephones are provided wheelchair accessible telephones complying with section 704.2 must be provided in accordance with Table 217.2.

A commenter stated that requiring installation of telephones within the proposed reach range requirements would adversely impact public and telephone owners and operators. According to the commenter, individuals without disabilities will not use telephones that are installed within the reach range requirements because they may be inconvenienced by having to stoop to operate these telephones, and, therefore, owners and operators will lose revenue due to less use of public telephones.

This comment misunderstands the scoping requirements for wheelchair accessible telephones. Section 217.2 of the 2010 Standards provides that where one or more single units are provided, only one unit per floor, level, or exterior site is required to be wheelchair accessible. However, where banks of telephones are provided, only one telephone in each bank is required to be wheelchair accessible. The Department believes these scoping requirements for wheelchair accessible telephones are reasonable and will not result in burdensome obligations or lost revenue for owners and operators.

---

705 Detectable Warnings

705.1 General. Detectable warnings shall consist of a surface of truncated domes and shall comply with 705.

705.1.1 Dome Size. Truncated domes in a detectable warning surface shall have a base diameter of 0.9 inch (23 mm) minimum and 1.4 inches (36 mm) maximum, a top diameter of 50 percent of the base diameter minimum to 65 percent of the base diameter maximum, and a height of 0.2 inch (5.1 mm).

705.1.2 Dome Spacing. Truncated domes in a detectable warning surface shall have a center-to-center spacing of 1.6 inches (41 mm) minimum and 2.4 inches (61 mm) maximum, and a base-to-base spacing of 0.65 inch (17 mm) minimum, measured between the most adjacent domes on a square grid.

705.1.3 Contrast. Detectable warning surfaces shall contrast visually with adjacent walking surfaces either light-on-dark, or dark-on-light.

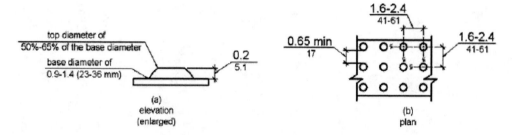

Figure 705.1 Size and Spacing of Truncated Domes

705.2 Platform Edges. Detectable warning surfaces at platform boarding edges shall be 24 inches (610 mm) wide and shall extend the full length of the public use areas of the platform.

706 Assistive Listening Systems

706.1 General. Assistive listening systems required in assembly areas shall comply with 706.

Advisory

706.1 General. Assistive listening systems are generally categorized by their mode of transmission. There are hard-wired systems and three types of wireless systems: induction loop, infrared, and FM radio transmission. Each has different advantages and disadvantages that can help determine which system is best for a given application. For example, an FM system may be better than an infrared system in some open-air assemblies since infrared signals are less effective in sunlight. On the other hand, an infrared system is typically a better choice than an FM system where confidential transmission is important because it will be contained within a given space.

The technical standards for assistive listening systems describe minimum performance levels for volume, interference, and distortion. Sound pressure levels (SPL), expressed in decibels, measure output sound volume. Signal-to-noise ratio (SNR or S/N), also expressed in decibels, represents the relationship between the loudness of a desired sound (the signal) and the background noise in a space or piece of equipment. The higher the SNR, the more intelligible the signal. The peak clipping level limits the distortion in signal output produced when high-volume sound waves are manipulated to serve assistive listening devices.

Selecting or specifying an effective assistive listening system for a large or complex venue requires assistance from a professional sound engineer. The Access Board has published technical assistance on assistive listening devices and systems.

706.2 Receiver Jacks. Receivers required for use with an assistive listening system shall include a 1/8 inch (3.2 mm) standard mono jack.

706.3 Receiver Hearing-Aid Compatibility. Receivers required to be hearing-aid compatible shall interface with telecoils in hearing aids through the provision of neckloops.

Advisory

706.3 Receiver Hearing-Aid Compatibility. Neckloops and headsets that can be worn as neckloops are compatible with hearing aids. Receivers that are not compatible include earbuds, which may require removal of hearing aids, earphones, and headsets that must be worn over the ear, which can create disruptive interference in the transmission and can be uncomfortable for people wearing hearing aids.

706.4 Sound Pressure Level. Assistive listening systems shall be capable of providing a sound pressure level of 110 dB minimum and 118 dB maximum with a dynamic range on the volume control of 50 dB.

706.5 Signal-to-Noise Ratio. The signal-to-noise ratio for internally generated noise in assistive listening systems shall be 18 dB minimum.

706.6 Peak Clipping Level. Peak clipping shall not exceed 18 dB of clipping relative to the peaks of speech.

Guidance

Signs. Section 216.10 of the 2010 Standards requires each covered assembly area to provide signs at each auditorium to inform patrons that assistive listening systems are available. However, an exception to this requirement permits assembly areas that have ticket offices or ticket windows to display the required signs at the ticket window.

A commenter recommended eliminating the exception at 216.10 because, for example, people who buy tickets through the mail, by subscription, or on-line may not need to stop at a ticket office or window upon arrival at the assembly area. The Department believes that an individual's decision to purchase tickets before arriving at a performance does not limit the discretion of the assembly operator to use the ticket window to provide other services to its patrons. The Department retained the exception at 216.10 to permit the venue operator some flexibility in determining how to meet the needs of its patrons.

Audible Communication. The 1991 Standards, at section 4.1.3(19)(b), require assembly areas, where audible communication is integral to the use of the space, to provide an assistive listening system if they have an audio amplification system or an occupant load of 50 or more people and have fixed seating. The 2010 Standards at section 219 require assistive listening systems in spaces where communication is integral to the space and audio amplification is provided and in courtrooms.

The 1991 Standards require receivers to be provided for at least four percent (4%) of the total number of fixed seats. The 2010 Standards, at section 219.3, revise the percentage of receivers required according to a table that correlates the required number of receivers to the seating capacity of the facility. Small facilities will continue to provide receivers for four percent (4%) of the seats. The required percentage declines as the size of the facility increases. The changes also require at least twenty-five percent (25%), but no fewer than two, of the receivers to be hearing-aid compatible. Assembly areas served by an induction loop assistive listening system will not have to provide hearing-aid compatible receivers.

Commenters were divided in their opinion of this change. The Department believes that the reduction in the required number of assistive listening systems for larger assembly areas will meet the needs of individuals with disabilities. The new requirement to provide hearing-aid compatible receivers should make assistive listening systems more usable for people who have been underserved until now.

Concerns were raised that the requirement to provide assistive listening systems may have an adverse impact on restaurants. This comment misunderstands the scope of coverage. The 2010 Standards define the term "assembly area" to include facilities used for entertainment, educational, or civic gatherings. A restaurant would fall within this category only if it is presenting programs to educate or entertain diners, and it provides an audio amplification system.

Same Management or Building. The 2010 Standards add a new exception that allows multiple assembly areas that are in the same building and under the same management, such as theaters in a multiplex cinema and lecture halls in a college building, to calculate the number of receivers required based on the total number of seats in all the assembly areas, instead of each assembly area separately, where the receivers are compatible with the assistive listening systems used in each of the assembly areas.

Mono Jacks, Sound Pressure, Etc. Section 4.33.7 of the 1991 Standards does not contain specific technical requirements for assistive listening systems. The 2010 Standards at section 706 require assistive listening systems to have standard mono jacks and will require hearing-aid compatible receivers to have neck loops to interface with telecoils in hearing aids. The 2010 Standards also specify sound pressure level, signal-to-noise ratio, and peak clipping level. Currently available assistive listening systems typically meet these technical requirements.

707 Automatic Teller Machines and Fare Machines

707.1 General. Automatic teller machines and fare machines shall comply with 707.

707.2 Clear Floor or Ground Space. A clear floor or ground space complying with 305 shall be provided.

EXCEPTION: Clear floor or ground space shall not be required at drive-up only automatic teller machines and fare machines.

707.3 Operable Parts. Operable parts shall comply with 309. Unless a clear or correct key is provided, each operable part shall be able to be differentiated by sound or touch, without activation.

EXCEPTION: Drive-up only automatic teller machines and fare machines shall not be required to comply with 309.2 and 309.3.

707.4 Privacy. Automatic teller machines shall provide the opportunity for the same degree of privacy of input and output available to all individuals.

707.5 Speech Output. Machines shall be speech enabled. Operating instructions and orientation, visible transaction prompts, user input verification, error messages, and all displayed information for full use shall be accessible to and independently usable by individuals with vision impairments. Speech shall be delivered through a mechanism that is readily available to all users, including but not limited to, an industry standard connector or a telephone handset. Speech shall be recorded or digitized human, or synthesized.

EXCEPTIONS:

1. Audible tones shall be permitted instead of speech for visible output that is not displayed for security purposes, including but not limited to, asterisks representing personal identification numbers.

2. Advertisements and other similar information shall not be required to be audible unless they convey information that can be used in the transaction being conducted.

3. Where speech synthesis cannot be supported, dynamic alphabetic output shall not be required to be audible.

707.5.1 User Control. Speech shall be capable of being repeated or interrupted. Volume control shall be provided for the speech function.

EXCEPTION: Speech output for any single function shall be permitted to be automatically interrupted when a transaction is selected.

707.5.2 Receipts. Where receipts are provided, speech output devices shall provide audible balance inquiry information, error messages, and all other information on the printed receipt necessary to complete or verify the transaction.

EXCEPTIONS:

1. Machine location, date and time of transaction, customer account number, and the machine identifier shall not be required to be audible.

2. Information on printed receipts that duplicates information available on-screen shall not be required to be presented in the form of an audible receipt.

3. Printed copies of bank statements and checks shall not be required to be audible.

707.6 Input. Input devices shall comply with 707.6.

707.6.1 Input Controls. At least one tactilely discernible input control shall be provided for each function. Where provided, key surfaces not on active areas of display screens, shall be raised above surrounding surfaces. Where membrane keys are the only method of input, each shall be tactilely discernable from surrounding surfaces and adjacent keys.

707.6.2 Numeric Keys. Numeric keys shall be arranged in a 12-key ascending or descending telephone keypad layout. The number five key shall be tactilely distinct from the other keys.

Advisory

707.6.2 Numeric Keys. Telephone keypads and computer keyboards differ in one significant feature, ascending versus descending numerical order. Both types of keypads are acceptable, provided the computer-style keypad is organized similarly to the number pad located at the right on most computer keyboards, and does not resemble the line of numbers located above the computer keys.

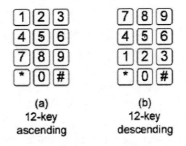

(a)
12-key
ascending

(b)
12-key
descending

Figure 707.6.2 Numeric Key Layout

707.6.3 Function Keys. Function keys shall comply with 707.6.3.

707.6.3.1 Contrast. Function keys shall contrast visually from background surfaces. Characters and symbols on key surfaces shall contrast visually from key surfaces. Visual contrast shall be either light-on-dark or dark-on-light.

EXCEPTION: Tactile symbols required by 707.6.3.2 shall not be required to comply with 707.6.3.1.

707.6.3.2 Tactile Symbols. Function key surfaces shall have tactile symbols as follows: Enter or Proceed key: raised circle; Clear or Correct key: raised left arrow; Cancel key: raised letter ex; Add Value key: raised plus sign; Decrease Value key: raised minus sign.

707.7 Display Screen. The display screen shall comply with 707.7.

EXCEPTION: Drive-up only automatic teller machines and fare machines shall not be required to comply with 707.7.1.

707.7.1 Visibility. The display screen shall be visible from a point located 40 inches (1015 mm) above the center of the clear floor space in front of the machine.

707.7.2 Characters. Characters displayed on the screen shall be in a sans serif font. Characters shall be 3/16 inch (4.8 mm) high minimum based on the uppercase letter "I". Characters shall contrast with their background with either light characters on a dark background or dark characters on a light background.

707.8 Braille Instructions. Braille instructions for initiating the speech mode shall be provided. Braille shall comply with 703.3.

Guidance

Section 707 of the 2010 Standards adds specific technical requirements for speech output, privacy, tactilely-discernible input controls, display screens, and Braille instructions to the general accessibility requirements set out in the 1991 Standards. Machines shall be speech enabled and exceptions are provided that cover when audible tones are permitted, when advertisements or similar information are provided, and where speech synthesis cannot be supported. The 1991 Standards require these machines to be accessible to and independently usable by persons with visual impairments, but do not contain any technical specifications.

---

708 Two-Way Communication Systems

708.1 General. Two-way communication systems shall comply with 708.

Advisory
708.1 General. Devices that do not require handsets are easier to use by people who have a limited reach.

708.2 Audible and Visual Indicators. The system shall provide both audible and visual signals.

Advisory
708.2 Audible and Visual Indicators. A light can be used to indicate visually that assistance is on the way. Signs indicating the meaning of visual signals should be provided.

708.3 Handsets. Handset cords, if provided, shall be 29 inches (735 mm) long minimum.

708.4 Residential Dwelling Unit Communication Systems. Communications systems between a residential dwelling unit and a site, building, or floor entrance shall comply with 708.4.

708.4.1 Common Use or Public Use System Interface. The common use or public use system interface shall include the capability of supporting voice and TTY communication with the residential dwelling unit interface.

708.4.2 Residential Dwelling Unit Interface. The residential dwelling unit system interface shall include a telephone jack capable of supporting voice and TTY communication with the common use or public use system interface.

Guidance

New provisions of the 2010 Standards at sections 230.1 and 708 require two-way communications systems to be equipped with visible as well as audible signals.

CHAPTER 8: SPECIAL ROOMS, SPACES AND ELEMENTS

801 General

801.1 Scope. The provisions of Chapter 8 shall apply where required by Chapter 2 or where referenced by a requirement in this document.

Advisory

801.1 Scope. Facilities covered by these requirements are also subject to the requirements of the other chapters. For example, 806 addresses guest rooms in transient lodging facilities while 902 contains the technical specifications for dining surfaces. If a transient lodging facility contains a restaurant, the restaurant must comply with requirements in other chapters such as those applicable to certain dining surfaces.

802 Wheelchair Spaces, Companion Seats, and Designated Aisle Seats

802.1 Wheelchair Spaces. Wheelchair spaces shall comply with 802.1.

802.1.1 Floor or Ground Surface. The floor or ground surface of wheelchair spaces shall comply with 302. Changes in level are not permitted.

EXCEPTION: Slopes not steeper than 1:48 shall be permitted.

802.1.2 Width. A single wheelchair space shall be 36 inches (915 mm) wide minimum Where two adjacent wheelchair spaces are provided, each wheelchair space shall be 33 inches (840 mm) wide minimum.

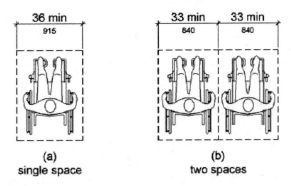

Figure 802.1.2 Width of Wheelchair Spaces in Assembly Areas

802.1.3 Depth. Where a wheelchair space can be entered from the front or rear, the wheelchair space shall be 48 inches (1220 mm) deep minimum. Where a wheelchair space can be entered only from the side, the wheelchair space shall be 60 inches (1525 mm) deep minimum.

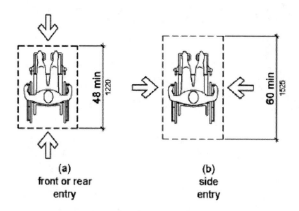

Figure 802.1.3 Depth of Wheelchair Spaces in Assembly Areas

802.1.4 Approach. Wheelchair spaces shall adjoin accessible routes. Accessible routes shall not overlap wheelchair spaces.

Advisory

802.1.4 Approach. Because accessible routes serving wheelchair spaces are not permitted to overlap the clear floor space at wheelchair spaces, access to any wheelchair space cannot be through another wheelchair space.

802.1.5 Overlap. Wheelchair spaces shall not overlap circulation paths.

Advisory

802.1.5 Overlap. The term "circulation paths" used in Section 802.1.5 means aisle width required by applicable building or life safety codes for the specific assembly occupancy. Where the circulation path provided is wider than the required aisle width, the wheelchair space may intrude into that portion of the circulation path that is provided in excess of the required aisle width.

802.2 Lines of Sight. Lines of sight to the screen, performance area, or playing field for spectators in wheelchair spaces shall comply with 802.2.

802.2.1 Lines of Sight Over Seated Spectators. Where spectators are expected to remain seated during events, spectators in wheelchair spaces shall be afforded lines of sight complying with 802.2.1.

802.2.1.1 Lines of Sight Over Heads. Where spectators are provided lines of sight over the heads of spectators seated in the first row in front of their seats, spectators seated in wheelchair spaces shall be afforded lines of sight over the heads of seated spectators in the first row in front of wheelchair spaces.

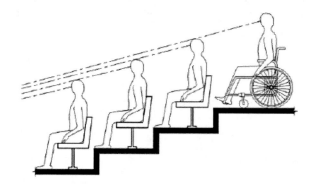

Figure 802.2.1.1 Lines of Sight Over the Heads of Seated Spectators

802.2.1.2 Lines of Sight Between Heads. Where spectators are provided lines of sight over the shoulders and between the heads of spectators seated in the first row in front of their seats, spectators seated in wheelchair spaces shall be afforded lines of sight over the shoulders and between the heads of seated spectators in the first row in front of wheelchair spaces.

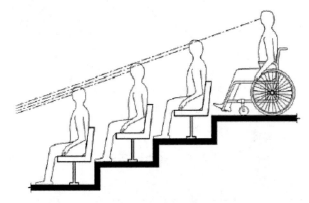

Figure 802.2.1.2 Lines of Sight Between the Heads of Seated Spectators

802.2.2 Lines of Sight Over Standing Spectators. Where spectators are expected to stand during events, spectators in wheelchair spaces shall be afforded lines of sight complying with 802.2.2.

802.2.2.1 Lines of Sight Over Heads. Where standing spectators are provided lines of sight over the heads of spectators standing in the first row in front of their seats, spectators seated in wheelchair spaces shall be afforded lines of sight over the heads of standing spectators in the first row in front of wheelchair spaces.

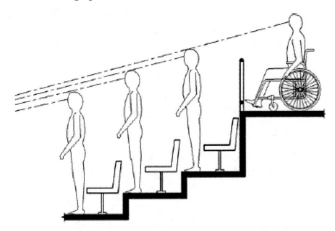

Figure 802.2.2.1 Lines of Sight Over the Heads of Standing Spectators

802.2.2.2 Lines of Sight Between Heads. Where standing spectators are provided lines of sight over the shoulders and between the heads of spectators standing in the first row in front of their seats, spectators seated in wheelchair spaces shall be afforded lines of sight over the shoulders and between the heads of standing spectators in the first row in front of wheelchair spaces.

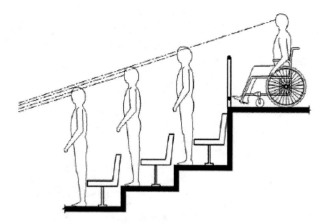

Figure 802.2.2.2 Lines of Sight Between the Heads of Standing Spectators

802.3 Companion Seats. Companion seats shall comply with 802.3.

802.3.1 Alignment. In row seating, companion seats shall be located to provide shoulder alignment with adjacent wheelchair spaces. The shoulder alignment point of the wheelchair space shall be measured 36 inches (915 mm) from the front of the wheelchair space. The floor surface of the companion seat shall be at the same elevation as the floor surface of the wheelchair space.

802.3.2 Type. Companion seats shall be equivalent in size, quality, comfort, and amenities to the seating in the immediate area. Companion seats shall be permitted to be movable.

802.4 Designated Aisle Seats. Designated aisle seats shall comply with 802.4.

802.4.1 Armrests. Where armrests are provided on the seating in the immediate area, folding or retractable armrests shall be provided on the aisle side of the seat.

802.4.2 Identification. Each designated aisle seat shall be identified by a sign or marker.

Advisory

802.4.2 Identification. Seats with folding or retractable armrests are intended for use by individuals who have difficulty walking. Consider identifying such seats with signs that contrast (light-on-dark or dark-on-light) and that are also photo luminescent.

---

803 Dressing, Fitting, and Locker Rooms

803.1 General. Dressing, fitting, and locker rooms shall comply with 803.

Advisory

803.1 General. Partitions and doors should be designed to ensure people using accessible dressing and fitting rooms privacy equivalent to that afforded other users of the facility. Section 903.5 requires dressing room bench seats to be installed so that they are at the same height as a typical wheelchair seat, 17 inches (430 mm) to 19 inches (485 mm). However, wheelchair seats can be lower than dressing room benches for people of short stature or children using wheelchairs.

803.2 Turning Space. Turning space complying with 304 shall be provided within the room.

803.3 Door Swing. Doors shall not swing into the room unless a clear floor or ground space complying with 305.3 is provided beyond the arc of the door swing.

803.4 Benches. A bench complying with 903 shall be provided within the room.

803.5 Coat Hooks and Shelves. Coat hooks provided within the room shall be located within one of the reach ranges specified in 308. Shelves shall be 40 inches (1015 mm) minimum and 48 inches (1220 mm) maximum above the finish floor or ground.

Guidance

Dressing rooms, fitting rooms, and locker rooms are required to comply with the accessibility requirements of sections 222 and 803 of the 2010 Standards. Where these types of rooms are provided in clusters, five percent (5%) but at least one room in each cluster must comply. Some commenters stated that clothing and retail stores would have to expand and reconfigure accessible dressing, fitting and locker rooms to meet the changed provision for clear floor space alongside the end of the bench. Commenters explained that meeting the new requirement would result in a loss of sales and inventory space. Other commenters also expressed opposition to the changed requirement in locker rooms for similar reasons.

The Department reminds the commenters that the requirements in the 2010 Standards for the clear floor space to be beside the short axis of the bench in an accessible dressing, fitting, or locker room apply only to new construction and alterations. The requirements for alterations in the 2010 Standards at section 202.3 do not include the requirement from the 1991 Standards at section 4.1.6(1)(c) that if alterations to single elements, when considered together, amount to an alteration of a room or space in a building or facility, the entire space shall be made accessible. Therefore, under the 2010 Standards, the alteration requirements only apply to specific elements or spaces that are being altered. So providing the clear floor space at the end of the bench as required by the 2010 Standards instead of in front of the bench as is allowed by the 1991 Standards would only be required when the bench in the accessible dressing room is altered or when the entire dressing room area is altered.

804 Kitchens and Kitchenettes

804.1 General. Kitchens and kitchenettes shall comply with 804.

804.2 Clearance. Where a pass through kitchen is provided, clearances shall comply with 804.2.1. Where a U-shaped kitchen is provided, clearances shall comply with 804.2.2.

EXCEPTION: Spaces that do not provide a cooktop or conventional range shall not be required to comply with 804.2.

Advisory

804.2 Clearance. Clearances are measured from the furthest projecting face of all opposing base cabinets, counter tops, appliances, or walls, excluding hardware.

804.2.1 Pass Through Kitchen. In pass through kitchens where counters, appliances or cabinets are on two opposing sides, or where counters, appliances or cabinets are opposite a parallel wall, clearance between all opposing base cabinets, counter tops, appliances, or walls within kitchen work areas shall be 40 inches (1015 mm) minimum. Pass through kitchens shall have two entries.

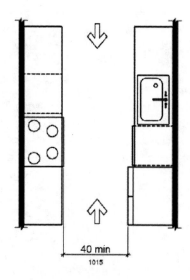

Figure 804.2.1 Pass Through Kitchens

804.2.2 U-Shaped. In U-shaped kitchens enclosed on three contiguous sides, clearance between all opposing base cabinets, counter tops, appliances, or walls within kitchen work areas shall be 60 inches (1525 mm) minimum.

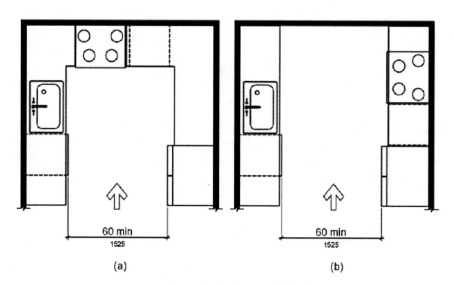

Figure 804.2.2 U-Shaped Kitchens

804.3 Kitchen Work Surface. In residential dwelling units required to comply with 809, at least one 30 inches (760 mm) wide minimum section of counter shall provide a kitchen work surface that complies with 804.3.

804.3.1 Clear Floor or Ground Space. A clear floor space complying with 305 positioned for a forward approach shall be provided. The clear floor or ground space shall be centered on the kitchen work surface and shall provide knee and toe clearance complying with 306.

> **EXCEPTION:** Cabinetry shall be permitted under the kitchen work surface provided that all of the following conditions are met:
>
> **(a)** the cabinetry can be removed without removal or replacement of the kitchen work surface;
>
> **(b)** the finish floor extends under the cabinetry; and
>
> **(c)** the walls behind and surrounding the cabinetry are finished.

804.3.2 Height. The kitchen work surface shall be 34 inches (865 mm) maximum above the finish floor or ground.

> **EXCEPTION:** A counter that is adjustable to provide a kitchen work surface at variable heights, 29 inches (735 mm) minimum and 36 inches (915 mm) maximum, shall be permitted.

804.3.3 Exposed Surfaces. There shall be no sharp or abrasive surfaces under the work surface counters.

804.4 Sinks. Sinks shall comply with 606.

804.5 Storage. At least 50 percent of shelf space in storage facilities shall comply with 811.

804.6 Appliances. Where provided, kitchen appliances shall comply with 804.6.

804.6.1 Clear Floor or Ground Space. A clear floor or ground space complying with 305 shall be provided at each kitchen appliance. Clear floor or ground spaces shall be permitted to overlap.

804.6.2 Operable Parts. All appliance controls shall comply with 309.

> **EXCEPTIONS:**
>
> **1.** Appliance doors and door latching devices shall not be required to comply with 309.4.
>
> **2.** Bottom-hinged appliance doors, when in the open position, shall not be required to comply with 309.3.

804.6.3 Dishwasher. Clear floor or ground space shall be positioned adjacent to the dishwasher door. The dishwasher door, in the open position, shall not obstruct the clear floor or ground space for the dishwasher or the sink.

804.6.4 Range or Cooktop. Where a forward approach is provided, the clear floor or ground space shall provide knee and toe clearance complying with 306. Where knee and toe space is provided, the underside of the range or cooktop shall be insulated or otherwise configured to prevent burns, abrasions, or electrical shock. The location of controls shall not require reaching across burners.

804.6.5 Oven. Ovens shall comply with 804.6.5.

804.6.5.1 Side-Hinged Door Ovens. Side-hinged door ovens shall have the work surface required by 804.3 positioned adjacent to the latch side of the oven door.

804.6.5.2 Bottom-Hinged Door Ovens. Bottom-hinged door ovens shall have the work surface required by 804.3 positioned adjacent to one side of the door.

804.6.5.3 Controls. Ovens shall have controls on front panels.

804.6.6 Refrigerator/Freezer. Combination refrigerators and freezers shall have at least 50 percent of the freezer space 54 inches (1370 mm) maximum above the finish floor or ground. The clear floor or ground space shall be positioned for a parallel approach to the space dedicated to a refrigerator/freezer with the centerline of the clear floor or ground space offset 24 inches (610 mm) maximum from the centerline of the dedicated space.

805 Medical Care and Long-Term Care Facilities

805.1 General. Medical care facility and long-term care facility patient or resident sleeping rooms required to provide mobility features shall comply with 805.

805.2 Turning Space. Turning space complying with 304 shall be provided within the room.

805.3 Clear Floor or Ground Space. A clear floor space complying with 305 shall be provided on each side of the bed. The clear floor space shall be positioned for parallel approach to the side of the bed.

805.4 Toilet and Bathing Rooms. Toilet and bathing rooms that are provided as part of a patient or resident sleeping room shall comply with 603. Where provided, no fewer than one water closet, one lavatory, and one bathtub or shower shall comply with the applicable requirements of 603 through 610.

806 Transient Lodging Guest Rooms

806.1 General. Transient lodging guest rooms shall comply with 806. Guest rooms required to provide mobility features shall comply with 806.2. Guest rooms required to provide communication features shall comply with 806.3.

806.2 Guest Rooms with Mobility Features. Guest rooms required to provide mobility features shall comply with 806.2.

Advisory

806.2 Guest Rooms. The requirements in Section 806.2 do not include requirements that are common to all accessible spaces. For example, closets in guest rooms must comply with the applicable provisions for storage specified in scoping.

806.2.1 Living and Dining Areas. Living and dining areas shall be accessible.

806.2.2 Exterior Spaces. Exterior spaces, including patios, terraces and balconies, that serve the guest room shall be accessible.

806.2.3 Sleeping Areas. At least one sleeping area shall provide a clear floor space complying with 305 on both sides of a bed. The clear floor space shall be positioned for parallel approach to the side of the bed.

EXCEPTION: Where a single clear floor space complying with 305 positioned for parallel approach is provided between two beds, a clear floor or ground space shall not be required on both sides of a bed.

806.2.4 Toilet and Bathing Facilities. At least one bathroom that is provided as part of a guest room shall comply with 603. No fewer than one water closet, one lavatory, and one bathtub or shower shall comply with applicable requirements of 603 through 610. In addition, required roll-in shower compartments shall comply with 608.2.2 or 608.2.3. Toilet and bathing fixtures required to comply with 603 through 610 shall be permitted to be located in more than one toilet or bathing area, provided that travel between fixtures does not require travel between other parts of the guest room.

806.2.4.1 Vanity Counter Top Space. If vanity counter top space is provided in non-accessible guest toilet or bathing rooms, comparable vanity counter top space, in terms of size and proximity to the lavatory, shall also be provided in accessible guest toilet or bathing rooms.

Advisory

806.2.4.1 Vanity Counter Top Space. This provision is intended to ensure that accessible guest rooms are provided with comparable vanity counter top space.

806.2.5 Kitchens and Kitchenettes. Kitchens and kitchenettes shall comply with 804.

806.2.6 Turning Space. Turning space complying with 304 shall be provided within the guest room.

806.3 Guest Rooms with Communication Features. Guest rooms required to provide communication features shall comply with 806.3.

Advisory

806.3 Guest Rooms with Communication Features. In guest rooms required to have accessible communication features, consider ensuring compatibility with adaptive equipment used by people with hearing impairments. To ensure communication within the facility, as well as on commercial lines, provide telephone interface jacks that are compatible with both digital and analog signal use. If an audio headphone jack is provided on a speaker phone, a cutoff switch can be included in the jack so that insertion of the jack cuts off the speaker. If a telephone-like handset is used, the external speakers can be turned off when the handset is removed from the cradle. For headset or external amplification system compatibility, a standard subminiature jack installed in the telephone will provide the most flexibility.

806.3.1 Alarms. Where emergency warning systems are provided, alarms complying with 702 shall be provided.

806.3.2 Notification Devices. Visible notification devices shall be provided to alert room occupants of incoming telephone calls and a door knock or bell. Notification devices shall not be connected to visible alarm signal appliances. Telephones shall have volume controls compatible with the telephone system and shall comply with 704.3. Telephones shall be served by an electrical outlet complying with 309 located within 48 inches (1220 mm) of the telephone to facilitate the use of a TTY.

Guidance

Scoping. The minimum number of guest rooms required to be accessible in transient lodging facilities is covered by section 224 of the 2010 Standards. Scoping requirements for guest rooms with mobility features and guest rooms with communication features are addressed at section 224.2 and section 224.4, respectively. Under the 1991 Standards all newly constructed guest rooms with mobility features must provide communication features. Under the 2010 Standards, in section 224.5, at least one guest room with mobility features must also provide communication features. Additionally, not more than ten percent (10%) of the guest rooms required to provide mobility features and also equipped with communication features can be used to satisfy the minimum number of guest rooms required to provide communication features.

Some commenters opposed requirements for guest rooms accessible to individuals with mobility disabilities stating that statistics provided by the industry demonstrate that all types of accessible guest rooms are unused. They further claimed that the requirements of the 2010 Standards are too burdensome to meet in new construction, and that the requirements will result in a loss of living space in places of transient lodging. Other commenters urged the Department to increase the number of guest rooms required to be accessible. The number of guest rooms accessible to individuals with mobility disabilities and the number accessible to persons who are deaf or who are hard of hearing in the 2010 Standards are consistent with the 1991 Standards and with the IBC. The Department continues to receive complaints about the lack of accessible guest rooms throughout the country. Accessible guest rooms are used not only by individuals using mobility devices such as wheelchairs and scooters, but also by individuals with other mobility disabilities including persons who use walkers, crutches, or canes.

Data provided by the Disability Statistics Center at the University of California, San Francisco demonstrated that the number of adults who use wheelchairs has been increasing at the rate of six percent (6%) per year from 1969 to 1999; and by 2010, it was projected that two percent (2%) of the adult population would use wheelchairs. In addition to persons who use wheelchairs, three percent (3%) of adults used crutches, canes, walkers, and other mobility devices in 1999; and the number was projected to increase to four percent (4%) by 2010. Thus, in 2010, up to six percent (6%) of the population may need accessible guest rooms.

Dispersion. The 2010 Standards, in section 224.5, set scoping requirements for dispersion in facilities covered by the transient lodging provisions. This section covers guest rooms with mobility features and guest rooms with communication features and applies in new construction and alterations. The primary requirement is to provide choices of types of guest rooms, number of beds, and other amenities comparable to the choices provided to other guests. An advisory in section 224.5 provides guidance that "factors to be considered in providing an equivalent range of options may include, but are not limited to, room size, bed size, cost, view, bathroom fixtures such as hot tubs and spas, smoking and nonsmoking, and the number of rooms provided."

Commenters asked the Department to clarify what is meant by various terms used in section 224.5 such as "classes," "types," "options," and "amenities." Other commenters asked the Department to clarify and simplify the dispersion requirements set forth in section 224.5 of the 2010 Standards, in particular the scope of the term "amenities." One commenter expressed concern that views, if considered an amenity, would further complicate room categories and force owners and operators to make an educated guess. Other commenters stated that views should only be a dispersion criteria if view is a factor for pricing room rates.

These terms are not to be considered terms of art, but should be used as in their normal course. For example, "class" is defined by Webster's Dictionary as "a division by quality." "Type" is defined as "a group of * * * things that share common traits or characteristics distinguishing them as an identifiable group or

---

class." Accordingly, these terms are not intended to convey different concepts, but are used as synonyms. In the 2010 Standards, section 224.5 and its advisory require dispersion in such a varied range of hotels and lodging facilities that the Department believes that the chosen terms are appropriate to convey what is intended. Dispersion required by this section is not "one size fits all" and it is imperative that each covered entity consider its individual circumstance as it applies this requirement. For example, a facility would consider view as an amenity if some rooms faced mountains, a beach, a lake, or other scenery that was considered to be a premium. A facility where view was not marketed or requested by guests would not factor the view as an amenity for purposes of meeting the dispersion requirement.

Section 224.5 of the 2010 Standards requires that guest rooms with mobility features and guest rooms with communication features "shall be dispersed among the various classes of guest rooms, and shall provide choices of types of guest rooms, number of beds, and other amenities comparable to the choices provided to other guests. When the minimum number of guest rooms required is not sufficient to allow for complete dispersion, guest rooms shall be dispersed in the following priority: guest room type, number of beds and amenities."

This general dispersion requirement is intended to effectuate Congress' directive that a percentage of each class of hotel rooms is to be fully accessible to persons with disabilities. See H.R. Rep. No. 101-485 (II) at 391. Accordingly, the promise of the ADA in this instance is that persons with disabilities will have an equal opportunity to benefit from the various options available to hotel guests without disabilities, from single occupancy guest rooms with limited features (and accompanying limited price tags) to luxury suites with lavish features and choices. The inclusion of section 224.5 of the 2010 Standards is not new. Substantially similar language is contained in section 9.1.4 of the 1991 Standards.

Commenters raised concerns that the factors included in the advisory to section 224.5 of the 2010 Standards have been expanded. The advisory provides: "[f]actors to be considered in providing an equivalent range of options may include, but are not limited to, room size, bed size, cost, view, bathroom fixtures such as hot tubs and spas, smoking and nonsmoking, and the number of rooms provided."

As previously discussed, the advisory materials provided in the 2010 Standards are meant to be illustrative and do not set out specific requirements. In this particular instance, the advisory materials for section 224.5 set out some of the common types of amenities found at transient lodging facilities, and include common sense concepts such as view, bathroom fixtures, and smoking status. The intention of these factors is to indicate to the hospitality industry the sorts of considerations that the Department, in its enforcement efforts since the enactment of the ADA, has considered as amenities that should be made available to persons with disabilities, just as they are made available to guests without disabilities.

Commenters offered several suggestions for addressing dispersion. One option included the flexibility to use an equivalent facilitation option similar to that provided in section 9.1.4(2) of the 1991 Standards.

The 2010 Standards eliminated all specific references to equivalent facilitation. Since Congress made it clear that each class of hotel room is to be available to individuals with disabilities, the Department declines to adopt such a specific limitation in favor of the specific requirement for new construction and alterations found in section 224.5 of the 2010 Standards.

In considering the comments of the hospitality industry from the ANPRM and the Department's enforcement efforts in this area, the Department sought comment in the NPRM on whether the dispersion requirements should be applied proportionally, or whether the requirements of section 224.5 of the 2010 Standards would be complied with if access to at least one guest room of each type were to be provided.

One commenter expressed concern about requiring different guest room types to be proportionally represented in the accessible guest room pool as opposed to just having each type represented. Some commenters also expressed concern about accessible guest rooms created in pre-1993 facilities and they requested that such accessible guest rooms be safe harbored just as they are safe harbored under the 1991 Standards. In addition, one commenter requested that the proposed dispersion requirements in section 224.5 of the 2010 Standards not be applied to pre-1993 facilities even when they are altered. Some commenters also offered a suggestion for limitations to the dispersion requirements as an alternative to safe harboring pre-1993 facilities. The suggestion included: (1) Guest rooms´ interior or exterior footprints may remain unchanged in order to meet the dispersion requirements; (2) Dispersion should only be required among the types of rooms affected by an alteration; and (3) Subject to (1) and (2) above and technical feasibility, a facility would need to provide only one guest room in each guest room type such as single, double and suites. One commenter requested an exception to the dispersion criteria that applies to both existing and new multi-story timeshare facilities. This requested exception waives dispersion based on views to the extent that up to eight units may be vertically stacked in a single location.

Section 224.1.1 of the 2010 Standards sets scoping requirements for alterations to transient lodging guest rooms. The advisory to section 224.1.1 further explains that compliance with 224.5 is more likely to be achieved if all of the accessible guest rooms are not provided in the same area of the facility, when accessible guest rooms are added as a result of subsequent alterations.

Some commenters requested a specific exemption for small hotels of 300 or fewer guest rooms from dispersion regarding smoking rooms. The ADA requires that individuals with disabilities be provided with the same range of options as persons without disabilities, and, therefore, the Department declines to add such an exemption. It is noted, however, that the existence of this language in the advisory does not require a place of transient lodging that does not offer smoking guest rooms at its facility to do so only for individuals with disabilities.

Guest Rooms with Mobility Features. Scoping provisions for guest rooms with mobility features are provided in section 224.2 of the 2010 Standards. Scoping requirements for alterations are included in 224.1.1. These scoping requirements in the 2010 Standards are consistent with the 1991 Standards.

One commenter expressed opposition to the new scoping provisions for altered guest rooms, which, according to the commenter, require greater numbers of accessible guest rooms with mobility features.

Section 224.1.1 of the 2010 Standards provides scoping requirements for alterations to guest rooms in existing facilities. Section 224.1.1 modifies the scoping requirements for new construction in section 224 by limiting the application of section 224 requirements only to those guest rooms being altered or added until the number of such accessible guest rooms complies with the minimum number required for new construction in section 224.2 of the 2010 Standards. The minimum required number of accessible guest rooms is based on the total number of guest rooms altered or added instead of the total number of guest rooms provided. These requirements are consistent with the requirements in the 1991 Standards. Language in the 2010 Standards clarifies the provision of section 104.2 of the 2010 Standards which requires rounding up values to the next whole number for calculations of percentages in scoping.

Guest Rooms with Communication Features. The revisions at section 224.4 of the 2010 Standards effect no substantive change from the 1991 Standards with respect to the number of guest rooms required to provide communication features. The scoping requirement is consolidated into a single table, instead of appearing in three sections as in the 1991 Standards. The revised provisions also limit the overlap between guest rooms required to provide mobility features and guest rooms required to provide communication features. Section 224.5 of the 2010 Standards requires that at least one guest room providing mobility features must also provide communications features. At least one, but not more than ten percent (10%), of the guest rooms required to provide mobility features can also satisfy the minimum number of guest rooms required to provide communication features.

Commenters suggested that the requirements for scoping and dispersion of guest rooms for persons with mobility impairments and guest rooms with communication features are too complex for the industry to effectively implement.

The Department believes the requirements for guest rooms with communications features in the 2010 Standards clarify the requirements necessary to provide equal opportunity for travelers with disabilities. Additional technical assistance will be made available to address questions before the rule goes into effect.

Visible Alarms in Guest Rooms with Communication Features. The 1991 Standards at sections 9.3.1 and 4.28.4 require transient lodging guest rooms with communication features to provide either permanently installed visible alarms that are connected to the building fire alarm system or portable visible alarms that are connected to a standard 110-volt electrical outlet and are both activated by the building fire alarm system and provide a visible alarm when the single station smoke detector is activated. Section 215.4 of the 2010 Standards no longer includes the portable visible alarm option and instead requires that transient lodging guest rooms with communication features be equipped with a fire alarm system which includes permanently installed audible and visible alarms in accordance with NFPA 72 National Fire Alarm Code (1999 or 2002 edition). Such guest rooms with communication features are also required by section 806.3.2 of the 2010 Standards to be equipped with visible notification devices that alert room occupants of incoming telephone calls and a door knock or bell.

The 2010 Standards add a new exception for alterations to existing facilities that exempts existing fire alarm systems from providing visible alarms, unless the fire alarm system itself is upgraded or replaced, or a new fire alarm system is installed. Transient lodging facilities that alter guest rooms are not required to provide permanently installed visible alarms complying with the NFPA 72 if the existing fire alarm system has not been upgraded or replaced, or a new fire alarm system has not been installed.

Commenters representing small providers of transient lodging raised concerns about the proposed changes to prohibit the use of portable visible alarms used in transient lodging guest rooms. These commenters recommended retaining requirements that allow the use of portable visible alarms.

Persons who are deaf or hard of hearing have reported that portable visible alarms used in transient lodging guest rooms are deficient because the alarms are not activated by the building fire alarm system, and the alarms do not work when the building power source goes out in emergencies. The 2010 Standards are consistent with the model building, fire, and life safety codes as applied to newly constructed transient lodging facilities. One commenter sought confirmation of its understanding of visible alarm requirements from the Department. This commenter interpreted the exception to section 215.1 of the 2010 Standards and the Department's commentary to the NPRM to mean that if a transient lodging facility does not have permanently installed visible alarms in its communication accessible guest rooms, it will not be required to provide such alarms until such time that its fire alarm system is upgraded or replaced, or a new fire alarm system is installed. In addition, this commenter also understood that, if a hotel already has permanently installed visible alarms in all of its mobility accessible guest rooms, it would not have to relocate such visible alarms and other communication features in those rooms to other guest rooms to comply with the ten percent (10%) overlap requirement until the alarm system is upgraded or replaced.

This commenter's interpretation and understanding are consistent with the Department's position in this matter. Section 215.4 of the 2010 Standards requires that guest rooms required to have communication features be equipped with a fire alarm system complying with section 702. Communication accessible guest rooms are required to have all of the communication features described in section 806.3 of the 2010 Standards including a fire alarm system which provides both audible and visible alarms. The exception to section 215.1 of the 2010 Standards, which applies only to fire alarm requirements for guest rooms with communication features in existing facilities, exempts the visible alarm requirement until such time as the existing fire alarm system is upgraded or replaced, or a new fire alarm system is installed. If guest rooms in existing facilities are altered and they are required by section 224 of the 2010 Standards to have communication features, such guest rooms are required by section 806.3 to have all other communication features including notification devices.

Vanity Counter Space. Section 806.2.4.1 of the 2010 Standards requires that if vanity countertop space is provided in inaccessible transient lodging guest bathrooms, comparable vanity space must be provided in accessible transient lodging guest bathrooms.

A commenter questioned whether in existing facilities vanity countertop space may be provided through the addition of a shelf. Another commenter found the term "comparable" vague and expressed concern about confusion the new requirement would cause. This commenter suggested that the phrase "equal area in square inches" be used instead of comparable vanity space.

In some circumstances, the addition of a shelf in an existing facility may be a reasonable way to provide a space for travelers with disabilities to use their toiletries and other personal items. However, this is a determination that must be made on a case-by-case basis. Comparable vanity countertop space need not be one continuous surface and need not be exactly the same size as the countertops in comparable guest bathrooms. For example, accessible shelving within reach of the lavatory could be stacked to provide usable surfaces for toiletries and other personal items.

Shower and Sauna Doors in Transient Lodging Facilities. Section 9.4 of the 1991 Standards and section 206.5.3 of the 2010 Standards both require passage doors in transient lodging guest rooms that do not provide mobility features to provide at least 32 inches of clear width. Congress directed this requirement to be included so that individuals with disabilities could visit guests in other rooms. *See* H. Rept. 101-485, pt. 2, at 118 (1990); S. Rept. 101-116, at 70 (1989). Section 224.1.2 of the 2010 Standards adds a new exception to clarify that shower and sauna doors in such inaccessible guest rooms are exempt from the requirement for passage doors to provide at least 32 inches of clear width. Two commenters requested that saunas and steam rooms in existing facilities be exempt from the section 224.1.2 requirement and that the requirement be made applicable to new construction only.

The exemption to the section 224.1.2 requirement for a 32-inch wide clearance at doors to shower and saunas applies only to those showers and saunas in guest rooms which are not required to have mobility features. Showers and saunas in other locations, including those in common use areas and guest rooms with mobility features, are required to comply with the 32-inch clear width standard as well as other applicable accessibility standards. Saunas come in a variety of types: portable, pre-built, pre-cut, and custom-made. All saunas except for custom-made saunas are made to manufacturers′ standard dimensions. The Department is aware that creating the required 32-inch clearance at existing narrower doorways may not always be technically feasible. However, the Department believes that owners and operators will have an opportunity to provide the required doorway clearance, unless doing so is technically infeasible, when an alteration to an existing sauna is undertaken. Therefore, the Department has retained these requirements.

Platform Lifts in Transient Lodging Guest Rooms and Dwelling Units. The 1991 Standards, at section 4.1.3(5), exception 4, and the 2010 Standards, at sections 206.7 and 206.7.6, both limit the locations where platform lifts are permitted to be used as part of an accessible route. The 2010 Standards add a new scoping requirement that permits platform lifts to be used to connect levels within transient lodging guest rooms and dwelling units with mobility features.

806 Transient Lodging Guest Rooms

In the NPRM, the Department included floor plans showing examples of accessible guest rooms and bathrooms designs with mobility features to illustrate how compliance with the 2010 Standards could be accomplished with little or no additional space compared to designs that comply with the 1991 Standards.

Commenters noted that the Department′s plans showing accessible transient lodging guest rooms compliant with the 2010 Standards were not common in the transient lodging industry and also noted that the plans omitted doors at sleeping room closets.

The Department agrees that the configuration of the accessible bathrooms is somewhat different from past designs used by the industry, but this was done to meet the requirements of the 2010 Standards. The plans were provided to show that, with some redesign, the 2010 Standards do not normally increase the square footage of an accessible sleeping room or bathroom with mobility features in new construction. The Department has also modified several accessible guest room plans to show that doors can be installed on closets and comply with the 2010 Standards.

A commenter stated that the Department′s drawings suggest that the fan coil units for heat and air conditioning are overhead, while the typical sleeping room usually has a vertical unit, or a packaged terminal air conditioning unit within the room. The Department′s drawings are sample plans, showing the layout of the space, relationship of elements to each other, and required clear floor and turning spaces. It was not the intent of the Department to provide precise locations for all elements, including heating and air conditioning units.

Commenters noted that in guest rooms with two beds, each bed was positioned close to a wall, reducing access on one side. Another commenter stated that additional housekeeping time is needed to clean the room when beds are placed closer to walls. The 2010 Standards require that, when two beds are provided, there must be at least 36 inches of clear space between the beds. The plans provided in the NPRM showed two bed arrangements with adequate clear width complying with the 1991 Standards and the 2010 Standards. Additional space can be provided on the other side of the beds to facilitate housekeeping as long as the clear floor space between beds is at least 36 inches wide.

Commenters stated that chases in sleeping room bathrooms that route plumbing and other utilities can present challenges when modifying existing facilities. In multi-story facilities, relocating or re-routing these elements may not be possible, limiting options for providing access. The Department recognizes that relocating mechanical chases in multi-story facilities may be difficult or impossible to accomplish. While these issues do not exist in new facilities, altered existing facilities must comply with the 2010 Standards to the extent that it is technically feasible to do so. When an alteration cannot fully comply because it is technically infeasible to do so, the alteration must still be designed to comply to the greatest extent feasible.

Commenters noted that on some of the Department's plans where a vanity is located adjacent to a bathtub, the vanity may require more maintenance due to exposure to water. The Department agrees that it would be advisable that items placed next to a bathtub or shower be made of materials that are not susceptible to water damage.

Transient Lodging Guest Room Floor Plans and Related Text

The Department has included the following floor plans showing application of the requirements of the 2010 Standards without significant loss of guest room living space in transient lodging compared to the 1991 Standards.

Plan 1A: 13-Foot Wide Accessible Guest Room

This drawing shows an accessible 13-foot wide guest room with features that comply with the 2010 Standards. Features include a standard bathtub with a seat, comparable vanity, clothes closet with swinging doors, and door connecting to adjacent guest room. Furnishings include a king bed and additional seating.

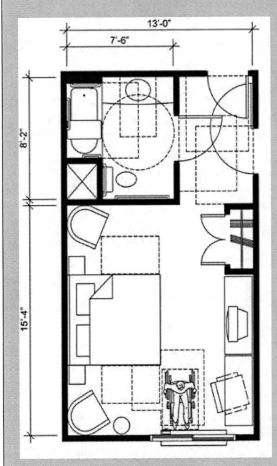

The following accessible features are provided in the bathroom:

- Comparable vanity counter top space (section 806);
- Bathtub with a lavatory at the control end (section 607.2);
- Removable bathtub seat (section 607.3);
- Clearance in front of the bathtub extends its full length and is 30 inches wide min. (section 607.2);
- Recessed bathtub location permits shorter rear grab bar at water closet (section 604.5.2);
- Circular turning space in room (section 603.2.1);
- Required clear floor spaces at fixtures and turning space overlap (section 603.2.2);
- Turning space includes knee and toe clearance at lavatory (section 304.3);
- Water closet clearance is 60 inches at back wall and 56 inches deep (section 604.3);
- Centerline of the water closet at 16-18 inches from side wall (section 604.2); and
- No other fixtures or obstructions located within required water closet clearance (section 604.3).

The following accessible features are provided in the living area:

- T-shaped turning space (section 304.3.2);
- Accessible route (section 402);
- Clear floor space on both sides of the bed (section 806.2.3);
- Maneuvering clearances at all doors (section 404.2);Accessible operable window (section 309); and
- Accessible controls for the heat and air conditioning (section 309).

Plan 1B: 13-Foot Wide Accessible Guest Room

This drawing shows an accessible 13-foot wide guest room with features that comply with the 2010 Standards. Features include a standard bathtub with a seat, comparable vanity, clothes closet with swinging doors, and door connecting to adjacent guest room. Furnishings include two beds.

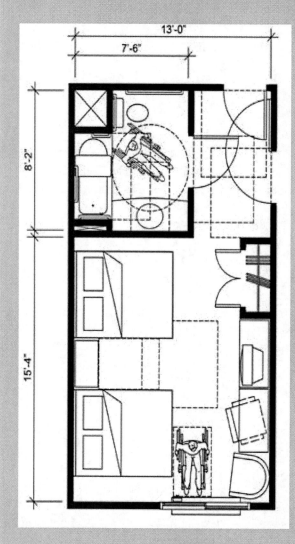

The following accessible features are provided in the bathroom:

- Comparable vanity counter top space (section 806);
- Bathtub with a lavatory at the control end (section 607.2);
- Removable bathtub seat (section 607.3);
- Clearance in front of the bathtub extends its full length and is 30 inches wide min. (section 607.2);
- Recessed bathtub location permits shorter rear grab bar at water closet (section 604.5.2);
- Circular turning space in room (section 603.2.1);
- Required clear floor spaces at fixtures and turning space overlap (section 603.2.2);
- Turning space includes knee and toe clearance at lavatory (section 304.3);
- Water closet clearance is 60 inches at back wall and 56 inches deep (section 604.3);
- Centerline of the water closet at 16-18 inches from side wall (section 604.2); and
- No other fixtures or obstructions located within required water closet clearance (section 604.3);

The following accessible features are provided in the living area:

- T-shaped turning space (section 304.3.2);
- Accessible route (section 402);
- Clear floor space between beds (section 806.2.3);
- Maneuvering clearances at all doors (section 404.2);
- Accessible operable window (section 309); and
- Accessible controls for the heat and air conditioning (section 309).

Plan 2A: 13-Foot Wide Accessible Guest Room

This drawing shows an accessible 13-foot wide guest room with features that comply with the 2010 Standards. Features include a standard roll-in shower with a seat, comparable vanity, wardrobe, and door connecting to adjacent guest room. Furnishings include a king bed and additional seating.

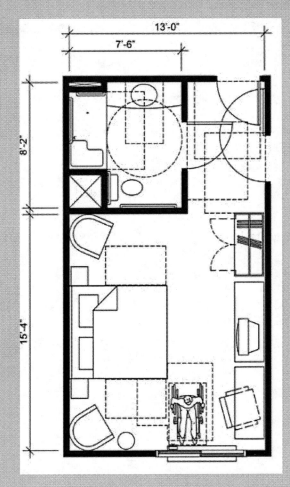

The following accessible features are provided in the bathroom:

- Comparable vanity counter top space (section 806);
- Standard roll-in type shower with folding seat (section 608.2.2);
- Recessed roll-in shower location permits shorter rear grab bar at water closet (section 604.5.2);
- Clear floor space adjacent to shower min. 30 inches wide by 60 inches long (section 608.2.2);
- Circular turning space in room (section 603.2.1);
- Required clear floor spaces at fixtures and turning space overlap (section 603.2.2);
- Turning space includes knee and toe clearance at lavatory (section 304.3);
- Water closet clearance is 60 inches at back wall and 56 inches deep (section 604.3);
- Centerline of the water closet at 16-18 inches from side wall (section 604.2); and
- No other fixtures or obstructions located within required water closet clearance (section 604.3).

The following accessible features are provided in the living area:

- T-shaped turning space (section 304.3.2);
- Accessible route (section 402);
- Clear floor space on both sides of the bed (section 806.2.3);
- Maneuvering clearances at all doors (section 404.2);
- Accessible operable window (section 309); and
- Accessible controls for the heat and air conditioning (section 309).

Plan 2B: 13-Foot Wide Accessible Guest Room

This drawing shows an accessible 13-foot wide guest room with features that comply with the 2010 Standards. Features include an alternate roll-in shower with a seat, comparable vanity, wardrobe, and door connecting to adjacent guest room. Furnishings include two beds.

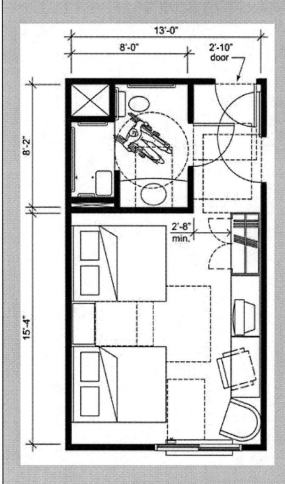

The following accessible features are provided in the bathroom:

- Comparable vanity counter top space (section 806);
- Alternate roll-in type shower with folding seat is 36 inches deep and 60 inches wide (section 608.2.3);
- Alternate roll-in shower has a 36-inch wide entry at one end of the long side of the compartment (section 608.2.3);
- Recessed alternate roll-in shower location permits shorter rear grab bar at water closet (section 604.5.2);
- Circular turning space in room (section 603.2.1);
- Required clear floor spaces at fixtures and turning space overlap (section 603.2.2);
- Turning space includes knee and toe clearance at lavatory (section 304.3);
- Water closet clearance is 60 inches at back wall and 56 inches deep (section 604.3);
- Centerline of the water closet at 16-18 inches from side wall (section 604.2); and
- No other fixtures or obstructions located within required water closet clearance (section 604.3)

The following accessible features are provided in the living area:

- T-shaped turning space (section 304.3.2);
- Accessible route (section 402);
- Clear floor space between beds (section 806.2.3);
- Maneuvering clearances at all doors (section 404.2);
- Accessible operable window (section 309); and
- Accessible controls for the heat and air conditioning (section 309).

Plan 3A: 12-Foot Wide Accessible Guest Room

This drawing shows an accessible 12-foot wide guest room with features that comply with the 2010 Standards. Features include a bathtub with a seat, comparable vanity, open clothes closet, and door connecting to adjacent guest room. Furnishings include a king bed and additional seating.

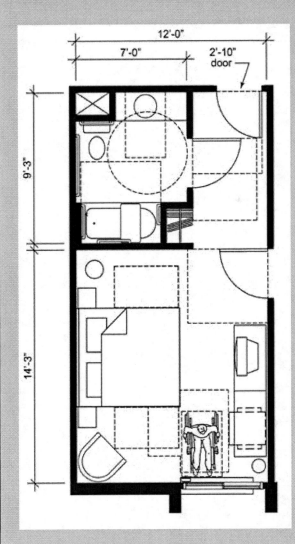

The following accessible features are provided in the bathroom:

- Comparable vanity counter top space (section 806);
- Bathtub (section 607.2);
- Removable bathtub seat (section 607.3);
- Clearance in front of the bathtub extends its full length and is 30 inches wide min. (section 607.2);
- Recessed lavatory with vanity countertop permits shorter rear grab bar at water closet (section 604.5.2);
- Circular turning space in room (section 603.2.1);
- Required clear floor spaces at fixtures and turning space overlap (section 603.2.2);
- Turning space includes knee and toe clearance at lavatory (section 304.3);
- Water closet clearance is 60 inches at back wall and 56 inches deep (section 604.3);
- Centerline of the water closet at 16-18 inches from side wall (section 604.2); and
- No other fixtures or obstructions located within required water closet clearance (section 604.3).

The following accessible features are provided in the living area:

- T-shaped turning space (section 304.3.2);
- Accessible route (section 402);
- Clear floor space on both sides of the bed (section 806.2.3);
- Maneuvering clearances at all doors (section 404.2);
- Accessible operable window (section 309); and
- Accessible controls for the heat and air conditioning (section 309).

Plan 3B: 12-Foot Wide Accessible Guest Room

This drawing shows an accessible 12-foot wide guest room with features that comply with the 2010 Standards. Features include a standard roll-in shower with a seat, comparable vanity, wardrobe, and door connecting to adjacent guest room. Furnishings include two beds.

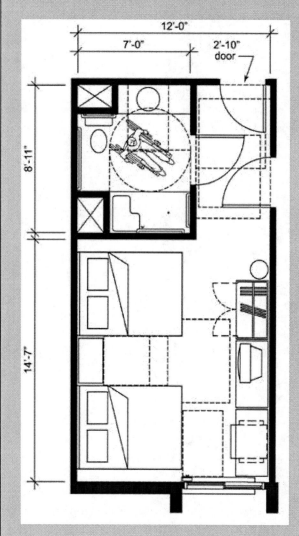

The following accessible features are provided in the bathroom:

- The following accessible features are provided in the bathroom:
- Comparable vanity counter top space (section 806);
- Standard roll-in type shower with folding seat (section 608.2.2);
- Recessed lavatory with vanity counter top permits shorter rear grab bar at water closet (section 604.5.2);
- Clear floor space adjacent to shower min. 30 inches wide by 60 inches long (section 608.2.2);
- Circular turning space in room (section 603.2.1);
- Required clear floor spaces at fixtures and turning space overlap (section 603.2.2);
- Turning space includes knee and toe clearance at lavatory (section 304.3);
- Water closet clearance is 60 inches at back wall and 56 inches deep (section 604.3);
- Centerline of the water closet at 16-18 inches from side wall (section 604.2); and

No other fixtures or obstructions located within required water closet clearance (section 604.3). The following accessible features are provided in the living area:

- T-shaped turning space (section 304.3.2);
- Accessible route (section 402);
- Clear floor space between beds (section 806.2.3);
- Maneuvering clearances at all doors (section 404.2);
- Accessible operable window (section 309); and
- Accessible controls for the heat and air conditioning (section 309).

Plan 4A: 13-Foot Wide Accessible Guest Room

This drawing shows an accessible 13-foot wide guest room with features that comply with the 2010 Standards. Features include a standard roll-in shower with a seat, comparable vanity, clothes closet with swinging doors, and door connecting to adjacent guest room. Furnishings include a king bed and additional seating.

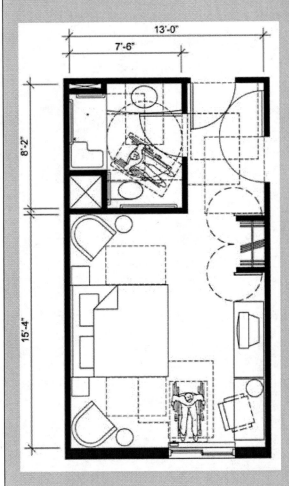

The following accessible features are provided in the bathroom:

- Comparable vanity counter top space (section 806);
- Standard roll-in type shower with folding seat (section 608.2.2);
- Clear floor space adjacent to shower min. 30 inches wide by 60 inches long (section 608.2.2);
- Recessed roll-in shower location permits shorter rear grab bar at water closet (section 604.5.2);
- Circular turning space in room (section 603.2.1);
- Required clear floor spaces at fixtures and turning space overlap (section 603.2.2);
- Turning space includes knee and toe clearance at lavatory (section 304.3);
- Water closet clearance is 60 inches at back wall and 56 inches deep (section 604.3);
- Centerline of the water closet at 16-18 inches from side wall (section 604.2); and
- No other fixtures or obstructions located within required water closet clearance (section 604.3).
- 30-inch wide by 48-inch long minimum clear floor space provided beyond the arc of the swing of the entry door (section 603.2.3 exception 2).

The following accessible features are provided in the living area:

- T-shaped turning space (section 304.3.2);
- Accessible route (section 402);
- Clear floor space on both sides of the bed (section 806.2.3);
- Maneuvering clearances at all doors (section 404.2);
- Accessible operable window (section 309); and
- Accessible controls for the heat and air conditioning (section 309). 13'-0" 7'-6" 15'-4

Plan 4B: 13-Foot Wide Accessible Guest Room

This drawing shows an accessible 13-foot wide guest room with features that comply with the 2010 Standards. Features include an alternate roll-in shower with a seat, comparable vanity, wardrobe, and door connecting to adjacent guest room. Furnishings include two beds.

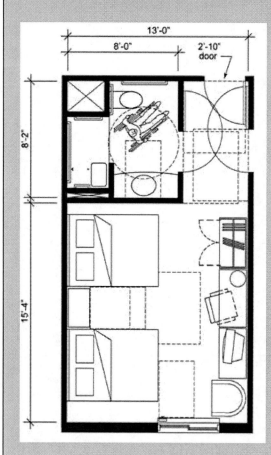

The following accessible features are provided in the bathroom:

- Comparable vanity counter top space (section 806);
- Alternate roll-in type shower with folding seat is 36 inches deep and 60 inches wide (section 608.2.3);
- Alternate roll-in shower has a 36-inch wide entry at one end of the long end of the compartment (section 608.2.3);
- Recessed alternate roll-in shower location permits shorter rear grab bar at water closet (section 604.5.2);
- Circular turning space in room (section 603.2.1);
- Required clear floor spaces at fixtures and turning space overlap (section 603.2.2);
- Turning space includes knee and toe clearance at lavatory (section 304.3);
- Water closet clearance is 60 inches at back wall and 56 inches deep (section 604.3);
- Centerline of the water closet at 16-18 inches from side wall (section 604.2); and
- No other fixtures or obstructions located within required water closet clearance (section 604.3).

The following accessible features are provided in the living area:

- T-shaped turning space (section 304.3.2);
- Accessible route (section 402);
- Clear floor space between beds (section 806.2.3);
- Maneuvering clearances at all doors (section 404.2);
- Accessible operable window (section 309); and
- Accessible controls for the heat and air conditioning (section 309).

Plan 5A: 13-Foot Wide Accessible Guest Room

This drawing shows an accessible 13-foot wide guest room with features that comply with the 2010 Standards. Features include a transfer shower, comparable vanity, clothes closet with swinging door, and door connecting to adjacent guest room. Furnishings include a king bed and additional seating.

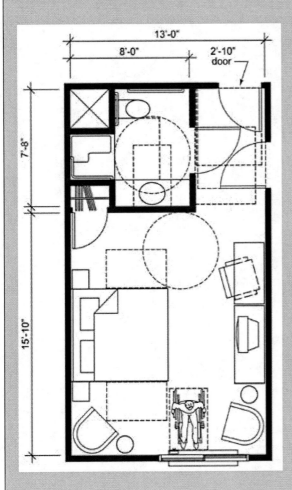

The following accessible features are provided in the bathroom:

- Comparable vanity counter top space (section 806);
- Transfer shower (section 603.2);
- Shower seat (section 610.3);
- Clearance in front of the shower extends beyond the seat and is 36 inches wide min. (section 607.2);
- Recessed transfer shower location permits shorter rear grab bar at water closet (section 604.5.2);
- Circular turning space in room (section 603.2.1);
- Required clear floor spaces at fixtures and turning space overlap (section 603.2.2);
- Water closet clearance is 60 inches at back wall and 56 inches deep (section 604.3);
- Centerline of the water closet at 16 inches from side wall (section 604.2); and
- No other fixtures or obstructions located within required water closet clearance (section 604.3).

The following accessible features are provided in the living area:

- Circular turning space (section 304.3.2);
- Accessible route (section 402);
- Clear floor space on both sides of the bed (section 806.2.3);
- Maneuvering clearances at all doors (section 404.2);
- Accessible operable window (section 229); and
- Accessible controls for the heat and air conditioning (section 309).

Plan 5B: 13-Foot Wide Accessible Guest Room

This drawing shows an accessible 13-foot wide guest room with features that comply with the 2010 Standards. Features include a transfer shower, comparable vanity, open clothes closet, and door connecting to adjacent guest room. Furnishings include two beds.

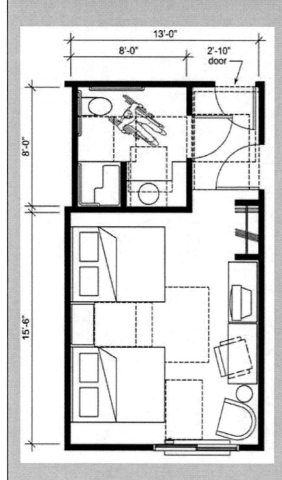

The following accessible features are provided in the bathroom:

- Comparable vanity counter top space (section 806);
- Transfer shower (section 603.2);
- Shower seat (section 610.3);
- Clearance in front of the shower extends beyond the seat and is 36 inches wide min. (section 607.2);
- Lavatory with vanity counter top recessed to permit shorter rear grab bar at water closet (section 604.5.2);
- T-shaped turning space in room (section 603.2.1);
- Required clear floor spaces at fixtures and turning space overlap (section 603.2.2);
- Water closet clearance is 60 inches at back wall and 56 inches deep (section 604.3);
- Centerline of the water closet at 16-18 inches from side wall (section 604.2); and
- No other fixtures or obstructions located within required water closet clearance (section 604.3).

The following accessible features are provided in the living area:

- T-shaped turning space (section 304.3.2);
- Accessible route (section 402);
- Clear floor space between beds (section 806.2.3);
- Maneuvering clearances at all doors (section 404.2);
- Accessible operable window (section 229); and
- Accessible controls for the heat and air conditioning (section 309).

Plan 6A: 12-Foot Wide Accessible Guest Room

This drawing shows an accessible 12-foot wide guest room with features that comply with the 2010 Standards. Features include a transfer shower, water closet length (rim to rear wall) 24 inches maximum, comparable vanity, clothes closet with swinging door, and door connecting to adjacent guest room. Furnishings include a king bed and additional seating.

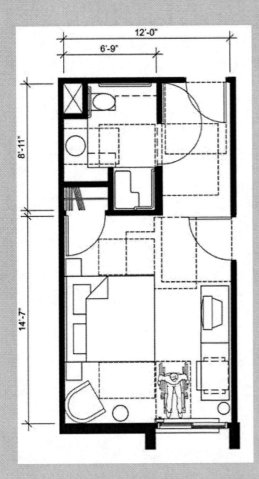

The following accessible features are provided in the bathroom:

- Comparable vanity counter top space (section 806);
- Transfer shower (section 603.2);
- Shower seat (section 610.3);
- Clearance in front of the shower extends beyond the seat and is 36 inches wide min. (section 607.2);
- Recessed lavatory with vanity counter top permits shorter rear grab bar at water closet (section 604.5.2);
- T-shaped turning space in room (section 603.2.1);
- Required clear floor spaces at fixtures and turning space overlap (section 603.2.2);
- Water closet clearance is 60 inches at back wall and 56 inches deep (section 604.3);
- Centerline of the water closet at 16 inches from side wall (section 604.2); and
- No other fixtures or obstructions located within required water closet clearance (section 604.3).

The following accessible features are provided in the living area:

- T-shaped turning space (section 304.3.2);
- Accessible route (section 402);
- Clear floor space on both sides of the bed (section 806.2.3);
- Maneuvering clearances at all doors (section 404.2);
- Accessible operable window (section 229); and
- Accessible controls for the heat and air conditioning (section 309).

Plan 6B: 12-Foot Wide Accessible Guest Room

This drawing shows an accessible 12-foot wide guest room with features that comply with the 2010 Standards. Features include a transfer shower, water closet length (rim to rear wall) 24 inches maximum, comparable vanity, wardrobe, and door connecting to adjacent guest room. Furnishings include two beds.

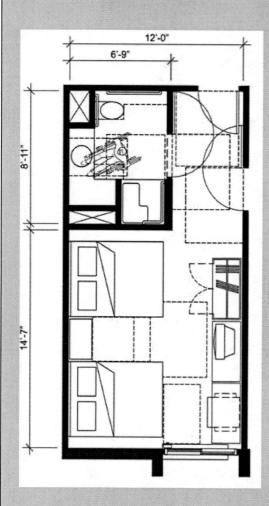

The following accessible features are provided in the bathroom:

- Comparable vanity counter top space (section 806);
- Transfer shower (section 603.2);
- Shower seat (section 610.3);
- Clearance in front of the shower extends beyond the seat and is 36 inches wide min. (section 607.2);
- Recessed lavatory with vanity counter top permits shorter rear grab bar at water closet (section 604.5.2);
- T-shaped turning space in room (section 603.2.1);
- Required clear floor spaces at fixtures and turning space overlap (section 603.2.2);
- Water closet clearance is 60 inches at back wall and 56 inches deep (section 604.3);
- Centerline of the water closet at 16 inches from side wall (section 604.2); and
- No other fixtures or obstructions located within required water closet clearance (section 604.3).

The following accessible features are provided in the living area:

- Circular turning space (section 304.3.2);
- Accessible route (section 402);
- Clear floor space between beds (section 806.2.3);
- Maneuvering clearances at all doors (section 404.2);
- Accessible operable window (section 229); and
- Accessible controls for the heat and air conditioning (section 309).

807 Holding Cells and Housing Cells

807.1 General. Holding cells and housing cells shall comply with 807.

807.2 Cells with Mobility Features. Cells required to provide mobility features shall comply with 807.2.

807.2.1 Turning Space. Turning space complying with 304 shall be provided within the cell.

807.2.2 Benches. Where benches are provided, at least one bench shall comply with 903.

807.2.3 Beds. Where beds are provided, clear floor space complying with 305 shall be provided on at least one side of the bed. The clear floor space shall be positioned for parallel approach to the side of the bed.

807.2.4 Toilet and Bathing Facilities. Toilet facilities or bathing facilities that are provided as part of a cell shall comply with 603. Where provided, no fewer than one water closet, one lavatory, and one bathtub or shower shall comply with the applicable requirements of 603 through 610.

Advisory

807.2.4 Toilet and Bathing Facilities. In holding cells, housing cells, or rooms required to be accessible, these requirements do not require a separate toilet room.

807.3 Cells with Communication Features. Cells required to provide communication features shall comply with 807.3.

807.3.1 Alarms. Where audible emergency alarm systems are provided to serve the occupants of cells, visible alarms complying with 702 shall be provided.

EXCEPTION: Visible alarms shall not be required where inmates or detainees are not allowed independent means of egress.

807.3.2 Telephones. Telephones, where provided within cells, shall have volume controls complying with 704.3.

808 Courtrooms

808.1 General. Courtrooms shall comply with 808.

808.2 Turning Space. Where provided, areas that are raised or depressed and accessed by ramps or platform lifts with entry ramps shall provide unobstructed turning space complying with 304.

808.3 Clear Floor Space. Each jury box and witness stand shall have, within its defined area, clear floor space complying with 305.

EXCEPTION: In alterations, wheelchair spaces are not required to be located within the defined area of raised jury boxes or witness stands and shall be permitted to be located outside these spaces where ramp or platform lift access poses a hazard by restricting or projecting into a means of egress required by the appropriate administrative authority.

808.4 Judges' Benches and Courtroom Stations. Judges' benches, clerks' stations, bailiffs' stations, deputy clerks' stations, court reporters' stations and litigants' and counsel stations shall comply with 902.

809 Residential Dwelling Units

809.1 General. Residential dwelling units shall comply with 809. Residential dwelling units required to provide mobility features shall comply with 809.2 through 809.4. Residential dwelling units required to provide communication features shall comply with 809.5.

809.2 Accessible Routes. Accessible routes complying with Chapter 4 shall be provided within residential dwelling units in accordance with 809.2.

EXCEPTION: Accessible routes shall not be required to or within unfinished attics or unfinished basements.

809.2.1 Location. At least one accessible route shall connect all spaces and elements which are a part of the residential dwelling unit. Where only one accessible route is provided, it shall not pass through bathrooms, closets, or similar spaces.

809.2.2 Turning Space. All rooms served by an accessible route shall provide a turning space complying with 304.

EXCEPTION: Turning space shall not be required in exterior spaces 30 inches (760 mm) maximum in depth or width.

809.2.2 Turning Space. It is generally acceptable to use required clearances to provide wheelchair turning space. For example, in kitchens, 804.3.1 requires at least one work surface with clear floor space complying with 306 to be centered beneath. If designers elect to provide clear floor space that is at least 36 inches (915 mm) wide, as opposed to the required 30 inches (760 mm) wide, that clearance can be part of a T-turn, thereby maximizing efficient use of the kitchen area. However, the overlap of turning space must be limited to one segment of the T-turn so that back-up maneuvering is not restricted. It would, therefore, be unacceptable to use both the clearances under the work surface and the sink as part of a T-turn. See Section 304.3.2 regarding T-turns.

809.3 Kitchen. Where a kitchen is provided, it shall comply with 804.

809.4 Toilet Facilities and Bathing Facilities. At least one bathroom shall comply with 603. No fewer than one of each type of fixture provided shall comply with applicable requirements of 603 through 610. Toilet and bathing fixtures required to comply with 603 through 610 shall be located in the same toilet and bathing area, such that travel between fixtures does not require travel between other parts of the residential dwelling unit.

Advisory

809.4 Toilet Facilities and Bathing Facilities. In an effort to promote space efficiency, vanity counter top space in accessible residential dwelling units is often omitted. This omission does not promote equal access or equal enjoyment of the unit. Where comparable units have vanity counter tops, accessible units should also have vanity counter tops located as close as possible to the lavatory for convenient access to toiletries.

809.5 Residential Dwelling Units with Communication Features. Residential dwelling units required to provide communication features shall comply with 809.5.

809.5.1 Building Fire Alarm System. Where a building fire alarm system is provided, the system wiring shall be extended to a point within the residential dwelling unit in the vicinity of the residential dwelling unit smoke detection system.

809.5.1.1 Alarm Appliances. Where alarm appliances are provided within a residential dwelling unit as part of the building fire alarm system, they shall comply with 702.

809.5.1.2 Activation. All visible alarm appliances provided within the residential dwelling unit for building fire alarm notification shall be activated upon activation of the building fire alarm in the portion of the building containing the residential dwelling unit.

809.5.2 Residential Dwelling Unit Smoke Detection System. Residential dwelling unit smoke detection systems shall comply with NFPA 72 (1999 or 2002 edition) (incorporated by reference, see "Referenced Standards" in Chapter 1).

809.5.2.1 Activation. All visible alarm appliances provided within the residential dwelling unit for smoke detection notification shall be activated upon smoke detection.

809.5.3 Interconnection. The same visible alarm appliances shall be permitted to provide notification of residential dwelling unit smoke detection and building fire alarm activation.

809.5.4 Prohibited Use. Visible alarm appliances used to indicate residential dwelling unit smoke detection or building fire alarm activation shall not be used for any other purpose within the residential dwelling unit.

809.5.5 Residential Dwelling Unit Primary Entrance. Communication features shall be provided at the residential dwelling unit primary entrance complying with 809.5.5.

809.5.5.1 Notification. A hard-wired electric doorbell shall be provided. A button or switch shall be provided outside the residential dwelling unit primary entrance. Activation of the button or switch shall initiate an audible tone and visible signal within the residential dwelling unit. Where visible doorbell signals are located in sleeping areas, they shall have controls to deactivate the signal.

809.5.5.2 Identification. A means for visually identifying a visitor without opening the residential dwelling unit entry door shall be provided and shall allow for a minimum 180 degree range of view.

Advisory

809.5.5.2 Identification. In doors, peepholes that include prisms clarify the image and should offer a wide-angle view of the hallway or exterior for both standing persons and wheelchair users. Such peepholes can be placed at a standard height and permit a view from several feet from the door.

809.5.6 Site, Building, or Floor Entrance. Where a system, including a closed-circuit system, permitting voice communication between a visitor and the occupant of the residential dwelling unit is provided, the system shall comply with 708.4.

810 Transportation Facilities

810.1 General. Transportation facilities shall comply with 810.

810.2 Bus Boarding and Alighting Areas. Bus boarding and alighting areas shall comply with 810.2.

Advisory

810.2 Bus Boarding and Alighting Areas. At bus stops where a shelter is provided, the bus stop pad can be located either within or outside of the shelter.

810.2.1 Surface. Bus stop boarding and alighting areas shall have a firm, stable surface.

810.2.2 Dimensions. Bus stop boarding and alighting areas shall provide a clear length of 96 inches (2440 mm) minimum, measured perpendicular to the curb or vehicle roadway edge, and a clear width of 60 inches (1525 mm) minimum, measured parallel to the vehicle roadway.

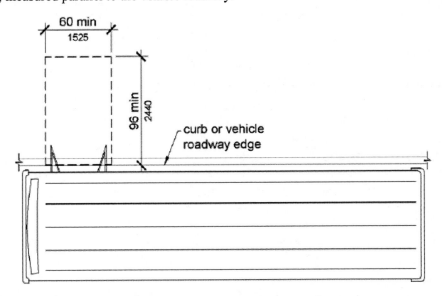

Figure 810.2.2 Dimensions of Bus Boarding and Alighting Areas

810.2.3 Connection. Bus stop boarding and alighting areas shall be connected to streets, sidewalks, or pedestrian paths by an accessible route complying with 402.

810.2.4 Slope. Parallel to the roadway, the slope of the bus stop boarding and alighting area shall be the same as the roadway, to the maximum extent practicable. Perpendicular to the roadway, the slope of the bus stop boarding and alighting area shall not be steeper than 1:48.

810.3 Bus Shelters. Bus shelters shall provide a minimum clear floor or ground space complying with 305 entirely within the shelter. Bus shelters shall be connected by an accessible route complying with 402 to a boarding and alighting area complying with 810.2.

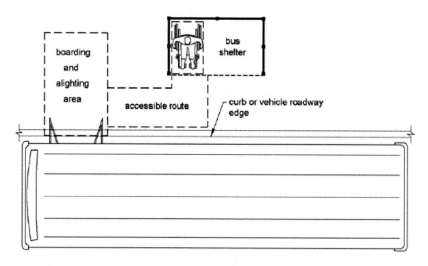

Figure 810.3 Bus Shelters

810.4 Bus Signs. Bus route identification signs shall comply with 703.5.1 through 703.5.4, and 703.5.7 and 703.5.8. In addition, to the maximum extent practicable, bus route identification signs shall comply with 703.5.5.

EXCEPTION: Bus schedules, timetables and maps that are posted at the bus stop or bus bay shall not be required to comply.

810.5 Rail Platforms. Rail platforms shall comply with 810.5.

810.5.1 Slope. Rail platforms shall not exceed a slope of 1:48 in all directions.

EXCEPTION: Where platforms serve vehicles operating on existing track or track laid in existing roadway, the slope of the platform parallel to the track shall be permitted to be equal to the slope (grade) of the roadway or existing track.

810.5.2 Detectable Warnings. Platform boarding edges not protected by platform screens or guards shall have detectable warnings complying with 705 along the full length of the public use area of the platform.

810.5.3 Platform and Vehicle Floor Coordination. Station platforms shall be positioned to coordinate with vehicles in accordance with the applicable requirements of 36 CFR Part 1192. Low-level platforms shall be 8 inches (205 mm) minimum above top of rail.

EXCEPTION: Where vehicles are boarded from sidewalks or street-level, low-level platforms shall be permitted to be less than 8 inches (205 mm).

Advisory

810.5.3 Platform and Vehicle Floor Coordination. The height and position of a platform must be coordinated with the floor of the vehicles it serves to minimize the vertical and horizontal gaps, in accordance with the ADA Accessibility Guidelines for Transportation Vehicles (36 CFR Part 1192). The vehicle guidelines, divided by bus, van, light rail, rapid rail, commuter rail, intercity rail, are available at http://www.access-board.gov/. The preferred alignment is a high platform, level with the vehicle floor. In some cases, the vehicle guidelines permit use of a low platform in conjunction with a lift or ramp. Most such low platforms must have a minimum height of eight inches above the top of the rail. Some vehicles are designed to be boarded from a street or the sidewalk along the street and the exception permits such boarding areas to be less than eight inches high.

810.6 Rail Station Signs. Rail station signs shall comply with 810.6.

> **EXCEPTION.** Signs shall not be required to comply with 810.6.1 and 810.6.2 where audible signs are remotely transmitted to hand-held receivers, or are user- or proximity-actuated.

Advisory

810.6 Rail Station Signs Exception. Emerging technologies such as an audible sign systems using infrared transmitters and receivers may provide greater accessibility in the transit environment than traditional Braille and raised letter signs. The transmitters are placed on or next to print signs and transmit their information to an infrared receiver that is held by a person. By scanning an area, the person will hear the sign. This means that signs can be placed well out of reach of Braille readers, even on parapet walls and on walls beyond barriers. Additionally, such signs can be used to provide wayfinding information that cannot be efficiently conveyed on Braille signs.

810.6.1 Entrances. Where signs identify a station or its entrance, at least one sign at each entrance shall comply with 703.2 and shall be placed in uniform locations to the maximum extent practicable. Where signs identify a station that has no defined entrance, at least one sign shall comply with 703.2 and shall be placed in a central location.

810.6.2 Routes and Destinations. Lists of stations, routes and destinations served by the station which are located on boarding areas, platforms, or mezzanines shall comply with 703.5. At least one tactile sign identifying the specific station and complying with 703.2 shall be provided on each platform or boarding area. Signs covered by this requirement shall, to the maximum extent practicable, be placed in uniform locations within the system.

> **EXCEPTION:** Where sign space is limited, characters shall not be required to exceed 3 inches (75 mm).

Advisory

810.6.2 Routes and Destinations. Route maps are not required to comply with the informational sign requirements in this document.

810.6.3 Station Names. Stations covered by this section shall have identification signs complying with 703.5. Signs shall be clearly visible and within the sight lines of standing and sitting passengers from within the vehicle on both sides when not obstructed by another vehicle.

Advisory

810.6.3 Station Names. It is also important to place signs at intervals in the station where passengers in the vehicle will be able to see a sign when the vehicle is either stopped at the station or about to come to a stop in the station. The number of signs necessary may be directly related to the size of the lettering displayed on the sign.

810.7 Public Address Systems. Where public address systems convey audible information to the public, the same or equivalent information shall be provided in a visual format.

810.8 Clocks. Where clocks are provided for use by the public, the clock face shall be uncluttered so that its elements are clearly visible. Hands, numerals and digits shall contrast with the background either light-on-dark or dark-on-light. Where clocks are installed overhead, numerals and digits shall comply with 703.5.

810.9 Escalators. Where provided, escalators shall comply with the sections 6.1.3.5.6 and 6.1.3.6.5 of ASME A17.1 (incorporated by reference, see "Referenced Standards" in Chapter 1) and shall have a clear width of 32 inches (815 mm) minimum.

> **EXCEPTION:** Existing escalators in key stations shall not be required to comply with 810.9.

810.10 Track Crossings. Where a circulation path serving boarding platforms crosses tracks, it shall comply with 402.

> **EXCEPTION:** Openings for wheel flanges shall be permitted to be 2 1/2 inches (64 mm) maximum.

Figure 810.10 (Exception) Track Crossings

Guidance

Detectable Warnings. Detectable warnings provide a distinctively textured surface of truncated domes. The 1991 Standards at sections 4.1.3(15), 4.7.7, 4.29.2, 4.29.5, 4.29.6, and 10.3.1(8) require detectable warnings at curb ramps, hazardous vehicular areas, reflecting pools, and transit platform edges. The 2010 Standards at sections 218, 810.5, 705.1, and 705.2 only require detectable warnings at transit platform edges. The technical specifications for the diameter and spacing of the truncated domes have also been changed. The 2010 Standards also delete the requirement for the material used to contrast in resiliency or sound-on-cane contact from adjoining walking surfaces at interior locations.

The 2010 Standards apply to detectable warnings on developed sites. They do not apply to the public right-of-way. Scoping for detectable warnings at all locations other than transit platform edges has been eliminated from the 2010 Standards. However, because detectable warnings have been shown to significantly benefit individuals with disabilities at transit platform edges, the 2010 Standards provide scoping and technical requirements for detectable warnings at transit platform edges.

---

811 Storage

811.1 General. Storage shall comply with 811.

811.2 Clear Floor or Ground Space. A clear floor or ground space complying with 305 shall be provided.

811.3 Height. Storage elements shall comply with at least one of the reach ranges specified in 308.

811.4 Operable Parts. Operable parts shall comply with 309.

Guidance

Section 225 of the 2010 Standards provides that where storage is provided in accessible spaces, at least one of each type shall comply with the 2010 Standards. Self-service shelving is required to be on an accessible route, but is not required to comply with the reach range requirements. These requirements are consistent with the 1991 Standards.

Section 225.3 adds a new scoping requirement for self-storage facilities. Facilities with 200 or fewer storage spaces will be required to make at least five percent (5%) of the storage spaces accessible. Facilities with more than 200 storage spaces will be required to provide ten accessible storage spaces, plus two percent (2%) of the total storage spaces over 200.

Sections 225.2.1 and 811 of the 2010 Standards require lockers to meet accessibility requirements. Where lockers are provided in clusters, five percent (5%) but at least one locker in each cluster will have to comply. Under the 1991 Standards, only one locker of each type provided must be accessible.

Commenters recommended that the Department adopt language requiring public accommodations to provide access to all self-service shelves and display areas available to customers. Other commenters opposed this requirement as too burdensome to retail and other entities and claimed that significant revenue would be lost if this requirement were to be implemented.

Other commenters raised concerns that section 225.2.2 of the 2010 Standards scopes only self-service shelving whereas section 4.1.3(12)(b) of the 1991 Standards applies to both "shelves or display units."

Although "display units" were not included in the 2010 Standards under the belief that displays are not to be touched and therefore by definition cannot be "self-service," both the 2010 Standards and the 1991 Standards should be read broadly to apply to all types of shelves, racks, hooks, and similar self-service merchandising fittings, including self-service display units. Such fixtures are permitted to be installed above or below the reach ranges possible for many persons with disabilities so that space available for merchandising is used as efficiently as possible.

CHAPTER 9: BUILT-IN ELEMENTS

901 General

901.1 Scope. The provisions of Chapter 9 shall apply where required by Chapter 2 or where referenced by a requirement in this document.

902 Dining Surfaces and Work Surfaces

902.1 General. Dining surfaces and work surfaces shall comply with 902.2 and 902.3.

  EXCEPTION: Dining surfaces and work surfaces for children's use shall be permitted to comply with 902.4.

Advisory

902.1 General. Dining surfaces include, but are not limited to, bars, tables, lunch counters, and booths. Examples of work surfaces include writing surfaces, study carrels, student laboratory stations, baby changing and other tables or fixtures for personal grooming, coupon counters, and where covered by the ABA scoping provisions, employee work stations.

902.2 Clear Floor or Ground Space. A clear floor space complying with 305 positioned for a forward approach shall be provided. Knee and toe clearance complying with 306 shall be provided.

902.3 Height. The tops of dining surfaces and work surfaces shall be 28 inches (710 mm) minimum and 34 inches (865 mm) maximum above the finish floor or ground.

902.4 Dining Surfaces and Work Surfaces for Children's Use. Accessible dining surfaces and work surfaces for children's use shall comply with 902.4.

  EXCEPTION: Dining surfaces and work surfaces that are used primarily by children 5 years and younger shall not be required to comply with 902.4 where a clear floor or ground space complying with 305 positioned for a parallel approach is provided.

902.4.1 Clear Floor or Ground Space. A clear floor space complying with 305 positioned for forward approach shall be provided. Knee and toe clearance complying with 306 shall be provided, except that knee clearance 24 inches (610 mm) minimum above the finish floor or ground shall be permitted.

902.4.2 Height. The tops of tables and counters shall be 26 inches (660 mm) minimum and 30 inches (760 mm) maximum above the finish floor or ground.

Guidance

  Section 226.1 of the 2010 Standards require that where dining surfaces are provided for the consumption of food or drink, at least five percent (5%) of the seating spaces and standing spaces at the dining surfaces comply with section 902. Section 902.2 requires the provision of accessible knee and toe clearance.

  Commenters stated that basing accessible seating on seating spaces and standing spaces potentially represents a significant increase in scoping, particularly given the ambiguity in what represents a "standing space" and urged a return to the 1991 Standard of requiring accessible seating based on fixed dining tables. The scoping change merely takes into account that tables may vary in size so that basing the calculation on the number of tables rather than on the number of individuals that may be accommodated by the tables could unnecessarily restrict opportunities for persons with disabilities. The revised scoping permits greater flexibility by allowing designers to disperse accessible seating and standing spaces throughout the dining area. Human factors data, which is readily available to designers, provides information about the amount of space required for both eating and drinking while seated or standing.

---

903 Benches

903.1 General. Benches shall comply with 903.

903.2 Clear Floor or Ground Space. Clear floor or ground space complying with 305 shall be provided and shall be positioned at the end of the bench seat and parallel to the short axis of the bench.

903.3 Size. Benches shall have seats that are 42 inches (1065 mm) long minimum and 20 inches (510 mm) deep minimum and 24 inches (610 mm) deep maximum.

903.4 Back Support. The bench shall provide for back support or shall be affixed to a wall. Back support shall be 42 inches (1065 mm) long minimum and shall extend from a point 2 inches (51 mm) maximum above the seat surface to a point 18 inches (455 mm) minimum above the seat surface. Back support shall be 2 1/2 inches (64 mm) maximum from the rear edge of the seat measured horizontally.

Advisory

903.4 Back Support. To assist in transferring to the bench, consider providing grab bars on a wall adjacent to the bench, but not on the seat back. If provided, grab bars cannot obstruct transfer to the bench.

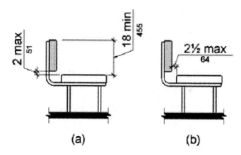

Figure 903.4 Bench Back Support

903.5 Height. The top of the bench seat surface shall be 17 inches (430 mm) minimum and 19 inches (485 mm) maximum above the finish floor or ground.

903.6 Structural Strength. Allowable stresses shall not be exceeded for materials used when a vertical or horizontal force of 250 pounds (1112 N) is applied at any point on the seat, fastener, mounting device, or supporting structure.

903.7 Wet Locations. Where installed in wet locations, the surface of the seat shall be slip resistant and shall not accumulate water.

904 Check-Out Aisles and Sales and Service Counters

904.1 General. Check-out aisles and sales and service counters shall comply with the applicable requirements of 904.

904.2 Approach. All portions of counters required to comply with 904 shall be located adjacent to a walking surface complying with 403.

Advisory

904.2 Approach. If a cash register is provided at the sales or service counter, locate the accessible counter close to the cash register so that a person using a wheelchair is visible to sales or service personnel and to minimize the reach for a person with a disability.

904.3 Check-Out Aisles. Check-out aisles shall comply with 904.3.

904.3.1 Aisle. Aisles shall comply with 403.

904.3.2 Counter. The counter surface height shall be 38 inches (965 mm) maximum above the finish floor or ground. The top of the counter edge protection shall be 2 inches (51 mm) maximum above the top of the counter surface on the aisle side of the check-out counter.

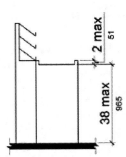

Figure 904.3.2 Check-Out Aisle Counters

904.3.3 Check Writing Surfaces. Where provided, check writing surfaces shall comply with 902.3.

904.4 Sales and Service Counters. Sales counters and service counters shall comply with 904.4.1 or 904.4.2. The accessible portion of the counter top shall extend the same depth as the sales or service counter top.

> **EXCEPTION:** In alterations, when the provision of a counter complying with 904.4 would result in a reduction of the number of existing counters at work stations or a reduction of the number of existing mail boxes, the counter shall be permitted to have a portion which is 24 inches (610 mm) long minimum complying with 904.4.1 provided that the required clear floor or ground space is centered on the accessible length of the counter.

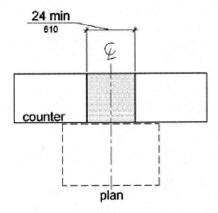

Figure 904.4 (Exception) Alteration of Sales and Service Counters

904.4.1 Parallel Approach. A portion of the counter surface that is 36 inches (915 mm) long minimum and 36 inches (915 mm) high maximum above the finish floor shall be provided. A clear floor or ground space complying with 305 shall be positioned for a parallel approach adjacent to the 36 inch (915 mm) minimum length of counter.

EXCEPTION: Where the provided counter surface is less than 36 inches (915 mm) long, the entire counter surface shall be 36 inches (915 mm) high maximum above the finish floor.

904.4.2 Forward Approach. A portion of the counter surface that is 30 inches (760 mm) long minimum and 36 inches (915 mm) high maximum shall be provided. Knee and toe space complying with 306 shall be provided under the counter. A clear floor or ground space complying with 305 shall be positioned for a forward approach to the counter.

904.5 Food Service Lines. Counters in food service lines shall comply with 904.5.

904.5.1 Self-Service Shelves and Dispensing Devices. Self-service shelves and dispensing devices for tableware, dishware, condiments, food and beverages shall comply with 308.

904.5.2 Tray Slides. The tops of tray slides shall be 28 inches (710 mm) minimum and 34 inches (865 mm) maximum above the finish floor or ground.

904.6 Security Glazing. Where counters or teller windows have security glazing to separate personnel from the public, a method to facilitate voice communication shall be provided. Telephone handset devices, if provided, shall comply with 704.3.

Advisory

904.6 Security Glazing. Assistive listening devices complying with 706 can facilitate voice communication at counters or teller windows where there is security glazing which promotes distortion in audible information. Where assistive listening devices are installed, place signs complying with 703.7.2.4 to identify those facilities which are so equipped. Other voice communication methods include, but are not limited to, grilles, slats, talk-through baffles, intercoms, or telephone handset devices.

Guidance

Check-Out Aisles and Sales and Service Counters. The 1991 Standards, at section 7.2, and the 2010 Standards, at section 904.4, contain technical requirements for sales and service counters. The 1991 Standards generally require sales and service counters to provide an accessible portion at least 36 inches long and no higher than 36 inches above the finish floor. The nondiscrimination requirements of the ADA regulations require the level of service provided at the accessible portion of any sales and service counter to be the same as the level of service provided at the inaccessible portions of the counter.

The 2010 Standards specify different lengths for the accessible portion of sales and service counters based on the type of approach provided. Where a forward approach is provided, the accessible portion of the counter must be at least 30 inches long and no higher than 36 inches, and knee and toe space must be provided under the counter. The requirement that knee and toe space be provided where only clear floor space for a forward approach to a sales and service counter is provided is not a new requirement. It is a clarification of the ongoing requirement that part of the sales and service counter be accessible. This requirement applies to the entire accessible part of sales and service counters and requires that the accessible clear floor or ground space adjacent to those counters be kept clear of merchandise, equipment, and other items so that the accessible part of the counter is readily accessible to and usable by individuals with disabilities. The accessible part of the counter must also be staffed and provide an equivalent level of service as that provided to all customers.

Where clear floor space for a parallel approach is provided, the accessible portion of the counter must be at least 36 inches long and no higher than 36 inches above the finish floor. A clear floor or ground space that is at least 48 inches long x 30 inches wide must be provided positioned for a parallel approach adjacent to the 36-inch minimum length of counter.

Section 904.4 of the 2010 Standards includes an exception for alterations to sales and service counters in existing facilities. It permits the accessible portion of the counter to be at least 24 inches long, where providing a longer accessible counter will result in a reduction in the number of existing counters at work stations or existing mailboxes, provided that the required clear floor or ground space is centered on the accessible length of the counter.

Section 904.4 of the 2010 Standards also clarifies that the accessible portion of the counter must extend the same depth as the sales or service counter top. Where the counter is a single-height counter, this requirement applies across the entire depth of the counter top. Where the counter is a split-height counter, this requirement applies only to the customer side of the counter top. The employee-side of the counter top may be higher or lower than the customer-side of the counter top.

Commenters recommended that the Department consider a regulatory alternative exempting small retailers from the new knee and toe clearance requirement and retaining existing wheelchair accessibility standards for sales and service counters. These commenters believed that the knee and toe clearance requirements will cause a reduction in the sales and inventory space at check-out aisles and other sales and service counters.

Both the 1991 and the 2010 Standards permit covered entities to determine whether they will provide a forward or a parallel approach to sales and service counters. So any facility that does not wish to provide the knee or toe clearance required for a front approach to such a counter may avoid that option. However, the Department believes that permitting a forward approach without requiring knee and toe clearance is not adequate to provide accessibility because the person using a wheelchair will be prevented from coming close enough to the counter to see the merchandise or to transact business with a degree of convenience that is comparable to that provided to other customers.

A parallel approach to sales and service counters also can provide the accessibility required by the 2010 Standards. Individuals using wheelchairs can approach sales and service counters from the side, and, assuming the necessary elements, features, or merchandise necessary to complete a business transaction are within the reach range requirements for a side approach, the needs of individuals with disabilities can be met effectively.

Section 227 of the 2010 Standards clarifies the requirements for food service lines. Queues and waiting lines serving counters or check-out aisles, including those for food service, must be accessible to individuals with disabilities.

CHAPTER 10: RECREATION FACILITIES

1001 General

1001.1 Scope. The provisions of Chapter 10 shall apply where required by Chapter 2 or where referenced by a requirement in this document.

Advisory

1001.1 Scope. Unless otherwise modified or specifically addressed in Chapter 10, all other ADAAG provisions apply to the design and construction of recreation facilities and elements. The provisions in Section 1001.1 apply wherever these elements are provided. For example, office buildings may contain a room with exercise equipment to which these sections would apply.

1002 Amusement Rides

1002.1 General. Amusement rides shall comply with 1002.

1002.2 Accessible Routes. Accessible routes serving amusement rides shall comply with Chapter 4.

EXCEPTIONS:

1. In load or unload areas and on amusement rides, where compliance with 405.2 is not structurally or operationally feasible, ramp slope shall be permitted to be 1:8 maximum.

2. In load or unload areas and on amusement rides, handrails provided along walking surfaces complying with 403 and required on ramps complying with 405 shall not be required to comply with 505 where compliance is not structurally or operationally feasible.

Advisory

1002.2 Accessible Routes Exception 1. Steeper slopes are permitted on accessible routes connecting the amusement ride in the load and unload position where it is "structurally or operationally infeasible." In most cases, this will be limited to areas where the accessible route leads directly to the amusement ride and where there are space limitations on the ride, not the queue line. Where possible, the least possible slope should be used on the accessible route that serves the amusement ride.

1002.3 Load and Unload Areas. A turning space complying with 304.2 and 304.3 shall be provided in load and unload areas.

1002.4 Wheelchair Spaces in Amusement Rides. Wheelchair spaces in amusement rides shall comply with 1002.4.

1002.4.1 Floor or Ground Surface. The floor or ground surface of wheelchair spaces shall be stable and firm.

1002.4.2 Slope. The floor or ground surface of wheelchair spaces shall have a slope not steeper than 1:48 when in the load and unload position.

1002.4.3 Gaps. Floors of amusement rides with wheelchair spaces and floors of load and unload areas shall be coordinated so that, when amusement rides are at rest in the load and unload position, the vertical difference between the floors shall be within plus or minus 5/8 inches (16 mm) and the horizontal gap shall be 3 inches (75 mm) maximum under normal passenger load conditions.

EXCEPTION: Where compliance is not operationally or structurally feasible, ramps, bridge plates, or similar devices complying with the applicable requirements of 36 CFR 1192.83(c) shall be provided.

Advisory

*1002.4.3 Gaps Exception. 36 CFR 1192.83(c) ADA Accessibility Guidelines for Transportation Vehicles - Light Rail Vehicles and Systems - Mobility Aid Accessibility is available at **www.access-board.gov**. It includes provisions for bridge plates and ramps that can be used at gaps between wheelchair spaces and floors of load and unload areas.*

1002.4.4 Clearances. Clearances for wheelchair spaces shall comply with 1002.4.4.

EXCEPTIONS:

1. Where provided, securement devices shall be permitted to overlap required clearances.

2. Wheelchair spaces shall be permitted to be mechanically or manually repositioned.

3. Wheelchair spaces shall not be required to comply with 307.4.

Advisory

1002.4.4 Clearances Exception 3. This exception for protruding objects applies to the ride devices, not to circulation areas or accessible routes in the queue lines or the load and unload areas.

1002.4.4.1 Width and Length. Wheelchair spaces shall provide a clear width of 30 inches (760 mm) minimum and a clear length of 48 inches (1220 mm) minimum measured to 9 inches (230 mm) minimum above the floor surface.

1002.4.4.2 Side Entry. Where wheelchair spaces are entered only from the side, amusement rides shall be designed to permit sufficient maneuvering clearance for individuals using a wheelchair or mobility aid to enter and exit the ride.

Advisory

1002.4.4.2 Side Entry. The amount of clear space needed within the ride, and the size and position of the opening are interrelated. A 32 inch (815 mm) clear opening will not provide sufficient width when entered through a turn into an amusement ride. Additional space for maneuvering and a wider door will be needed where a side opening is centered on the ride. For example, where a 42 inch (1065 mm) opening is provided, a minimum clear space of 60 inches (1525 mm) in length and 36 inches (915mm) in depth is needed to ensure adequate space for maneuvering.

1002.4.4.3 Permitted Protrusions in Wheelchair Spaces. Objects are permitted to protrude a distance of 6 inches (150 mm) maximum along the front of the wheelchair space, where located 9 inches (230 mm) minimum and 27 inches (685 mm) maximum above the floor or ground surface of the wheelchair space. Objects are permitted to protrude a distance of 25 inches (635 mm) maximum along the front of the wheelchair space, where located more than 27 inches (685 mm) above the floor or ground surface of the wheelchair space.

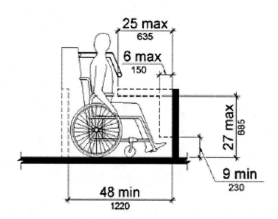

Figure 1002.4.4.3 Protrusions in Wheelchair Spaces in Amusement Rides

1002.4.5 Ride Entry. Openings providing entry to wheelchair spaces on amusement rides shall be 32 inches (815 mm) minimum clear.

1002.4.6 Approach. One side of the wheelchair space shall adjoin an accessible route when in the load and unload position.

1002.4.7 Companion Seats. Where the interior width of the amusement ride is greater than 53 inches (1345 mm), seating is provided for more than one rider, and the wheelchair is not required to be centered within the amusement ride, a companion seat shall be provided for each wheelchair space.

1002.4.7.1 Shoulder-to-Shoulder Seating. Where an amusement ride provides shoulder-to-shoulder seating, companion seats shall be shoulder-to-shoulder with the adjacent wheelchair space.

> **EXCEPTION:** Where shoulder-to-shoulder companion seating is not operationally or structurally feasible, compliance with this requirement shall be required to the maximum extent practicable.

1002.5 Amusement Ride Seats Designed for Transfer. Amusement ride seats designed for transfer shall comply with 1002.5 when positioned for loading and unloading.

Advisory

1002.5 Amusement Ride Seats Designed for Transfer. The proximity of the clear floor or ground space next to an element and the height of the element one is transferring to are both critical for a safe and independent transfer. Providing additional clear floor or ground space both in front of and diagonal to the element will provide flexibility and will increase usability for a more diverse population of individuals with disabilities. Ride seats designed for transfer should involve only one transfer. Where possible, designers are encouraged to locate the ride seat no higher than 17 to 19 inches (430 to 485 mm) above the load and unload surface. Where greater distances are required for transfers, providing gripping surfaces, seat padding, and avoiding sharp objects in the path of transfer will facilitate the transfer.

1002.5.1 Clear Floor or Ground Space. A clear floor or ground space complying with 305 shall be provided in the load and unload area adjacent to the amusement ride seats designed for transfer.

1002.5.2 Transfer Height. The height of amusement ride seats designed for transfer shall be 14 inches (355 mm) minimum and 24 inches (610 mm) maximum measured from the surface of the load and unload area.

1002.5.3 Transfer Entry. Where openings are provided for transfer to amusement ride seats, the openings shall provide clearance for transfer from a wheelchair or mobility aid to the amusement ride seat.

1002.5.4 Wheelchair Storage Space. Wheelchair storage spaces complying with 305 shall be provided in or adjacent to unload areas for each required amusement ride seat designed for transfer and shall not overlap any required means of egress or accessible route.

1002.6 Transfer Devices for Use with Amusement Rides. Transfer devices for use with amusement rides shall comply with 1002.6 when positioned for loading and unloading.

Advisory

1002.6 Transfer Devices for Use with Amusement Rides. Transfer devices for use with amusement rides should permit individuals to make independent transfers to and from their wheelchairs or mobility devices. There are a variety of transfer devices available that could be adapted to provide access onto an amusement ride. Examples of devices that may provide for transfers include, but are not limited to, transfer systems, lifts, mechanized seats, and custom designed systems. Operators and designers have flexibility in developing designs that will facilitate individuals to transfer onto amusement rides. These systems or devices should be designed to be reliable and sturdy.

Designs that limit the number of transfers required from a wheelchair or mobility device to the ride seat are encouraged. When using a transfer device to access an amusement ride, the least number of transfers and the shortest distance is most usable. Where possible, designers are encouraged to locate the transfer device seat no higher than 17 to 19 inches (430 to 485 mm) above the load and unload surface. Where greater distances are required for transfers, providing gripping surfaces, seat padding, and avoiding sharp objects in the path of transfer will facilitate the transfer. Where a series of transfers are required to reach the amusement ride seat, each vertical transfer should not exceed 8 inches (205 mm).

1002.6.1 Clear Floor or Ground Space. A clear floor or ground space complying with 305 shall be provided in the load and unload area adjacent to the transfer device.

1002.6.2 Transfer Height. The height of transfer device seats shall be 14 inches (355 mm) minimum and 24 inches (610 mm) maximum measured from the load and unload surface.

1002.6.3 Wheelchair Storage Space. Wheelchair storage spaces complying with 305 shall be provided in or adjacent to unload areas for each required transfer device and shall not overlap any required means of egress or accessible route.

Guidance

New and Altered Permanently Installed Amusement Rides. Section 234 of the 2010 Standards sets out scoping requirements and section 1002 sets out the technical requirements for the accessibility of permanently installed amusement rides. These requirements apply to newly designed and constructed amusement rides and used rides when certain alterations are made.

A commenter raised concerns that smaller amusement parks tend to purchase used rides more frequently than new rides, and that the conversion of a used ride to provide the required accessibility may be difficult to ensure because of the possible complications in modifying equipment to provide accessibility.

The Department agrees with this commenter. The Department notes, however, that the 2010 Standards will require modifications to existing amusement rides when a ride's structural and operational characteristics are altered to the extent that the ride's performance differs from that specified by the manufacturer or the original design. Such an extensive alteration to an amusement ride may well require that new load and unload areas be designed and constructed. When load and unload areas serving existing amusement rides are newly designed and constructed they must be level, provide wheelchair turning space, and be on an accessible route compliant with Chapter 4 of the 2010 Standards except as modified by section 1002.2 of the 2010 Standards.

Mobile or Portable Amusement Rides. The exception in section 234.1 of the 2010 Standards exempts mobile or portable amusement rides, such as those set up for short periods of time at carnivals, fairs or festivals, from having to comply with the 2010 Standards. However, even though the mobile/portable ride itself is not subject to the Standards, these facilities are still subject to the ADA's general requirement to ensure that individuals with disabilities have an equal opportunity to enjoy the services and amenities of these facilities.

Subject to these general requirements, mobile or portable amusement rides should be located on an accessible route and the load and unload areas serving a ride should provide a level wheelchair turning space to provide equal opportunity for individuals with disabilities to be able to participate on the amusement ride to the extent feasible.

One commenter noted that the exception in Section 234.1 of the 2010 Standards for mobile or portable amusement rides limits the opportunities of persons with disabilities to participate on amusement rides because traveling or temporary amusement rides by their nature come to their customers' town or a nearby town rather than the customer having to go to them and so are less expensive than permanent amusement parks. While the Department understands the commenter's concerns, the Department notes that most amusement rides are too complex to be reasonably modified or re-engineered to accommodate the majority of individuals with disabilities and that additional complexities and safety concerns are added when the rides are mobile or portable.

A commenter asked that section 234 of the 2010 Standards make clear that the requirements for accessible routes include the routes leading up to and including the loading and unloading areas of amusement rides. Sections 206.2.9 and 1002.2 of the 2010 Standards clarify that the requirements for accessible routes include the routes leading up to and including the loading and unloading areas of amusement rides.

A commenter requested that the final rule specifically allow for wheelchair access through the exit or other routes, or alternate means of wheelchair access routes to amusement rides. The commenter stated that the concept of wheelchair access through the exit or alternate routes was a base assumption for the 2010 Standards. The commenter noted that the concept is apparent in the signage and load/unload area provisions in Section 216.12 (" * * * where accessible unload areas also serve as accessible load areas, signs indicating the location of the accessible load and unload areas shall be provided at entries to queues and waiting lines"). The Department agrees with the commenter that accessible load and unload areas may be the same where signs that comply with section 216.12 are provided.

Wheelchair Space or Transfer Seat or Transfer Device. Sections 234.3 and 1002.4 - 1002.6 of the 2010 Standards provide that each new and altered amusement ride, except for mobile/portable rides and a few additional excepted rides, will be required to provide at least one type of access by means of one wheelchair space or one transfer seat or one transfer device (the design of the transfer device is not specified).

Commenters urged the Department to revise the requirements for wheelchair spaces and transfer seats and devices because most amusement rides are too complex to be reasonably modified or re-engineered to accommodate the majority of individuals with disabilities. They argued that the experience of amusement rides will be significantly reduced if the proposed requirements are implemented.

The 2004 ADAAG, which the Department adopted as part of the 2010 Standards, was developed with the assistance of an advisory committee that included representation from the design staffs of major amusement venues and from persons with disabilities. The Department believes that the resulting 2004 ADAAG reflected sensitivity to the complex problems posed in adapting existing rides by focusing on new rides that can be designed from the outset to be accessible.

To permit maximum design flexibility, the 2010 Standards permit designers to determine whether it is more appropriate to permit individuals who use wheelchairs to remain in their chairs on the ride, or to provide for transfer access.

Maneuvering Space in Load and Unload Areas. Sections 234.2 and 1002.3 of the 2010 Standards require that a level wheelchair turning space be provided at the load and unload areas of each amusement ride. The turning space must comply with sections 304.2 and 304.3.

Signs Required at Waiting Lines to Amusement Rides. Section 216.12 of the 2010 Standards requires signs at entries to queues and waiting lines identifying type and location of access for the amusement ride.

1003 Recreational Boating Facilities

1003.1 General. Recreational boating facilities shall comply with 1003.

1003.2 Accessible Routes. Accessible routes serving recreational boating facilities, including gangways and floating piers, shall comply with Chapter 4 except as modified by the exceptions in 1003.2.

1003.2.1 Boat Slips. Accessible routes serving boat slips shall be permitted to use the exceptions in 1003.2.1.

EXCEPTIONS:

1. Where an existing gangway or series of gangways is replaced or altered, an increase in the length of the gangway shall not be required to comply with 1003.2 unless required by 202.4.

2. Gangways shall not be required to comply with the maximum rise specified in 405.6.

3. Where the total length of a gangway or series of gangways serving as part of a required accessible route is 80 feet (24 m) minimum, gangways shall not be required to comply with 405.2.

4. Where facilities contain fewer than 25 boat slips and the total length of the gangway or series of gangways serving as part of a required accessible route is 30 feet (9145 mm) minimum, gangways shall not be required to comply with 405.2.

5. Where gangways connect to transition plates, landings specified by 405.7 shall not be required.

6. Where gangways and transition plates connect and are required to have handrails, handrail extensions shall not be required. Where handrail extensions are provided on gangways or transition plates, the handrail extensions shall not be required to be parallel with the ground or floor surface.

7. The cross slope specified in 403.3 and 405.3 for gangways, transition plates, and floating piers that are part of accessible routes shall be measured in the static position.

8. Changes in level complying with 303.3 and 303.4 shall be permitted on the surfaces of gangways and boat launch ramps.

Advisory

1003.2.1 Boat Slips Exception 3. The following example shows how exception 3 would be applied: A gangway is provided to a floating pier which is required to be on an accessible route. The vertical distance is 10 feet (3050 mm) between the elevation where the gangway departs the landside connection and the elevation of the pier surface at the lowest water level. Exception 3 permits the gangway to be 80 feet (24 m) long. Another design solution would be to have two 40 foot (12 m) plus continuous gangways joined together at a float, where the float (as the water level falls) will stop dropping at an elevation five feet below the landside connection. The length of transition plates would not be included in determining if the gangway(s) meet the requirements of the exception.

1003.2.2 Boarding Piers at Boat Launch Ramps. Accessible routes serving boarding piers at boat launch ramps shall be permitted to use the exceptions in 1003.2.2.

EXCEPTIONS:

1. Accessible routes serving floating boarding piers shall be permitted to use Exceptions 1, 2, 5, 6, 7 and 8 in 1003.2.1.

2. Where the total length of the gangway or series of gangways serving as part of a required accessible route is 30 feet (9145 mm) minimum, gangways shall not be required to comply with 405.2.

3. Where the accessible route serving a floating boarding pier or skid pier is located within a boat launch ramp, the portion of the accessible route located within the boat launch ramp shall not be required to comply with 405.

1003.3 Clearances. Clearances at boat slips and on boarding piers at boat launch ramps shall comply with 1003.3.

Advisory

1003.3 Clearances. Although the minimum width of the clear pier space is 60 inches (1525 mm), it is recommended that piers be wider than 60 inches (1525 mm) to improve the safety for persons with disabilities, particularly on floating piers.

1003.3.1 Boat Slip Clearance. Boat slips shall provide clear pier space 60 inches (1525 mm) wide minimum and at least as long as the boat slips. Each 10 feet (3050 mm) maximum of linear pier edge serving boat slips shall contain at least one continuous clear opening 60 inches (1525 mm) wide minimum.

EXCEPTIONS:

1. Clear pier space shall be permitted to be 36 inches (915 mm) wide minimum for a length of 24 inches (610 mm) maximum, provided that multiple 36 inch (915 mm) wide segments are separated by segments that are 60 inches (1525 mm) wide minimum and 60 inches (1525 mm) long minimum.

2. Edge protection shall be permitted at the continuous clear openings, provided that it is 4 inches (100 mm) high maximum and 2 inches (51 mm) wide maximum.

3. In existing piers, clear pier space shall be permitted to be located perpendicular to the boat slip and shall extend the width of the boat slip, where the facility has at least one boat slip complying with 1003.3, and further compliance with 1003.3 would result in a reduction in the number of boat slips available or result in a reduction of the widths of existing slips.

Advisory

1003.3.1 Boat Slip Clearance Exception 3. Where the conditions in exception 3 are satisfied, existing facilities are only required to have one accessible boat slip with a pier clearance which runs the length of the slip. All other accessible slips are allowed to have the required pier clearance at the head of the slip. Under this exception, at piers with perpendicular boat slips, the width of most "finger piers" will remain unchanged. However, where mooring systems for floating piers are replaced as part of pier alteration projects, an opportunity may exist for increasing accessibility. Piers may be reconfigured to allow an increase in the number of wider finger piers, and serve as accessible boat slips.

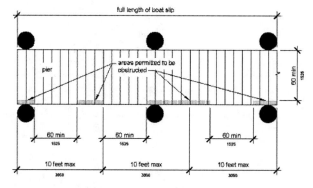

Figure 1003.3.1 Boat Slip Clearance

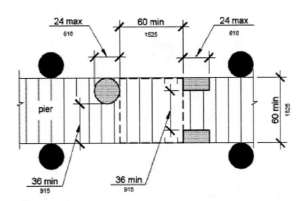

Figure 1003.3.1 (Exception 1) Clear Pier Space Reduction at Boat Slips

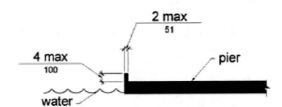

Figure 1003.3.1 (Exception 2) Edge Protection at Boat Slips

1003.3.2 Boarding Pier Clearances. Boarding piers at boat launch ramps shall provide clear pier space 60 inches (1525 mm) wide minimum and shall extend the full length of the boarding pier. Every 10 feet (3050 mm) maximum of linear pier edge shall contain at least one continuous clear opening 60 inches (1525 mm) wide minimum.

EXCEPTIONS:

1. The clear pier space shall be permitted to be 36 inches (915 mm) wide minimum for a length of 24 inches (610 mm) maximum provided that multiple 36 inch (915 mm) wide segments are separated by segments that are 60 inches (1525 mm) wide minimum and 60 inches (1525 mm) long minimum.

2. Edge protection shall be permitted at the continuous clear openings provided that it is 4 inches (100 mm) high maximum and 2 inches (51 mm) wide maximum.

Advisory

1003.3.2 Boarding Pier Clearances. These requirements do not establish a minimum length for accessible boarding piers at boat launch ramps. The accessible boarding pier should have a length at least equal to that of other boarding piers provided at the facility. If no other boarding pier is provided, the pier would have a length equal to what would have been provided if no access requirements applied. The entire length of accessible boarding piers would be required to comply with the same technical provisions that apply to accessible boat slips. For example, at a launch ramp, if a 20 foot (6100 mm) long accessible boarding pier is provided, the entire 20 feet (6100 mm) must comply with the pier clearance requirements in 1003.3. Likewise, if a 60 foot (18 m) long accessible boarding pier is provided, the pier clearance requirements in 1003.3 would apply to the entire 60 feet (18 m).

The following example applies to a boat launch ramp boarding pier: A chain of floats is provided on a launch ramp to be used as a boarding pier which is required to be accessible by 1003.3.2. At high water, the entire chain is floating and a transition plate connects the first float to the surface of the launch ramp. As the water level decreases, segments of the chain end up resting on the launch ramp surface, matching the slope of the launch ramp.

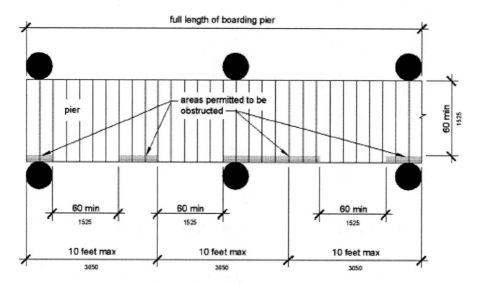

Figure 1003.3.2 Boarding Pier Clearance

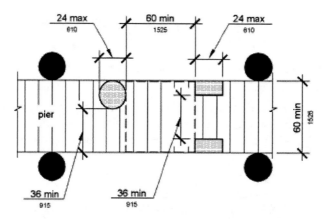

Figure 1003.3.2 (Exception 1) Clear Pier Space Reduction at Boarding Piers

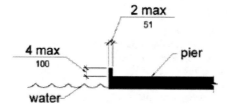

Figure 1003.3.2 (Exception 2) Edge Protection at Boarding Piers

Guidance

These sections require that accessible boat slips and boarding piers be provided. Most commenters approved of the requirements for recreational boating facility accessibility and urged the Department to keep regulatory language consistent with those provisions. They commented that the requirements appropriately reflect industry conditions. Individual commenters and disability organizations agreed that the 2010 Standards achieve acceptable goals for recreational boating facility access.

Accessible Route. Sections 206.2.10 and 1003.2 of the 2010 Standards require an accessible route to all accessible boating facilities, including boat slips and boarding piers at boat launch ramps. Section 1003.2.1 provides a list of exceptions applicable to structures such as gangways, transition plates, floating piers, and structures containing combinations of these elements that are affected by water level changes. The list of exceptions specifies alternate design requirements applicable to these structures which, because of water level variables, cannot comply with the slope, cross slope, and handrail requirements for fixed ramps contained in sections 403.3, 405.2, 405.3, 405.6, and 405.7 of the 2010 Standards. Exceptions 3 and 4 in Section 1003.2.1, which permit a slope greater than that specified in Section 405.2, are available for structures that meet specified length requirements. Section 206.7.10 permits the use of platform lifts as an alternative to gangways that are part of accessible routes.

Commenters raised concerns that because of water level fluctuations it may be difficult to provide accessible routes to all accessible boating facilities, including boat slips and boarding piers at boat launch ramps. One of the specific concerns expressed by several commenters relates to the limits for running slope permitted on gangways that are part of an accessible route as gangways may periodically have a steeper slope than is permitted for a fixed ramp. The exceptions contained in section 1003.2 of the 2010 Standards modify the requirements of Chapter 4. For example, where the total length of a gangway or series of gangways serving as an accessible route is 80 feet or more an exception permits the slope on gangways to exceed the maximum slope in section 405.2.

Some commenters suggested that permissible slope variations could be reduced further by introducing a formula that ties required gangway length to anticipated water level fluctuations. Such a formula would incorporate predictions of tidal level changes such as those issued by the National Oceanographic and Atmospheric Administration (NOAA) and the United States Geologic Survey (USGS). This suggested approach would be an alternative to the gangway length exceptions and limits in section 1003.2.1 of the 2010 Standards. These commenters noted that contemporary building materials and techniques make gangways of longer length and alternative configurations achievable. These commenters provided at least one example of a regional regulatory authority using this type of formula. While this approach may be successfully implemented and consistent with the goals of the ADA, the example provided was applied in a highly developed area containing larger facilities. The Department has considered that many facilities do not have sufficient resources available to take advantage of the latest construction materials and design innovations. Other commenters supported compliance exceptions for facilities that are subject to extreme tidal conditions. One commenter noted that if a facility is located in an area with limited space and extreme tidal variations, a disproportionately long gangway might intrude into water travel routes. The Department has considered a wide range of boating facility characteristics including size, water surface areas, tidal fluctuations, water conditions, variable resources, whether the facility is in a highly developed or remote location, and other factors. The Department has determined that the 2010 Standards provide sufficient flexibility for such broad application. Additionally, the length requirement for accessible routes in section 1003.2.1 provides an easily determinable compliance standard.

Accessible Boarding Piers. Where boarding piers are provided at boat launch ramps, sections 235.3 and 1003.3.2 of the 2010 Standards require that at least five percent (5%) of boarding piers, but at least one, must be accessible.

Accessible Boat Slips. Sections 235.2 and 1003.3.1 of the 2010 Standards require that a specified number of boat slips in each recreational boating facility meet specified accessibility standards. The number of accessible boat slips required by the 2010 Standards is set out in a chart in section 235.2. One accessible boat slip is required for facilities containing 25 or fewer total slips. The number of required accessible boat slips increases with the total number of slips at the facility. Facilities containing more than one thousand (1000) boat slips are required to provide twelve (12) accessible boat slips plus one for each additional one hundred slips at the facility.

One commenter asserted the need for specificity in the requirement for dispersion of accessible slips. Section

235.2.1 of the 2010 Standards addresses dispersion and requires that boat slips "shall be dispersed throughout the various types of boat slips provided." The commenter was concerned that if a marina could not put accessible slips all on one pier, it would have to reconstruct the entire facility to accommodate accessible piers, gangways, docks and walkways. The provision permits required accessible boat slips to be grouped together. The Department recognizes that economical and structural feasibility may produce this result. The 2010 Standards do not require the dispersion of the physical location of accessible boat slips. Rather, the dispersion must be among the various types of boat slips offered by the facility. Section 235.2.1 of the 2010 Standards specifies that if the required number has been met, no further dispersion is required. For example, if a facility offers five different ′types′ of boat slips but is only required to provide three according to the table in Section 235.2, that facility is not required to provide more than three accessible boat slips, but the three must be varied among the five ′types′ of boat slips available at the facility.

1004 Exercise Machines and Equipment

1004.1 Clear Floor Space. Exercise machines and equipment shall have a clear floor space complying with 305 positioned for transfer or for use by an individual seated in a wheelchair. Clear floor or ground spaces required at exercise machines and equipment shall be permitted to overlap.

Advisory

1004.1 Clear Floor Space. One clear floor or ground space is permitted to be shared between two pieces of exercise equipment. To optimize space use, designers should carefully consider layout options such as connecting ends of the row and center aisle spaces. The position of the clear floor space may vary greatly depending on the use of the equipment or machine. For example, to provide access to a shoulder press machine, clear floor space next to the seat would be appropriate to allow for transfer. Clear floor space for a bench press machine designed for use by an individual seated in a wheelchair, however, will most likely be centered on the operating mechanisms.

Guidance

Accessible Route to Exercise Machines and Equipment. Section 206.2.13 of the 2010 Standards requires an accessible route to serve accessible exercise machines and equipment.

Commenters raised concerns that the requirement to provide accessible routes to serve accessible exercise machines and equipment will be difficult for some facilities to provide, especially some transient lodging facilities that typically locate exercise machines and equipment in a single room. The Department believes that this requirement is a reasonable one in new construction and alterations because accessible exercise machines and equipment can be located so that an accessible route can serve more than one piece of equipment.

Exercise Machines and Equipment. Section 236 of the 2010 Standards requires at least one of each type of exercise machine to meet clear floor space requirements of section 1004.1. Types of machines are generally defined according to the muscular groups exercised or the kind of cardiovascular exercise provided.

Several commenters were concerned that existing facilities would have to reduce the number of available exercise equipment and machines in order to comply with the 2010 Standards. One commenter submitted prototype drawings showing equipment and machine layouts with and without the required clearance specified in the 2010 Standards. The accessible alternatives all resulted in a loss of equipment and machines. However, because these prototype layouts included certain possibly erroneous assumptions about the 2010 Standards, the Department wishes to clarify the requirements.

Section 1004.1 of the 2010 Standards requires a clear floor space "positioned for transfer or for use by an individual seated in a wheelchair" to serve at least one of each type of exercise machine and equipment. This requirement provides the designer greater flexibility regarding the location of the clear floor space than was employed by the commenter who submitted prototype layouts. The 2010 Standards do not require changes to exercise machines or equipment in order to make them more accessible to persons with disabilities. Even where machines or equipment do not have seats and typically are used by individuals in a standing position, at least one of each type of machine or equipment must have a clear floor space. Therefore, it is reasonable to assume that persons with disabilities wishing to use this type of machine or equipment can stand or walk, even if they use wheelchairs much of the time. As indicated in Advisory 1004.1, "the position of the clear floor space may vary greatly depending on the use of the equipment or machine." Where exercise equipment or machines require users to stand on them, the clear floor space need not be located parallel to the length of the machine or equipment in order to provide a lateral seat-to-platform transfer. It is permissible to locate the clear floor space for such machines or equipment in the aisle behind the device and to overlap the clear floor space and the accessible route.

Commenters were divided in response to the requirement for accessible exercise machines and equipment. Some supported requirements for accessible machines and equipment; others urged the Department not to require accessible machines and equipment because of the costs involved. The Department believes that the requirement strikes an appropriate balance in ensuring that persons with disabilities, particularly those who use wheelchairs, will have the opportunity to use the exercise equipment. Providing access to exercise machines and equipment recognizes the need and desires of individuals with disabilities to have the same opportunity as other patrons to enjoy the advantages of exercise and maintaining health.

1005 Fishing Piers and Platforms

1005.1 Accessible Routes. Accessible routes serving fishing piers and platforms, including gangways and floating piers, shall comply with Chapter 4.

EXCEPTIONS:

1. Accessible routes serving floating fishing piers and platforms shall be permitted to use Exceptions 1, 2, 5, 6, 7 and 8 in 1003.2.1.

2. Where the total length of the gangway or series of gangways serving as part of a required accessible route is 30 feet (9145 mm) minimum, gangways shall not be required to comply with 405.2.

1005.2 Railings. Where provided, railings, guards, or handrails shall comply with 1005.2.

1005.2.1 Height. At least 25 percent of the railings, guards, or handrails shall be 34 inches (865 mm) maximum above the ground or deck surface.

EXCEPTION: Where a guard complying with sections 1003.2.12.1 and 1003.2.12.2 of the International Building Code (2000 edition) or sections 1012.2 and 1012.3 of the International Building Code (2003 edition) (incorporated by reference, see "Referenced Standards" in Chapter 1) is provided, the guard shall not be required to comply with 1005.2.1.

1005.2.1.1 Dispersion. Railings, guards, or handrails required to comply with 1005.2.1 shall be dispersed throughout the fishing pier or platform.

Advisory

1005.2.1.1 Dispersion. Portions of the railings that are lowered to provide fishing opportunities for persons with disabilities must be located in a variety of locations on the fishing pier or platform to give people a variety of locations to fish. Different fishing locations may provide varying water depths, shade (at certain times of the day), vegetation, and proximity to the shoreline or bank.

1005.3 Edge Protection. Where railings, guards, or handrails complying with 1005.2 are provided, edge protection complying with 1005.3.1 or 1005.3.2 shall be provided.

Advisory

1005.3 Edge Protection. Edge protection is required only where railings, guards, or handrails are provided on a fishing pier or platform. Edge protection will prevent wheelchairs or other mobility devices from slipping off the fishing pier or platform. Extending the deck of the fishing pier or platform 12 inches (305 mm) where the 34 inch (865 mm) high railing is provided is an alternative design, permitting individuals using wheelchairs or other mobility devices to pull into a clear space and move beyond the face of the railing. In such a design, curbs or barriers are not required.

1005.3.1 Curb or Barrier. Curbs or barriers shall extend 2 inches (51 mm) minimum above the surface of the fishing pier or platform.

1005.3.2 Extended Ground or Deck Surface. The ground or deck surface shall extend 12 inches (305 mm) minimum beyond the inside face of the railing. Toe clearance shall be provided and shall be 30 inches (760 mm) wide minimum and 9 inches (230 mm) minimum above the ground or deck surface beyond the railing.

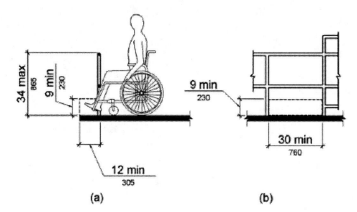

Figure 1005.3.2 Extended Ground or Deck Surface at Fishing Piers and Platforms

1005.4 Clear Floor or Ground Space. At each location where there are railings, guards, or handrails complying with 1005.2.1, a clear floor or ground space complying with 305 shall be provided. Where there are no railings, guards, or handrails, at least one clear floor or ground space complying with 305 shall be provided on the fishing pier or platform.

1005.5 Turning Space. At least one turning space complying with 304.3 shall be provided on fishing piers and platforms.

1006 Golf Facilities

1006.1 General. Golf facilities shall comply with 1006.

1006.2 Accessible Routes. Accessible routes serving teeing grounds, practice teeing grounds, putting greens, practice putting greens, teeing stations at driving ranges, course weather shelters, golf car rental areas, bag drop areas, and course toilet rooms shall comply with Chapter 4 and shall be 48 inches (1220 mm) wide minimum. Where handrails are provided, accessible routes shall be 60 inches (1525 mm) wide minimum.

> **EXCEPTION:** Handrails shall not be required on golf courses. Where handrails are provided on golf courses, the handrails shall not be required to comply with 505.

Advisory

1006.2 Accessible Routes. The 48 inch (1220 mm) minimum width for the accessible route is necessary to ensure passage of a golf car on either the accessible route or the golf car passage. This is important where the accessible route is used to connect the golf car rental area, bag drop areas, practice putting greens, practice teeing grounds, course toilet rooms, and course weather shelters. These are areas outside the boundary of the golf course, but are areas where an individual using an adapted golf car may travel. A golf car passage may not be substituted for other accessible routes to be located outside the boundary of the course. For example, an accessible route connecting an accessible parking space to the entrance of a golf course clubhouse is not covered by this provision.

Providing a golf car passage will permit a person that uses a golf car to practice driving a golf ball from the same position and stance used when playing the game. Additionally, the space required for a person using a golf car to enter and maneuver within the teeing stations required to be accessible should be considered.

1006.3 Golf Car Passages. Golf car passages shall comply with 1006.3.

1006.3.1 Clear Width. The clear width of golf car passages shall be 48 inches (1220 mm) minimum.

1006.3.2 Barriers. Where curbs or other constructed barriers prevent golf cars from entering a fairway, openings 60 inches (1525 mm) wide minimum shall be provided at intervals not to exceed 75 yards (69 m).

1006.4 Weather Shelters. A clear floor or ground space 60 inches (1525 mm) minimum by 96 inches (2440 mm) minimum shall be provided within weather shelters.

Guidance

Accessible Route. Sections 206.2.15, 1006.2, and 1006.3 of the 2010 Standards require an accessible route to connect all accessible elements within the boundary of the golf course and, in addition, to connect golf car rental areas, bag drop areas, teeing grounds, putting greens, and weather shelters. An accessible route also is required to connect any practice putting greens, practice teeing grounds, and teeing stations at driving ranges that are required to be accessible. An exception permits the accessible route requirements to be met, within the boundaries of the golf course, by providing a "golf car passage" (the path typically used by golf cars) if specifications for width and curb cuts are met.

Most commenters expressed the general viewpoint that nearly all golf courses provide golf cars and have either well-defined paths or permit the cars to drive on the course where paths are not present, and thus meet the accessible route requirement.

The Department received many comments requesting clarification of the term "golf car passage." Some commenters recommended additional regulatory language specifying that an exception from a pedestrian route requirement should be allowed only when a golf car passage provides unobstructed access onto the teeing ground, putting green, or other accessible element of the course so that an accessible golf car can have full access to those elements. These commenters cautioned that full and equal access would not be provided if a golfer were required to navigate a steep slope up or down a hill or a flight of stairs in order to get to the teeing ground, putting green, or other accessible element of the course.

Conversely, another commenter requesting clarification of the term "golf car passage" argued that golf courses typically do not provide golf car paths or pedestrian paths up to actual tee grounds or greens, many of which are higher or lower than the car path. This commenter argued that if golf car passages were required to extend onto teeing grounds and greens in order to qualify for an exception, then some golf courses would have to substantially regrade teeing grounds and greens at a high cost.

Some commenters argued that older golf courses, small nine-hole courses, and executive courses that do not have golf car paths would be unable to comply with the accessible route requirements because of the excessive cost involved. A commenter noted that, for those older courses that have not yet created an accessible pedestrian route or golf car passage, the costs and impacts to do so should be considered.

A commenter argued that an accessible route should not be required where natural terrain makes it infeasible to create an accessible route. Some commenters cautioned that the 2010 Standards would jeopardize the integrity of golf course designs that utilize natural terrain elements and elevation changes to set up shots and create challenging golf holes.

The Department has given careful consideration to the comments and has decided to adopt the 2010 Standards requiring that at least one accessible route connect accessible elements and spaces within the boundary of the golf course including teeing grounds, putting greens, and weather shelters, with an exception provided that golf car passages shall be permitted to be used for all or part of required accessible routes. In response to requests for clarification of the term "golf car passage," the Department points out that golf car passage is merely a pathway on which a motorized golf car can operate and includes identified or paved paths, teeing grounds, fairways, putting greens, and other areas of the course. Golf cars cannot traverse steps and exceedingly steep slopes. A nine-hole golf course or an executive golf course that lacks an identified golf car path but provides golf car passage to teeing grounds, putting greens, and other elements throughout the course may utilize the exception for all or part of the accessible pedestrian route. The exception in section 206.2.15 of the 2010 Standards does not exempt golf courses from their obligation to provide access to necessary elements of the golf course; rather, the exception allows a golf course to use a golf car passage for part or all of the accessible pedestrian route to ensure that persons with mobility disabilities can fully and equally participate in the recreational activity of playing golf.

Accessible Teeing Grounds, Putting Greens, and Weather Shelters. Sections 238.2 and 1006.4 of the 2010 Standards require that golf cars be able to enter and exit each putting green and weather shelter. Where two teeing grounds are provided, the forward teeing ground is required to be accessible (golf car can enter and exit). Where three or more teeing grounds are provided, at least two, including the forward teeing ground, must be accessible.

A commenter supported requirements for teeing grounds, particularly requirements for accessible teeing grounds, noting that accessible teeing grounds are essential to the full and equal enjoyment of the golfing experience.

A commenter recommended that existing golf courses be required to provide access to only one teeing ground per hole. The majority of commenters reported that most public and private golf courses already provide golf car passage to teeing grounds and greens. The Department has decided that it is reasonable to maintain the requirement. The 2010 Standards provide an exception for existing golf courses with three or more teeing grounds not to provide golf car passage to the forward teeing ground where terrain makes such passage infeasible.

Section 1006.3.2 of the 2010 Standards requires that where curbs or other constructed barriers prevent golf cars from entering a fairway, openings 60 inches wide minimum shall be provided at intervals not to exceed 75 yards.

A commenter disagreed with the requirement that openings 60 inches wide minimum be installed at least every 75 yards, arguing that a maximum spacing of 75 yards may not allow enough flexibility for terrain and hazard placements. To resolve this problem, the commenter recommended that the standards be modified to require that each golf car passage include one 60-inch wide opening for an accessible golf car to reach the tee, and that one opening be provided where necessary for an accessible golf car to reach a green. The requirement for openings where curbs or other constructed barriers may otherwise prevent golf cars from entering a fairway allows the distance between openings to be less than every 75 yards. Therefore, the Department believes that the language in section 1006.3.2 of the 2010 Standards allows appropriate flexibility. Where a paved path with curbs or other constructed barrier exists, the Department believes that it is essential that openings be provided to enable golf car passages to access teeing grounds, fairways and putting greens, and other required elements. Golf car passage is not restricted to a paved path with curbs. Golf car passage also includes fairways, teeing grounds, putting greens, and other areas on which golf cars operate.

Accessible Practice Putting Greens, Practice Teeing Grounds, and Teeing Stations at Driving Ranges. Section 238.3 of the 2010 Standards requires that five percent (5%) but at least one of each of practice putting greens, practice teeing grounds, and teeing stations at driving ranges must permit golf cars to enter and exit.

1007 Miniature Golf Facilities

1007.1 General. Miniature golf facilities shall comply with 1007.

1007.2 Accessible Routes. Accessible routes serving holes on miniature golf courses shall comply with Chapter 4. Accessible routes located on playing surfaces of miniature golf holes shall be permitted to use the exceptions in 1007.2.

> **EXCEPTIONS:**
>
> **1.** Playing surfaces shall not be required to comply with 302.2.
>
> **2.** Where accessible routes intersect playing surfaces of holes, a 1 inch (25 mm) maximum curb shall be permitted for a width of 32 inches (815 mm) minimum.
>
> **3.** A slope not steeper than 1:4 for a 4 inch (100 mm) maximum rise shall be permitted.
>
> **4.** Ramp landing slopes specified by 405.7.1 shall be permitted to be 1:20 maximum.
>
> **5.** Ramp landing length specified by 405.7.3 shall be permitted to be 48 inches (1220 mm) long minimum.
>
> **6.** Ramp landing size specified by 405.7.4 shall be permitted to be 48 inches (1220 mm) minimum by 60 inches (1525 mm) minimum.
>
> **7.** Handrails shall not be required on holes. Where handrails are provided on holes, the handrails shall not be required to comply with 505.

1007.3 Miniature Golf Holes. Miniature golf holes shall comply with 1007.3.

1007.3.1 Start of Play. A clear floor or ground space 48 inches (1220 mm) minimum by 60 inches (1525 mm) minimum with slopes not steeper than 1:48 shall be provided at the start of play.

1007.3.2 Golf Club Reach Range Area. All areas within holes where golf balls rest shall be within 36 inches (915 mm) maximum of a clear floor or ground space 36 inches (915 mm) wide minimum and 48 inches (1220 mm) long minimum having a running slope not steeper than 1:20. The clear floor or ground space shall be served by an accessible route.

Advisory

1007.3.2 Golf Club Reach Range Area. The golf club reach range applies to all holes required to be accessible. This includes accessible routes provided adjacent to or, where provided, on the playing surface of the hole.

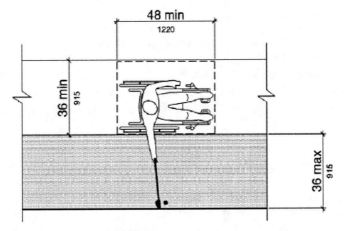

Note: Running Slope of Clear Floor or Ground Space Not Steeper Than 1:20

Figure 1007.3.2 Golf Club Reach Range Area

Guidance

Accessible Route to Miniature Golf Course Holes. Sections 206.2.16, 239.3, and 1007.2 of the 2010 Standards require an accessible route to connect accessible miniature golf course holes and the last accessible hole on the course directly to the course entrance or exit. Accessible holes are required to be consecutive with an exception permitting one break in the sequence of consecutive holes provided that the last hole on the miniature golf course is the last hole in the sequence.

Many commenters supported expanding the exception from one to multiple breaks in the sequence of accessible holes. One commenter noted that permitting accessible holes with breaks in the sequence would enable customers with disabilities to enjoy the landscaping, water and theme elements of the miniature golf course. Another commenter wrote in favor of allowing multiple breaks in accessible holes with a connecting accessible route.

Other commenters objected to allowing multiple breaks in the sequence of miniature golf holes. Commenters opposed to this change argued that allowing any breaks in the sequence of accessible holes at a miniature golf course would disrupt the flow of play for persons with disabilities and create a less socially integrated experience. A commenter noted that multiple breaks in sequence would not necessarily guarantee the provision of access to holes that are most representative of those with landscaping, water elements, or a fantasy-like experience.

The Department has decided to retain the exception without change. Comments did not provide a sufficient basis on which to conclude that allowing multiple breaks in the sequence of accessible holes would necessarily increase integration of accessible holes with unique features of miniature golf courses. Some designs of accessible holes with multiple breaks in the sequence might provide equivalent facilitation where persons with disabilities gain access to landscaping, water or theme elements not otherwise represented in a consecutive configuration of accessible holes. A factor that might contribute to equivalent facilitation would be an accessible route designed to bring persons with disabilities to a unique feature, such as a waterfall, that would otherwise not be served by an accessible route connecting consecutive accessible holes.

Specified exceptions are permitted for accessible route requirements when located on the playing surfaces near holes.

Accessible Miniature Golf Course Holes. Sections 239.2 and 1007.3 of the 2010 Standards require at least fifty percent (50%) of golf holes on miniature golf courses to be accessible, including providing a clear floor or ground space that is 48 inches minimum by 60 inches minimum with slopes not steeper than 1:48 at the start of play.

1008 Play Areas

1008.1 General. Play areas shall comply with 1008.

1008.2 Accessible Routes. Accessible routes serving play areas shall comply with Chapter 4 and 1008.2 and shall be permitted to use the exceptions in 1008.2.1 through 1008.2.3. Where accessible routes serve ground level play components, the vertical clearance shall be 80 inches high (2030 mm) minimum.

1008.2.1 Ground Level and Elevated Play Components. Accessible routes serving ground level play components and elevated play components shall be permitted to use the exceptions in 1008.2.1.

EXCEPTIONS:

1. Transfer systems complying with 1008.3 shall be permitted to connect elevated play components except where 20 or more elevated play components are provided no more than 25 percent of the elevated play components shall be permitted to be connected by transfer systems.

2. Where transfer systems are provided, an elevated play component shall be permitted to connect to another elevated play component as part of an accessible route.

1008.2.2 Soft Contained Play Structures. Accessible routes serving soft contained play structures shall be permitted to use the exception in 1008.2.2.

EXCEPTION: Transfer systems complying with 1008.3 shall be permitted to be used as part of an accessible route.

1008.2.3 Water Play Components. Accessible routes serving water play components shall be permitted to use the exceptions in 1008.2.3.

EXCEPTIONS:

1. Where the surface of the accessible route, clear floor or ground spaces, or turning spaces serving water play components is submerged, compliance with 302, 403.3, 405.2, 405.3, and 1008.2.6 shall not be required.

2. Transfer systems complying with 1008.3 shall be permitted to connect elevated play components in water.

Advisory

1008.2.3 Water Play Components. Personal wheelchairs and mobility devices may not be appropriate for submerging in water when using play components in water. Some may have batteries, motors, and electrical systems that when submerged in water may cause damage to the personal mobility device or wheelchair or may contaminate the water. Providing an aquatic wheelchair made of non-corrosive materials and designed for access into the water will protect the water from contamination and avoid damage to personal wheelchairs.

1008.2.4 Clear Width. Accessible routes connecting play components shall provide a clear width complying with 1008.2.4.

1008.2.4.1 Ground Level. At ground level, the clear width of accessible routes shall be 60 inches (1525 mm) minimum.

EXCEPTIONS:

1. In play areas less than 1000 square feet (93 m^2), the clear width of accessible routes shall be permitted to be 44 inches (1120 mm) minimum, if at least one turning space complying with 304.3 is provided where the restricted accessible route exceeds 30 feet (9145 mm) in length.

2. The clear width of accessible routes shall be permitted to be 36 inches (915 mm) minimum for a distance of 60 inches (1525 mm) maximum provided that multiple reduced width segments are separated by segments that are 60 inches (1525 mm) wide minimum and 60 inches (1525 mm) long minimum.

1008.2.4.2 Elevated. The clear width of accessible routes connecting elevated play components shall be 36 inches (915 mm) minimum.

EXCEPTIONS:

1. The clear width of accessible routes connecting elevated play components shall be permitted to be reduced to 32 inches (815 mm) minimum for a distance of 24 inches (610 mm) maximum provided that reduced width segments are separated by segments that are 48 inches (1220 mm) long minimum and 36 inches (915 mm) wide minimum.

2. The clear width of transfer systems connecting elevated play components shall be permitted to be 24 inches (610 mm) minimum.

1008.2.5 Ramps. Within play areas, ramps connecting ground level play components and ramps connecting elevated play components shall comply with 1008.2.5.

1008.2.5.1 Ground Level. Ramp runs connecting ground level play components shall have a running slope not steeper than 1:16.

1008.2.5.2 Elevated. The rise for any ramp run connecting elevated play components shall be 12 inches (305 mm) maximum.

1008.2.5.3 Handrails. Where required on ramps serving play components, the handrails shall comply with 505 except as modified by 1008.2.5.3.

EXCEPTIONS:

1. Handrails shall not be required on ramps located within ground level use zones.

2. Handrail extensions shall not be required.

1008.2.5.3.1 Handrail Gripping Surfaces. Handrail gripping surfaces with a circular cross section shall have an outside diameter of 0.95 inch (24 mm) minimum and 1.55 inches (39 mm) maximum. Where the shape of the gripping surface is non-circular, the handrail shall provide an equivalent gripping surface.

1008.2.5.3.2 Handrail Height. The top of handrail gripping surfaces shall be 20 inches (510 mm) minimum and 28 inches (710 mm) maximum above the ramp surface.

1008.2.6 Ground Surfaces. Ground surfaces on accessible routes, clear floor or ground spaces, and turning spaces shall comply with 1008.2.6.

Advisory

1008.2.6 Ground Surfaces. Ground surfaces must be inspected and maintained regularly to ensure continued compliance with the ASTM F 1951 standard. The type of surface material selected and play area use levels will determine the frequency of inspection and maintenance activities.

1008.2.6.1 Accessibility. Ground surfaces shall comply with ASTM F 1951 (incorporated by reference, see "Referenced Standards" in Chapter 1). Ground surfaces shall be inspected and maintained regularly and frequently to ensure continued compliance with ASTM F 1951.

1008.2.6.2 Use Zones. Ground surfaces located within use zones shall comply with ASTM F 1292 (1999 edition or 2004 edition) (incorporated by reference, see "Referenced Standards" in Chapter 1).

1008.3 Transfer Systems. Where transfer systems are provided to connect to elevated play components, transfer systems shall comply with 1008.3.

Advisory

1008.3 Transfer Systems. Where transfer systems are provided, consideration should be given to the distance between the transfer system and the elevated play components. Moving between a transfer platform and a series of transfer steps requires extensive exertion for some children. Designers should minimize the distance between the points where a child transfers from a wheelchair or mobility device and where the elevated play components are located. Where elevated play components are used to connect to another elevated play component instead of an accessible route, careful consideration should be used in the selection of the play components used for this purpose.

1008.3.1 Transfer Platforms. Transfer platforms shall be provided where transfer is intended from wheelchairs or other mobility aids. Transfer platforms shall comply with 1008.3.1.

1008.3.1.1 Size. Transfer platforms shall have level surfaces 14 inches (355 mm) deep minimum and 24 inches (610 mm) wide minimum.

1008.3.1.2 Height. The height of transfer platforms shall be 11 inches (280 mm) minimum and 18 inches (455 mm) maximum measured to the top of the surface from the ground or floor surface.

1008.3.1.3 Transfer Space. A transfer space complying with 305.2 and 305.3 shall be provided adjacent to the transfer platform. The 48 inch (1220 mm) long minimum dimension of the transfer space shall be centered on and parallel to the 24 inch (610 mm) long minimum side of the transfer platform. The side of the transfer platform serving the transfer space shall be unobstructed.

1008.3.1.4 Transfer Supports. At least one means of support for transferring shall be provided.

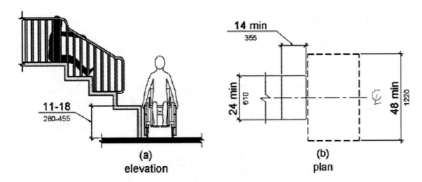

Figure 1008.3.1 Transfer Platforms

1008.3.2 Transfer Steps. Transfer steps shall be provided where movement is intended from transfer platforms to levels with elevated play components required to be on accessible routes. Transfer steps shall comply with 1008.3.2.

1008.3.2.1 Size. Transfer steps shall have level surfaces 14 inches (355 mm) deep minimum and 24 inches (610 mm) wide minimum.

1008.3.2.2 Height. Each transfer step shall be 8 inches (205 mm) high maximum.

1008.3.2.3 Transfer Supports. At least one means of support for transferring shall be provided.

Advisory

1008.3.2.3 Transfer Supports. Transfer supports are required on transfer platforms and transfer steps to assist children when transferring. Some examples of supports include a rope loop, a loop type handle, a slot in the edge of a flat horizontal or vertical member, poles or bars, or D rings on the corner posts.

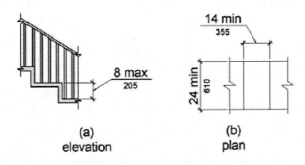

Figure 1008.3.2 Transfer Steps

1008.4 Play Components. Ground level play components on accessible routes and elevated play components connected by ramps shall comply with 1008.4.

1008.4.1 Turning Space. At least one turning space complying with 304 shall be provided on the same level as play components. Where swings are provided, the turning space shall be located immediately adjacent to the swing.

1008.4.2 Clear Floor or Ground Space. Clear floor or ground space complying with 305.2 and 305.3 shall be provided at play components.

Advisory

1008.4.2 Clear Floor or Ground Space. Clear floor or ground spaces, turning spaces, and accessible routes are permitted to overlap within play areas. A specific location has not been designated for the clear floor or ground spaces or turning spaces, except swings, because each play component may require that the spaces be placed in a unique location. Where play components include a seat or entry point, designs that provide for an unobstructed transfer from a wheelchair or other mobility device are recommended. This will enhance the ability of children with disabilities to independently use the play component.

When designing play components with manipulative or interactive features, consider appropriate reach ranges for children seated in wheelchairs. The following table provides guidance on reach ranges for children seated in wheelchairs. These dimensions apply to either forward or side reaches. The reach ranges are appropriate for use with those play components that children seated in wheelchairs may access and reach. Where transfer systems provide access to elevated play components, the reach ranges are not appropriate.

Children's Reach Ranges

Forward or Side Reach	Ages 3 and 4	Ages 5 through 8	Ages 9 through 12
High (maximum)	36 in (915 mm)	40 in (1015 mm)	44 in (1120 mm)
Low (minimum)	20 in (510 mm)	18 in (455 mm)	16 in (405 mm)

1008.4.3 Play Tables. Where play tables are provided, knee clearance 24 inches (610 mm) high minimum, 17 inches deep (430 mm) minimum, and 30 inches (760 mm) wide minimum shall be provided. The tops of rims, curbs, or other obstructions shall be 31 inches (785 mm) high maximum.

EXCEPTION: Play tables designed and constructed primarily for children 5 years and younger shall not be required to provide knee clearance where the clear floor or ground space required by 1008.4.2 is arranged for a parallel approach.

1008.4.4 Entry Points and Seats. Where play components require transfer to entry points or seats, the entry points or seats shall be 11 inches (280 mm) minimum and 24 inches (610 mm) maximum from the clear floor or ground space.

EXCEPTION: Entry points of slides shall not be required to comply with 1008.4.4.

1008.4.5 Transfer Supports. Where play components require transfer to entry points or seats, at least one means of support for transferring shall be provided.

Guidance

Section 240 of the 2010 Standards provides scoping for play areas and section 1008 provides technical requirements for play areas. Section 240.1 of the 2010 Standards sets requirements for play areas for children ages 2 and over and covers separate play areas within a site for specific age groups. Section 240.1 also provides four exceptions to the requirements that apply to family child care facilities, relocation of existing play components in existing play areas, amusement attractions, and alterations to play components where the ground surface is not altered.

Ground Surfaces. Section 1008.2.6 of the 2010 Standards provides technical requirements for accessible ground surfaces for play areas on accessible routes, clear floor or ground spaces, and turning spaces. These ground surfaces must follow special rules, incorporated by reference from nationally recognized standards for accessibility and safety in play areas, including those issued by the American Society for Testing and Materials (ASTM).

A commenter recommended that the Department closely examine the requirements for ground surfaces at play areas. The Department is aware that there is an ongoing controversy about play area ground surfaces arising from a concern that some surfaces that meet the ASTM requirements at the time of installation will become inaccessible if they do not receive constant maintenance. The Access Board is also aware of this issue and is working to develop a portable field test that will provide more relevant information on installed play surfaces. The Department would caution covered entities selecting among the ground surfacing materials that comply with the ASTM requirements that they must anticipate the maintenance costs that will be associated with some of the products. Permitting a surface to deteriorate so that it does not meet the 2010 Standards would be an independent violation of the Department's ADA regulations.

Accessible Route to Play Components. Section 206.2.17 of the 2010 Standards provides scoping requirements for accessible routes to ground level and elevated play components and to soft contained play structures. Sections 240.2 and 1008 of the 2010 Standards require that accessible routes be provided for play components. The accessible route must connect to at least one ground level play component of each different type provided (e.g., for different experiences such as rocking, swinging, climbing, spinning, and sliding). Table 240.2.1.2 sets requirements for the number and types of ground level play components required to be on accessible routes. When elevated play components are provided, an accessible route must connect at least fifty percent (50%) of the elevated play components. Section 240.2.1.2, provides an exception to the requirements for ground level play components if at least fifty percent (50%) of the elevated play components are connected by a ramp and at least three of the elevated play components connected by the ramp are different types of play components.

The technical requirements at section 1008 include provisions where if three or fewer entry points are provided to a soft contained play structure, then at least one entry point must be on an accessible route. In addition, where four or more entry points are provided to a soft contained play structure, then at least two entry points must be served by an accessible route.

If elevated play components are provided, fifty percent (50%) of the elevated components are required to be accessible. Where 20 or more elevated play components are provided, at least twenty five percent (25%) will have to be connected by a ramp. The remaining play components are permitted to be connected by a transfer system. Where less than 20 elevated play components are provided, a transfer system is permitted in lieu of a ramp.

A commenter noted that the 2010 Standards allow for the provision of transfer steps to elevated play structures based on the number of elevated play activities, but asserted that transfer steps have not been documented as an effective means of access.

The 2010 Standards recognize that play structures are designed to provide unique experiences and opportunities for children. The 2010 Standards provide for play components that are accessible to children who cannot transfer from their wheelchair, but they also provide opportunities for children who are able to transfer. Children often interact with their environment in ways that would be considered inappropriate for adults. Crawling and climbing, for example, are integral parts of the play experience for young children. Permitting the use of transfer platforms in play structures provides some flexibility for creative playground design.

Accessible Play Components. Accessible play components are required to be on accessible routes, including elevated play components that are required to be connected by ramps. These play components must also comply with other accessibility requirements, including specifications for clear floor space and seat heights (where provided).

A commenter expressed concerns that the general requirements of section 240.2.1 of the 2010 Standards and the advisory accompanying section 240.2.1 conflict. The comment asserts that section 240.2.1 of the 2010 Standards provides that the only requirement for integration of equipment is where there are two or more required ground level play components, while the advisory appears to suggest that all accessible components must be integrated.

The commenter misinterprets the requirement. The ADA mandates that persons with disabilities be able to participate in programs or activities in the most integrated setting appropriate to their needs. Therefore, all accessible play components must be integrated into the general playground setting. Section 240.2.1 of the 2010 Standards specifies that where there is more than one accessible ground level play component, the components must be both dispersed and integrated.

1009 Swimming Pools, Wading Pools, and Spas

1009.1 General. Where provided, pool lifts, sloped entries, transfer walls, transfer systems, and pool stairs shall comply with 1009.

1009.2 Pool Lifts. Pool lifts shall comply with 1009.2.

Advisory

1009.2 Pool Lifts. There are a variety of seats available on pool lifts ranging from sling seats to those that are preformed or molded. Pool lift seats with backs will enable a larger population of persons with disabilities to use the lift. Pool lift seats that consist of materials that resist corrosion and provide a firm base to transfer will be usable by a wider range of people with disabilities. Additional options such as armrests, head rests, seat belts, and leg support will enhance accessibility and better accommodate people with a wide range of disabilities.

1009.2.1 Pool Lift Location. Pool lifts shall be located where the water level does not exceed 48 inches (1220 mm).

EXCEPTIONS:

1. Where the entire pool depth is greater than 48 inches (1220 mm), compliance with 1009.2.1 shall not be required.

2. Where multiple pool lift locations are provided, no more than one pool lift shall be required to be located in an area where the water level is 48 inches (1220 mm) maximum.

1009.2.2 Seat Location. In the raised position, the centerline of the seat shall be located over the deck and 16 inches (405 mm) minimum from the edge of the pool. The deck surface between the centerline of the seat and the pool edge shall have a slope not steeper than 1:48.

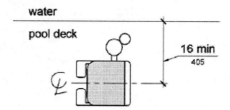

Figure 1009.2.2 Pool Lift Seat Location

1009.2.3 Clear Deck Space. On the side of the seat opposite the water, a clear deck space shall be provided parallel with the seat. The space shall be 36 inches (915 mm) wide minimum and shall extend forward 48 inches (1220 mm) minimum from a line located 12 inches (305 mm) behind the rear edge of the seat. The clear deck space shall have a slope not steeper than 1:48.

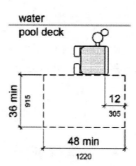

Figure 1009.2.3 Clear Deck Space at Pool Lifts

1009.2.4 Seat Height. The height of the lift seat shall be designed to allow a stop at 16 inches (405 mm) minimum to 19 inches (485 mm) maximum measured from the deck to the top of the seat surface when in the raised (load) position.

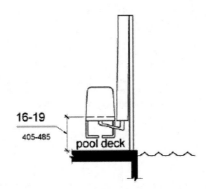

Figure 1009.2.4 Pool Lift Seat Height

1009.2.5 Seat Width. The seat shall be 16 inches (405 mm) wide minimum.

1009.2.6 Footrests and Armrests. Footrests shall be provided and shall move with the seat. If provided, the armrest positioned opposite the water shall be removable or shall fold clear of the seat when the seat is in the raised (load) position.

EXCEPTION: Footrests shall not be required on pool lifts provided in spas.

1009.2.7 Operation. The lift shall be capable of unassisted operation from both the deck and water levels. Controls and operating mechanisms shall be unobstructed when the lift is in use and shall comply with 309.4.

Advisory

1009.2.7 Operation. Pool lifts must be capable of unassisted operation from both the deck and water levels. This will permit a person to call the pool lift when the pool lift is in the opposite position. It is extremely important for a person who is swimming alone to be able to call the pool lift when it is in the up position so he or she will not be stranded in the water for extended periods of time awaiting assistance. The requirement for a pool lift to be independently operable does not preclude assistance from being provided.

1009.2.8 Submerged Depth. The lift shall be designed so that the seat will submerge to a water depth of 18 inches (455 mm) minimum below the stationary water level.

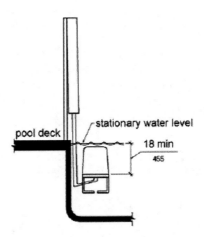

Figure 1009.2.8 Pool Lift Submerged Depth

1009.2.9 Lifting Capacity. Single person pool lifts shall have a weight capacity of 300 pounds. (136 kg) minimum and be capable of sustaining a static load of at least one and a half times the rated load.

Advisory

1009.2.9 Lifting Capacity. Single person pool lifts must be capable of supporting a minimum weight of 300 pounds (136 kg) and sustaining a static load of at least one and a half times the rated load. Pool lifts should be provided that meet the needs of the population they serve. Providing a pool lift with a weight capacity greater than 300 pounds (136 kg) may be advisable.

1009.3 Sloped Entries. Sloped entries shall comply with 1009.3.

Advisory

1009.3 Sloped Entries. Personal wheelchairs and mobility devices may not be appropriate for submerging in water. Some may have batteries, motors, and electrical systems that when submerged in water may cause damage to the personal mobility device or wheelchair or may contaminate the pool water. Providing an aquatic wheelchair made of non-corrosive materials and designed for access into the water will protect the water from contamination and avoid damage to personal wheelchairs or other mobility aids.

1009.3.1 Sloped Entries. Sloped entries shall comply with Chapter 4 except as modified in 1109.3.1 through 1109.3.3.

EXCEPTION: Where sloped entries are provided, the surfaces shall not be required to be slip resistant.

1009.3.2 Submerged Depth. Sloped entries shall extend to a depth of 24 inches (610 mm) minimum and 30 inches (760 mm) maximum below the stationary water level. Where landings are required by 405.7, at least one landing shall be located 24 inches (610 mm) minimum and 30 inches (760 mm) maximum below the stationary water level.

EXCEPTION: In wading pools, the sloped entry and landings, if provided, shall extend to the deepest part of the wading pool.

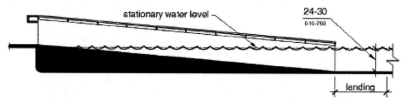

Figure 1009.3.2 Sloped Entry Submerged Depth

1009.3.3 Handrails. At least two handrails complying with 505 shall be provided on the sloped entry. The clear width between required handrails shall be 33 inches (840 mm) minimum and 38 inches (965 mm) maximum.

EXCEPTIONS:

1. Handrail extensions specified by 505.10.1 shall not be required at the bottom landing serving a sloped entry.

2. Where a sloped entry is provided for wave action pools, leisure rivers, sand bottom pools, and other pools where user access is limited to one area, the handrails shall not be required to comply with the clear width requirements of 1009.3.3.

3. Sloped entries in wading pools shall not be required to provide handrails complying with 1009.3.3. If provided, handrails on sloped entries in wading pools shall not be required to comply with 505.

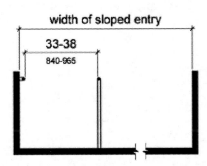

Figure 1009.3.3 Handrails for Sloped Entry

1009.4 Transfer Walls. Transfer walls shall comply with 1009.4.

1009.4.1 Clear Deck Space. A clear deck space of 60 inches (1525 mm) minimum by 60 inches (1525 mm) minimum with a slope not steeper than 1:48 shall be provided at the base of the transfer wall. Where one grab bar is provided, the clear deck space shall be centered on the grab bar. Where two grab bars are provided, the clear deck space shall be centered on the clearance between the grab bars.

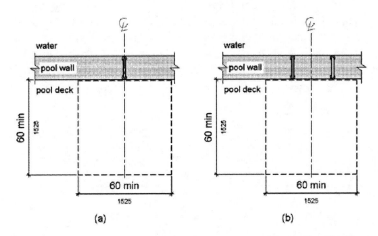

Figure 1009.4.1 Clear Deck Space at Transfer Walls

1009.4.2 Height. The height of the transfer wall shall be 16 inches (405 mm) minimum and 19 inches (485 mm) maximum measured from the deck.

Figure 1009.4.2 Transfer Wall Height

1009.4.3 Wall Depth and Length. The depth of the transfer wall shall be 12 inches (305 mm) minimum and 16 inches (405 mm) maximum. The length of the transfer wall shall be 60 inches (1525 mm) minimum and shall be centered on the clear deck space.

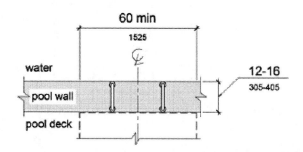

Figure 1009.4.3 Depth and Length of Transfer Walls

1009.4.4 Surface. Surfaces of transfer walls shall not be sharp and shall have rounded edges.

1009.4.5 Grab Bars. At least one grab bar complying with 609 shall be provided on the transfer wall. Grab bars shall be perpendicular to the pool wall and shall extend the full depth of the transfer wall. The top of the gripping surface shall be 4 inches (100 mm) minimum and 6 inches (150 mm) maximum above transfer walls. Where one grab bar is provided, clearance shall be 24 inches (610 mm) minimum on both sides of the grab bar. Where two grab bars are provided, clearance between grab bars shall be 24 inches (610 mm) minimum.

EXCEPTION: Grab bars on transfer walls shall not be required to comply with 609.4.

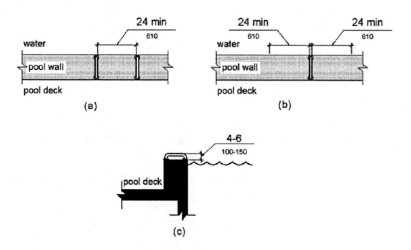

Figure 1009.4.5 Grab Bars for Transfer Walls

1009.5 Transfer Systems. Transfer systems shall comply with 1009.5.

1009.5.1 Transfer Platform. A transfer platform shall be provided at the head of each transfer system. Transfer platforms shall provide 19 inches (485 mm) minimum clear depth and 24 inches (610 mm) minimum clear width.

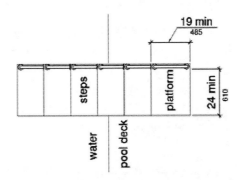

Figure 1009.5.1 Size of Transfer Platform

1009.5.2 Transfer Space. A transfer space of 60 inches (1525 mm) minimum by 60 inches (1525 mm) minimum with a slope not steeper than 1:48 shall be provided at the base of the transfer platform surface and shall be centered along a 24 inch (610 mm) minimum side of the transfer platform. The side of the transfer platform serving the transfer space shall be unobstructed.

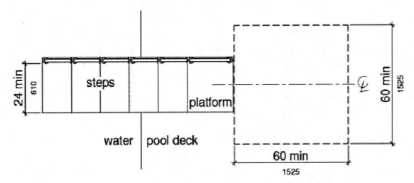

Figure 1009.5.2 Clear Deck Space at Transfer Platform

1009.5.3 Height. The height of the transfer platform shall comply with 1009.4.2.

1009.5.4 Transfer Steps. Transfer step height shall be 8 inches (205 mm) maximum. The surface of the bottom tread shall extend to a water depth of 18 inches (455 mm) minimum below the stationary water level.

Advisory

1009.5.4 Transfer Steps. Where possible, the height of the transfer step should be minimized to decrease the distance an individual is required to lift up or move down to reach the next step to gain access.

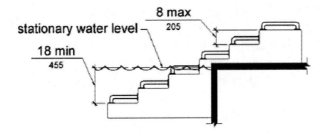

Figure 1009.5.4 Transfer Steps

1009.5.5 Surface. The surface of the transfer system shall not be sharp and shall have rounded edges.

1009.5.6 Size. Each transfer step shall have a tread clear depth of 14 inches (355 mm) minimum and 17 inches (430 mm) maximum and shall have a tread clear width of 24 inches (610 mm) minimum.

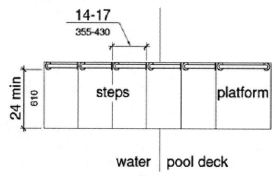

Figure 1009.5.6 Size of Transfer Steps

1009.5.7 Grab Bars. At least one grab bar on each transfer step and the transfer platform or a continuous grab bar serving each transfer step and the transfer platform shall be provided. Where a grab bar is provided on each step, the tops of gripping surfaces shall be 4 inches (100 mm) minimum and 6 inches (150 mm) maximum above each step and transfer platform. Where a continuous grab bar is provided, the top of the gripping surface shall be 4 inches (100 mm) minimum and 6 inches (150 mm) maximum above the step nosing and transfer platform. Grab bars shall comply with 609 and be located on at least one side of the transfer system. The grab bar located at the transfer platform shall not obstruct transfer.

EXCEPTION: Grab bars on transfer systems shall not be required to comply with 609.4.

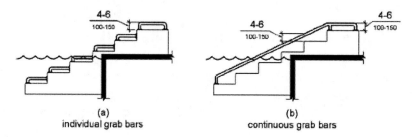

Figure 1009.5.7 Grab Bars

1009.6 Pool Stairs. Pool stairs shall comply with 1009.6.

1009.6.1 Pool Stairs. Pool stairs shall comply with 504.

> **EXCEPTION:** Pool step riser heights shall not be required to be 4 inches (100 mm) high minimum and 7 inches (180 mm) high maximum provided that riser heights are uniform.

1009.6.2 Handrails. The width between handrails shall be 20 inches (510 mm) minimum and 24 inches (610 mm) maximum. Handrail extensions required by 505.10.3 shall not be required on pool stairs.

Guidance

Accessible Means of Entry to Pools. Section 242 of the 2010 Standards requires at least two accessible means of entry for larger pools (300 or more linear feet) and at least one accessible entry for smaller pools. This section requires that at least one entry will have to be a sloped entry or a pool lift; the other could be a sloped entry, pool lift, a transfer wall, or a transfer system (technical specifications for each entry type are included at section 1009).

Many commenters supported the scoping and technical requirements for swimming pools. Other commenters stated that the cost of requiring facilities to immediately purchase a pool lift for each indoor and outdoor swimming pool would be very significant especially considering the large number of swimming pools at lodging facilities. One commenter requested that the Department clarify what would be an "alteration" to a swimming pool that would trigger the obligation to comply with the accessible means of entry in the 2010 Standards.

Alterations are covered by section 202.3 of the 2010 Standards and the definition of "alteration" is provided at section 106.5. A physical change to a swimming pool which affects or could affect the usability of the pool is considered to be an alteration. Changes to the mechanical and electrical systems, such as filtration and chlorination systems, are not alterations. Exception 2 to section 202.3 permits an altered swimming pool to comply with applicable requirements to the maximum extent feasible if full compliance is technically infeasible. "Technically infeasible" is also defined in section 106.5 of the 2010 Standards.

The Department also received comments suggesting that it is not appropriate to require two accessible means of entry to wave pools, lazy rivers, sand bottom pools, and other water amusements where there is only one point of entry. Exception 2 of Section 242.2 of the 2010 Standards exempts pools of this type from having to provide more than one accessible means of entry provided that the one accessible means of entry is a swimming pool lift compliant with section 1009.2, a sloped entry compliant with section 1009.3, or a transfer system compliant with section 1009.5 of the 2010 Standards.

Accessible Means of Entry to Wading Pools. Sections 242.3 and 1009.3 of the 2010 Standards require that at least one sloped means of entry is required into the deepest part of each wading pool.

Accessible Means of Entry to Spas. Sections 242.4 and 1009.2, 1009.4, and 1009.5 of the 2010 Standards require spas to meet accessibility requirements, including an accessible means of entry. Where spas are provided in clusters, five percent (5%) but at least one spa in each cluster must be accessible. A pool lift, a transfer wall, or a transfer system will be permitted to provide the required accessible means of entry.

1010 Shooting Facilities with Firing Positions

1010.1 Turning Space. A circular turning space 60 inches (1525 mm) diameter minimum with slopes not steeper than 1:48 shall be provided at shooting facilities with firing positions.